ANIMALS

VISUAL ENCYCLOPEDIA

ANIMALS

VISUAL ENCYCLOPEDIA

First edition published in 2011

Reprinted in 2013, 2017

Published by
Amber Books Ltd
74–77 White Lion Street
London N1 9PF
United Kingdom
Website: www.amberbooks.co.uk
Appstore: itunes.com/apps/amberbooksltd
Facebook: www.facebook.com/amberbooks
Twitter: @amberbooks

ISBN: 978-1-908273-01-7

Project Editor: Sarah Uttridge
Design: Andrew Easton

Printed in China

4 6 8 10 9 7 5 3 2

CONTENTS

INTRODUCTION 6

MAMMALS 8

BIRDS 164

REPTILES 282

AMPHIBIANS 308

FISH 322

INVERTEBRATES 388

Glossary 438

Index 440

INTRODUCTION

Scientists divide up life into five kingdoms: bacteria, amoeba-like creatures called protists, fungi, plants and, lastly, animals. There are around 1.5 million species of animals that have been described so far, and some estimates put the total number as high as 30 million, making the animal kingdom the dominant life force on Earth.

What makes an animal different to the other forms of life? Perhaps we should look first at what makes them similar; what makes them alive in the first place. All living things take in energy and nutrients from the surroundings and use them to grow their bodies and then reproduce – build new versions of themselves. By that logic a virus is not alive, because it cannot grow, but plants, animals and other organisms do it in some way or another.

Other Eaters

Animals are what scientists call heterotrophs, which translates as 'other feeders'. This contrasts with plants, which are autotrophic – or 'self feeding'. To put it another way, animals get their energy by consuming the bodies or products of other organisms. Plants use a different system, the process of photosynthesis. This harnesses the energy in sunlight to manufacture the plant's sugar fuels from two raw materials – water from the ground and carbon dioxide from the air.

Nevertheless, animals are not the only heterotrophic organisms on Earth. Many protists live this way, too, engulfing the bodies of smaller organisms in a battle being constantly waged at the microscopic level. (In fact, some protists are heterotrophs and autotrophs at the same time!) On the macroscopic scale, the fungi, which include mushrooms and molds, are also heterotrophs. They grow across the bodies of other organisms, digesting away the nutrients they need.

Mobile bodies

However, the fungi and plants also share a crucial similarity; their cells are always surrounded by a tough wall. This is what makes them solid structures rather than gooey blobs. Animal cells do not have this solid wall. In some cases, that means their bodies are little more than gooey blobs, but in general they have evolved alternative means of giving their bodies structure and solidity – bones, shells etc. The lack of the cell wall frees up an animal's body to be a moving entity, able to respond to the surroundings and actively collect the items it needs.

Animal diversity

The first animals evolved around 600 million years ago, and probably resembled today's sponges and jellyfish. Over all the time since then, these mobile, active organisms have evolved into the incredible variety of animals we see today, ranging from the giant whales to the minute mites that live in hair follicles, and from the high-speed falcons diving in for the kill to giant tortoises, seeing out a century-long lifetime at a more leisurely pace. This book contains the details of less than one-tenth of one percent of known animal species, but even this small number shows the incredible diversity of animal life, of which we humans are just one small part.

Above: A bald eagle survives by hunting and scavenging for fish and small mammals.

MAMMALS

There are about 4500 species of mammal, all of which feed their young on milk. The largest creatures on Earth today are mammal species, and we ourselves belong to this group.

Mammals are hairy creatures; all of them have at least a few hairs at some point of their development, most are covered head to foot in fur. Mammals are warm-blooded. In other words, they maintain a constant body temperature. As a result, mammals have been able to exploit more habitats than any other animal group, from the deep ocean to the polar ice and desert sands.

Left: The primary purpose of mammal hair is to keep the body warm and dry, but it has other uses. This male lion's mane is a signal of his great strength.

Australasian Marsupials

Although they also live in the Americas, New Guinea and Indonesia, marsupials are most associated with the Australian mainland. The mammals reproduce in a somewhat peculiar way. The females have no uterus in which to nurture a foetus, so the young complete their development in a pouch on their mother's belly.

Numbat

Myrmecobius fasciatus

Also known as the banded anteater, the numbat uses its long tongue to lick up termites and ants. It can eat 20,000 insects in one day. The numbat uses its powerful forelegs to rip into rotting logs and earth mounds to find prey. They are most active during the day and spend most of their time foraging alone.

FACT FILE	
Length:	28cm (11in)
Weight:	600g (21oz)
Distribution:	Southwestern Australia
Habitat:	Woodlands and grasslands
Diet:	Termites and ants
Status (IUCN Red List):	Endangered

Northern Quoll

Dasyurus hallucatus

Roughly the same size as a domestic cat, the quolls are sometimes referred to as 'native cats'. Like their namesake, quolls are predators, and a predilection for domestic fowl resulted in them being persecuted by farmers. Today, quolls are endangered. This species is restricted to pockets of habitat on Australia's north coast.

FACT FILE	
Length:	35cm (13¾in)
Weight:	525g (18oz)
Distribution:	Northern Australia
Habitat:	Rocky areas
Diet:	Reptiles, worms and insects
Status (IUCN Red List):	Endangered

Common Spiny Bandicoot

Echymipera kalubu

A regular night-time visitor to gardens and the coffee and fruit plantations of New Guinea, the common spiny bandicoot is a true omnivore, feasting on fallen fruits, insects and soft-bodied invertebrates. In its natural forest habitat, the animal tunnels through the deep layer of leaf litter that covers the ground.

FACT FILE	
Length:	38cm (15in)
Weight:	650g (23oz)
Distribution:	New Guinea
Habitat:	Forest
Diet:	Fruits, worms and slugs
Status (IUCN Red List):	Least concern

Koala

Phascolarctos cinereus

This species owes its undoubtedly cute appearance to its dependence on a diet of eucalyptus leaves. The plump, rounded body is filled with a long intestine for digesting this tough food. It maintains its teddy-bear posture in the leafy branches by gripping tightly with opposable thumbs on its forepaws.

FACT FILE	
Length:	82cm (32¼in)
Weight:	15kg (33lb)
Distribution:	Eastern Australia
Habitat:	Woodlands and forests
Diet:	Eucalyptus leaves
Status (IUCN Red List):	Least concern

Striped Possum

Dactylopsila trivirgata

The striped possum holds the record for having the largest brain compared to body weight of any marsupials. The agile animal lives in the treetops. It taps branches with a long middle finger to locate the burrows made under the bark by insect larvae. Once located, the possum gnaws through the wood to get to them.

FACT FILE	
Length:	26cm (10¼in)
Weight:	420g (15oz)
Distribution:	Northern Australia and N. Guinea
Habitat:	Tropical forest
Diet:	Insects
Status (IUCN Red List):	Least concern

Short-beaked Echidna

Tachyglossus aculeatus

The most primitive group of mammals is the monotremes. There are just three species surviving: the famed duck-billed platypus and two types of echidna, all confined to New Guinea and Australia. The monotremes produce milk like other mammals, but do not give birth to young, instead laying eggs like a bird or reptile.

FACT FILE	
Length:	45cm (17¾in)
Weight:	7kg (15lb 8oz)
Distribution:	Australia, Tasmania and N. Guinea
Habitat:	Desert, grassland and woodland
Diet:	Ants, termites and other insects
Status (IUCN Red List):	Least concern

Also known as the spiny anteater, the short-beaked echidna is the most common monotreme species. It licks up termites and ants with its long tongue. It finds food by smell, but may also pick up electrical impulses produced by prey animals. Female echidnas lay one egg at a time and brood it in a pouch on her underside.

SPINES
The echidna's protective spines are thickened hairs.
SPUR
Male echidnas have a spur on their hind legs, thought to be used in fighting. It is believed that the spurs of earlier monotremes were venomous. Only the platypus produces venom today.

American Oddities

Without the large herbivores of other continents, South American wildlife conforms to a different set of rules. As a result, it is home to some strange mammals, including one with a tongue almost as long as a human's arm, another that rolls into an armoured ball, and yet another that is so slow that it goes mouldy while still alive.

Grey Four-eyed Opossum

Philander opossum

South America is thought to be the home of the first marsupials. They are represented today by the opossums. The four-eyed opossum is so named because of the white spots above its eyes. Like this forest species, most opossums are generalists, and survive on a wide-ranging diet.

FACT FILE	
Length:	35cm (13¾in)
Weight:	450g (1lb)
Distribution:	Mexico to Argentina
Habitat:	Forests
Diet:	Insects, eggs, frogs and fruits
Status (IUCN Red List):	Least concern

Pale-throated Sloth

Bradypus tridactylus

The pale-throated sloth spends its days in the high branches of tropical forests, suspended from its hooked claws. It sleeps for 19 hours a day up there, and also feeds, mates and gives birth in the trees. Green algae grows on its long hairs, giving the animal a mouldy tinge. It cannot walk on land but is a good swimmer.

FACT FILE	
Length:	76cm (30in)
Weight:	5.5kg (12lb 2oz)
Distribution:	Central America to Argentina
Habitat:	Tropical forest
Diet:	Leaves, buds and twigs
Status (IUCN Red List):	Least concern

Giant Anteater

Myrmecophaga tridactyla

This species uses its powerful forelegs to rip into termite mounds and ant nests, to be greeted by a torrent of defending insects. The long tongue – 60cm (23½in) – sets to work, snaring a few insects with each lightning-paced lick. An adult can eat 30,000 ants in a single meal. A baby rides on its mother's back for about six months.

FACT FILE	
Length:	1.2m (4ft)
Weight:	39kg (86lb)
Distribution:	Belize to northern Argentina
Habitat:	Grasslands, swamps and forests
Diet:	Ants and termites
Status (IUCN Red List):	Vulnerable

Large Hairy Armadillo

Chaetophractus villosus

Along with the sloths and anteaters, the armadillos form a group of mammals called the xenarthrans. They are the only surviving relatives of a succession of huge beasts that roamed across the Americas a million years ago. This species of armadillo lives on the Gran Chaco, an inhospitable sun-baked scrubland.

FACT FILE	
Length:	32cm (12½in)
Weight:	2kg (4lb 6oz)
Distribution:	Paraguay to Bolivia
Habitat:	Semi-desert
Diet:	Insects, carrion and fruits
Status (IUCN Red List):	Least concern

Southern Three-banded Armadillo

Tolypeutes matacus

The name armadillo means 'little armoured one' in Spanish, and obviously refers to the bony plates that protect the back. The skin-covered plates are articulated in bands and, contrary to popular belief, most armadillos cannot roll into an armoured ball when threatened. However, the southern three-banded species is one of just two that can manage this feat.

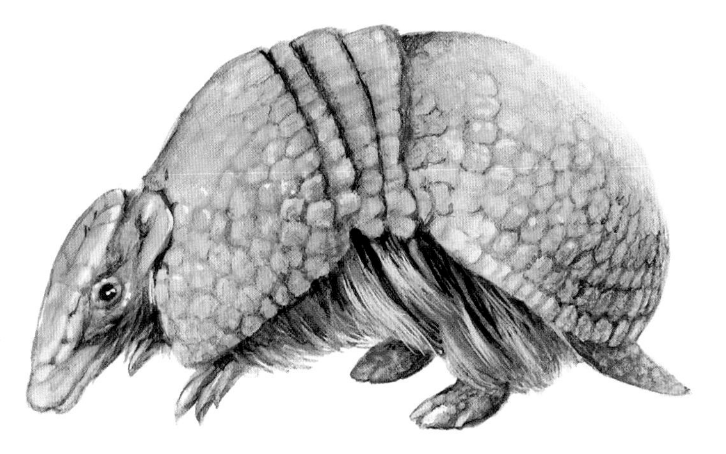

FACT FILE	
Length:	30cm (12in)
Weight:	1.5kg (3lb 5oz)
Distribution:	Argentina, Bolivia, southern Brazil
Habitat:	Marsh, grassland and woodland
Diet:	Ants and termites
Status (IUCN Red List):	Near threatened

Elephants and Relatives

Unsurprisingly for such an unusual animal, the elephant does not have many surviving close relatives. After all, if it did, these giant animals would not be regarded as unusual. Nevertheless, the elephants have an extended family, known as the Afrotherians, a group that contains a few less-well-known oddball species.

Asian Elephant

Elephas maximus

The Asian elephant is a domestic animal in its native territories. In fact, truly wild populations are very rare. Many untamed groups are believed to be feral, descended from escaped domestic stock. The Asian species differs from its African cousin by having a single projection on the tip of the trunk, smaller ears and a rounded back.

FACT FILE	
Length:	6m (19ft 7in); 3m (9ft 9in) tall
Weight:	6.5 tonnes (7 tons)
Distribution:	From India to Borneo
Habitat:	Forest
Diet:	Grass, leaves, shoots and fruits
Status (IUCN Red List):	Endangered

Western Tree Hyrax

Dendrohyrax dorsalis

It may look like a large rodent, but this animal is one of the closest living relatives of elephants. The nails on a hyrax's feet are arranged in a similar way to an elephant's, and the hyrax has two upper teeth extended into defensive tusks – although on a much smaller scale.

FACT FILE	
Length:	63cm (24¾in)
Weight:	3kg (6lb 10oz)
Distribution:	Central Africa
Habitat:	Forest
Diet:	Leaves, twigs, buds and fruits
Status (IUCN Red List):	Least concern

Dugong
Dugong dugon

The Afrotherian group is a mixed bag, as is amply illustrated by the dugong, an Indian ocean sea cow, which, despite its marine looks, is barely related to the whale or seal groups. The gentle giant – said to be an inspiration for the myth of mermaids – grazes on grasses that grow on the seabed of warm seas.

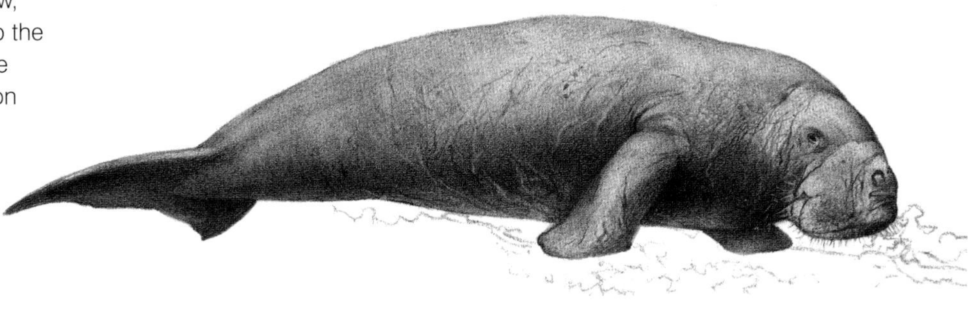

FACT FILE	
Length:	2.7m (8ft 9in)
Weight:	500kg (1100lb)
Distribution:	East African coast to N. Australia
Habitat:	Shallow seas
Diet:	Sea grass
Status (IUCN Red List):	Vulnerable

West Indian Manatee
Trichechus manatus

An Atlantic cousin to the dugong, the West Indian manatee has an even rarer cousin living along the west African coast. Manatees have rounder tail flukes than the dugong and pluck their aquatic plant foods with very dextrous lips. A manatee breathes air, like all mammals. Its lungs extend the length of its body, helping it to float.

FACT FILE	
Length:	3m (9ft 9in)
Weight:	600kg (1322lb)
Distribution:	Gulf of Mexico, Caribbean
Habitat:	Shallow seas and rivers
Diet:	Sea grass
Status (IUCN Red List):	Vulnerable

Aardvark
Orycteropus afer

The final member of the Afrotherians, the aardvark is the sole species in the whole mammal order Tubulidentata. (By contrast, the Rodentia order contains 2000 species.) Aardvark means 'earth pig' in Afrikaans, the name presumably associated with its tubular snout. Like anteaters, aardvarks dig out ant nests and lick up the exposed insects.

FACT FILE	
Length:	1.5m (5ft)
Weight:	70kg (154lb)
Distribution:	Sub-Saharan Africa
Habitat:	Dry grasslands and woods
Diet:	Ants and other insects
Status (IUCN Red List):	Least concern

African Elephant

Loxodonta africana

The largest land animal in the world, the African elephant has recently been divided into two separate species: the bush elephant, shown here, and the smaller forest elephant. The second species is confined to the jungles of Central Africa and is seldom seen, only its occasional rumbling calls giving it away.

FACT FILE	
Length:	7.5m (24ft); height 3.75m (12ft)
Weight:	7.5 tonnes (8.25 tons)
Distribution:	Sub-Saharan Africa
Habitat:	Grasslands, dry forest, marshes
Diet:	Roots, leaves, bark and fruits
Status (IUCN Red List):	Vulnerable

African elephants owe their huge size to the poor quality of their food. There are few nutrients in strips of bark and tough leaves, and so the species relies on the efficiency savings offered by a giant body. An adult eats about 200kg (440lb) and drinks 190 litres (50 gallons) of water every day to survive.

TUSKS
Both male and female African elephants have tusks. They are used to dig up roots, bulldoze tree trunks and as a weapon.

TRUNK
The long, flexible trunk is surprisingly dextrous. The double-pointed tip can pluck a blade of grass, while the main body is muscular enough to lift tree trunks.

EARS
The elephant's iconic ears have several functions: they are flapped during a threat display, and act as radiators, releasing excess heat to cool the animal.

TAIL
An elephant's thick skin is largely hairless. One of the few patches of hair is on the tip of the tail, which is used as a fly swat. The tail can also be used as a helping hand for young elephants struggling to keep up with the herd.

Moles

Everyone is familiar with what it is to be a mole – a life spent underground, burrowing through the darkness. However, this lifestyle has been taken on by members of several disparate groups of mammals, many of which are known as 'moles' and look very similar, despite hailing from very different lineages.

Hottentot Golden Mole

Amblysomus hottentotus

There are no true moles living in Africa. An unconnected group of small mammals called the Chrysochloridae, or golden moles, got there first. They are another example of Afrotherians, a small but significant set of mammals that also includes sea cows and elephants, and which broke away from other mammals 100 million years ago.

FACT FILE	
Length:	13cm (5in)
Weight:	85g (3oz)
Distribution:	Southern Africa
Habitat:	Soft soils
Diet:	Worms, grubs and snails
Status (IUCN Red List):	Least concern

Star-nosed Mole

Condylura cristata

Equipped with a super-sensitive snout, this species is a true record-breaker. Its 22-fingered nose can detect electrical impulses from prey as well as their smell, and it takes only 120 milliseconds for the mole to identify whether an animal is worth eating – quicker than any other animal on earth.

FACT FILE	
Length:	20cm (8in)
Weight:	70g (2½oz)
Distribution:	Eastern North America
Habitat:	Damp soil, riverbanks
Diet:	Worms and insects
Status (IUCN Red List):	Least concern

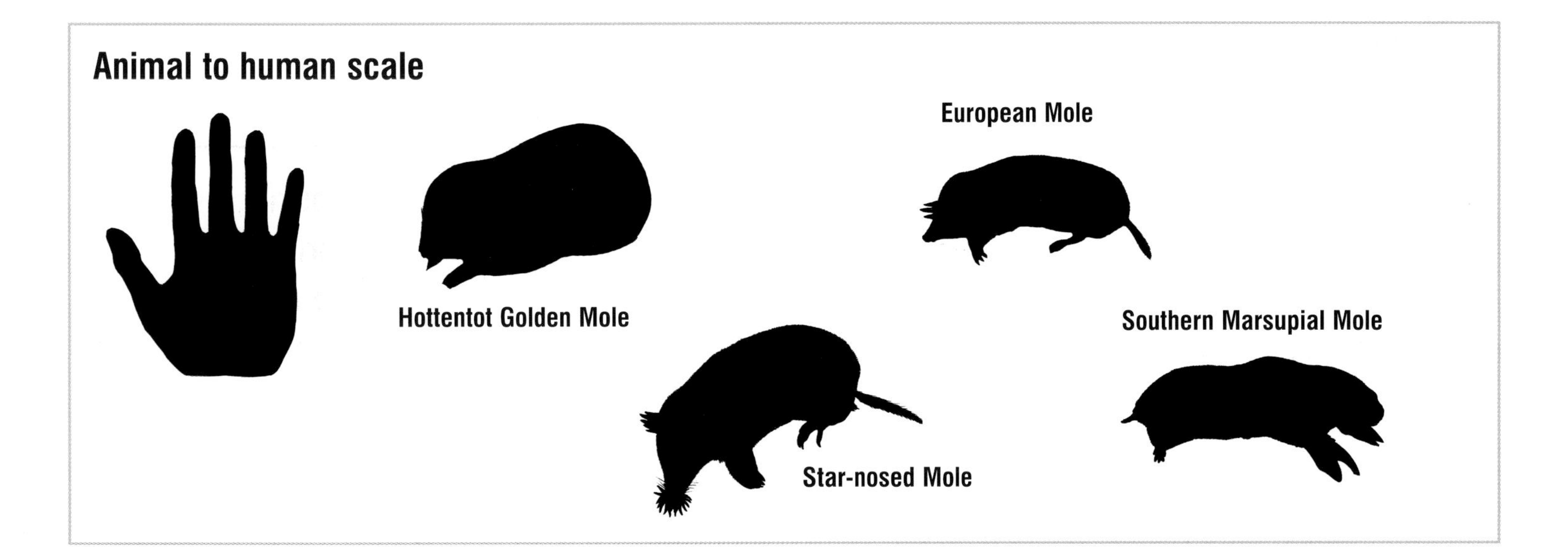

European Mole

Talpa europaea

This is the mole of storybooks that ruins lawns with its molehills. The digging is done by the animal's shovel-shaped forepaws. To aid life in a tunnel, the mole has no outer ears and its body is cylindrical. Contrary to popular belief, European moles do have working eyes, although there is little to look at underground.

FACT FILE	
Length:	15cm (6in)
Weight:	110g (4oz)
Distribution:	Northern Europe, western Siberia
Habitat:	Deep, soft soils
Diet:	Worms, insects and slugs
Status (IUCN Red List):	Least concern

Southern Marsupial Mole

Notoryctes typhlops

It looks like a mole, and it lives like one, but this species is more closely related to kangaroos and wombats. Like nearly all marsupials, this species rears young in a pouch, although in this case the pouch opens to the rear, so it does not fill with soil as the mole drags itself down tunnels.

FACT FILE	
Length:	18cm (7in)
Weight:	55g (2oz)
Distribution:	Southern Australia
Habitat:	Sandy soil
Diet:	Worms, grubs and lizards
Status (IUCN Red List):	Data deficient

Insectivores

Perhaps the most primitive group of mammals, the insectivores can be traced back more than 130 million years. The first mammals that evolved 140 million years earlier, even before the rise of the dinosaurs, are thought to have lived a similar lifestyle to today's insectivores, which include moles, hedgehogs and shrews.

Cuban Solenodon

Solenodon cubanus

This large species of insectivore is a very unusual animal. Its saliva contains a weak venom – almost unheard of among mammals. The venom is not deadly, and probably only stuns prey, making them easier to catch. Despite its relatively large size, the solenodon tunnels through soft ground, sniffing out food with its flexible snout.

FACT FILE	
Length:	33cm (13in)
Weight:	1kg (2lb 4oz)
Distribution:	Eastern Cuba
Habitat:	Caves and damp forests
Diet:	Insects, worms and fruits
Status (IUCN Red List):	Endangered

European Hedgehog

Erinaceus europaeus

Despite the hairs on its back being thickened into protective spines, the European hedgehog seldom comes out of hiding during the day. Instead, its muffled snuffles can be heard in gardens and hedgerows on warmer nights, where it is searching for worms and spiders, plus the eggs of ground-nesting birds.

FACT FILE	
Length:	26cm (10¼in)
Weight:	1kg (2lb 4oz)
Distribution:	Western Europe
Habitat:	Woodlands, fields and gardens
Diet:	Worms, insects, spiders and eggs
Status (IUCN Red List):	Least concern

Elegant Water Shrew

Nectogale elegans

Like other shrews, this species has a distinctive pointed snout; however, it also has adaptations for life in water. Its tail is fringed with hairs, making it into an effective paddle. The body fur is extremely fine and dense to create a waterproof coat, while the soles of the feet form disc-shaped suckers, ideal for scrabbling over wet rocks.

FACT FILE	
Length:	12cm (4¾in) plus tail
Weight:	28g (1oz)
Distribution:	Tibet and Himalayas
Habitat:	Mountain streams
Diet:	Small fish and crustaceans
Status (IUCN Red List):	Least concern

Bicoloured Shrew

Crocidura leucodon

Undoubtedly large for a shrew, this species is named for the pale underparts that contrast with the grey or chestnut fur on the back. Bicoloured shrews can produce 30 babies a year, in three or four separate litters. When a breeding nest is disturbed, the mother leads her young to safety in a nose-to-rump chain, known as a 'caravan'.

FACT FILE	
Length:	13cm (5in) plus tail
Weight:	13g (½oz)
Distribution:	Central Europe
Habitat:	Dry upland areas
Diet:	Frogs, lizards and invertebrates
Status (IUCN Red List):	Least concern

Asian House Shrew

Suncus murinus

Also known as the musk shrew, this species has few predators because it produces a nasty smell when under attack. This proves to be an effective deterrent against house cats and other domestic pest controllers, and so the house shrew is a common resident in many buildings in eastern Asia.

FACT FILE	
Length:	12cm (4¾in) plus tail
Weight:	33g (1.1oz)
Distribution:	Eastern Asia
Habitat:	Woodlands, fields and houses
Diet:	Insects
Status (IUCN Red List):	Least concern

Ground Pangolin

Manis gigantea

The ground pangolin looks more like a reptile than a mammal. The only hairs it has are its eyelashes. The rest of the body is tiled in thick horny scales. The pangolins have proved difficult to classify. For a long time they were grouped with plated armadillos and toothless anteaters, with which they share obvious similarities. However, today they form a distinct order, the Philodota.

FACT FILE	
Length:	1.4m (4ft 6in) plus tail
Weight:	18kg (39lb 10oz)
Distribution:	South Africa
Habitat:	Forest and grassland
Diet:	Ants and termites
Status (IUCN Red List):	Near-threatened

Giant pangolins are one of four Pangolin species. The other three live in southern and eastern Asia. Pangolins are also known as scaly anteaters, and for obvious reason. The sticky tongue laps up ants and termites, which are swallowed whole through the small and toothless mouth. The food is then ground into a pulp by a horny stomach lining.

TAIL
The tail makes up half of the body length. When threatened, the pangolin wraps its long tail around the body and rolls into a protective ball.

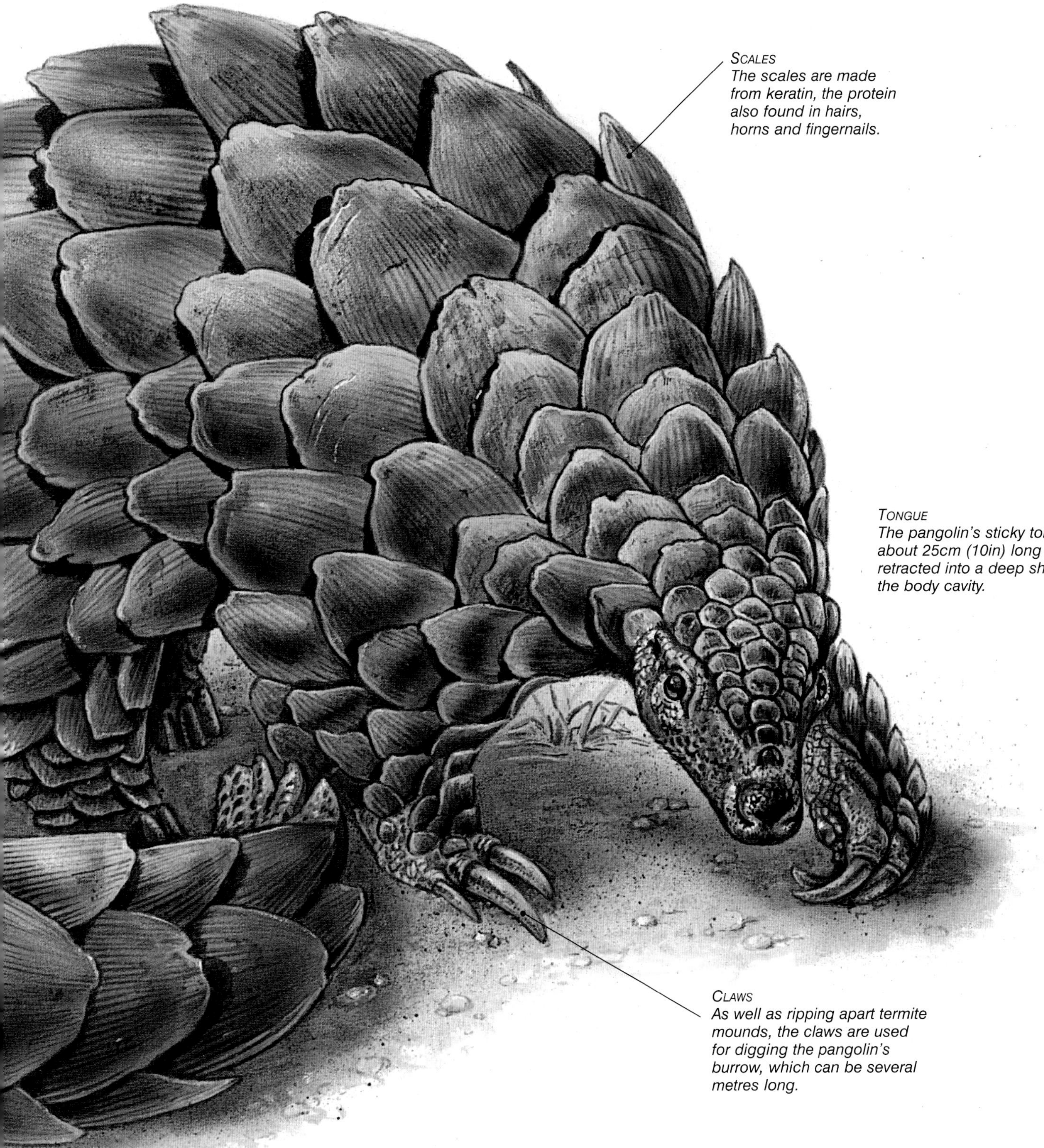

SCALES
The scales are made from keratin, the protein also found in hairs, horns and fingernails.

TONGUE
The pangolin's sticky tongue is about 25cm (10in) long and is retracted into a deep sheath in the body cavity.

CLAWS
As well as ripping apart termite mounds, the claws are used for digging the pangolin's burrow, which can be several metres long.

Big Bats

The bat order Chiroptera is roughly divided into two subgroups, the microchiroptera and the megachiroptera. The latter group is made up of the largest types of bat, known as flying foxes or, sometimes, fruit bats, after the group's main food source. Unlike smaller bats, larger bats do not use echolocation but rely on eyesight.

Long-tongued Nectar Bat

Macroglossus minimus

With a 33cm (13in) wingspan, this species cuts an imposing figure in the evening sky as it sets off from roosts in palm trees and under roofs to forage among large forest flowers, especially on banana plants. The bat is rarely seen alone, but flaps around in groups of a dozen or so.

FACT FILE	
Length:	82mm (3in)
Weight:	21g (¾oz)
Distribution:	Southern and Southeast Asia
Habitat:	Swamps and forests
Diet:	Pollen, nectar and soft fruits
Status (IUCN Red List):	Least concern

Queensland Tube-nosed Bat

Nyctimene robinsoni

This large Australian species gets its common name from its raised tubular nostrils, which can stick out from the face by up to 2cm (¾in). It is unclear what the tubes are for. The bats are solitary, roosting in trees by day and flying close to the ground, below the branches, while searching for fruits at night.

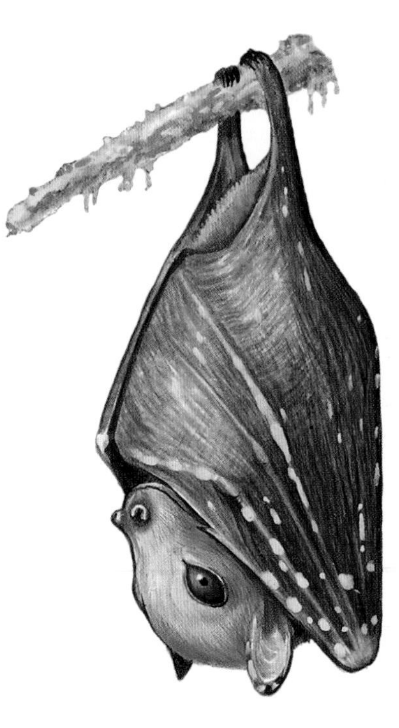

FACT FILE	
Length:	13cm (5in)
Weight:	55g (2oz)
Distribution:	East coast of Australia
Habitat:	Forests and orchards
Diet:	Fruits
Status (IUCN Red List):	Least concern

Egyptian Rousette

Rousettus aegyptiacus

This large fruit bats roosts in damp and dark places, such as caves, during the day. They live in groups of a few dozen, which can swell to nearly 1000 bats in the right conditions. The bats stream out of their roosts just after sunset to feast on a range of fruits, spreading their wings to a span of 60cm (23½in).

FACT FILE	
Length:	16.5cm (6½in)
Weight:	130g (4½oz)
Distribution:	Sub-Saharan Africa and Arabia
Habitat:	Forests, grassland and scrub
Diet:	Fruits
Status (IUCN Red List):	Least concern

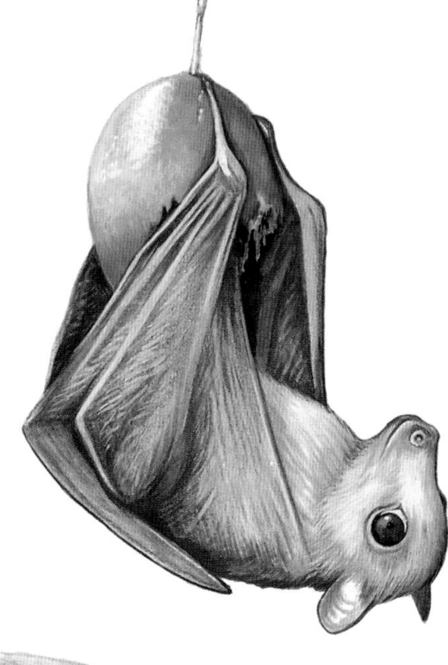

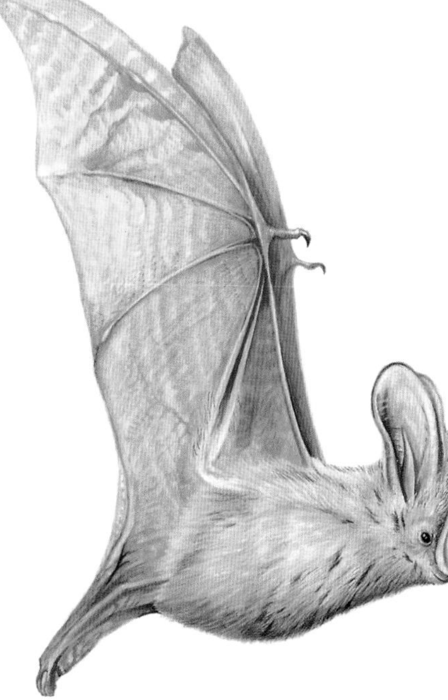

Yellow-winged Bat

Lavia frons

This insect-eating species does not hunt down its prey like smaller insectivorous bats. Instead, it hangs from a branch – often on a large thorny bush – and swoops on flying insects as they buzz past. Unusually, yellow-winged bats are monogamous. A pair roosts together in the same tree, and chases other bats away.

FACT FILE	
Length:	7cm (2¾in)
Weight:	28g (1oz)
Distribution:	Central Africa
Habitat:	Woodland and savannah
Diet:	Insects
Status (IUCN Red List):	Least concern

Small Bats

The smaller bat species tend to hunt insects on the wing during the night. They use an echolocation system to find prey – and avoid obstacles – in the darkness. They produce ultrasound calls, far too high-pitched for the human ear, and orientate themselves by listening to the echoes.

Greater Bulldog Bat

Noctilio leporinus

Also known as the fisherman bat, this species makes foraging runs across still water and hooks small fish by dragging its clawed feet through the water. The bat may store some of its food in pouches in the cheeks while it busies itself with another hunting run. If one bat spots another on a collision course, it emits a deep warning honk.

FACT FILE	
Length:	13cm (5in)
Weight:	78g (2¾oz)
Distribution:	South America and Caribbean
Habitat:	Streams,rivers and coastal waters
Diet:	Fish
Status (IUCN Red List):	Least concern

Common Vampire Bat

Desmodus rotundus

Bats have often been associated with the legend of vampires, and this species explains why. Unable to survive on anything other than the blood of living vertebrates, vampire bats cut small holes in the neck or leg of prey and lap from the trickle of blood. The bats' saliva contains an anticoagulant so wounds bleed for a long time.

FACT FILE	
Length:	8cm (3in)
Weight:	28g (1oz)
Distribution:	From Mexico to Chile
Habitat:	Warm, humid regions
Diet:	Blood
Status (IUCN Red List):	Least concern

White Bat

Ectophylla alba

Even for a bat, this species is a tiddler. White bats build 'tents' out of Heliconia leaves by nibbling the side veins so they hang down from the central rib. A single male lives underneath with a harem of five or six females. The bats' white fur affords them some protection, making the little bats look like patches of fungus or bird droppings.

FACT FILE	
Length:	4cm (1½in)
Weight:	6g (⅕oz)
Distribution:	Central America
Habitat:	Rainforests
Diet:	Fruit
Status (IUCN Red List):	Near threatened

Serotine Bat

Eptesicus serotinus

One of the largest of European bats, with a wingspan of around 37cm (14½in), the serotine tunes its echolocation calls to pick out large flying insects. The species often hunts in low-lying woodlands and frequently enters residential areas. Small groups may roost in rural buildings in summer.

FACT FILE	
Length:	7cm (2¾in)
Weight:	28g (1oz)
Distribution:	Europe
Habitat:	Lowlands
Diet:	Beetles, flies and moths
Status (IUCN Red List):	Least concern

Pocketed Free-tailed Bat

Nyctinomops femorosaccus

Unlike most bats, this species has a tail that extends beyond the skin membrane used in flight. The reference to pockets in its common name refers to the way the skin folds as the wings are retracted. This species of bats is fast-flying, and can be heard literally whistling through the air as it flies past.

FACT FILE	
Length:	11cm (4¼in)
Weight:	13g (½oz)
Distribution:	Southwestern US and Mexico
Habitat:	Desert
Diet:	Insects
Status (IUCN Red List):	Least concern

Cats

The cat family, Felidae, falls into two groups: the big cats and the small cats. As one would expect, the first group includes lions and tigers, but it also contains some medium-sized species, too. What links them is their ability to roar. The small cats can only snarl and purr.

Cheetah

Acinonyx jubatus

The fastest animal on four legs, the cheetah relies as much on its speed as on its feline stealth to bring down prey. While other cats have retractable claws, which are pulled in to keep them sharp, a cheetah's blunt claws are locked in the out position. The claws work like a sprinter's spikes, helping the cat to power up to speeds of 110km/h (68mph).

FACT FILE	
Length:	1.8m (6ft)
Weight:	40kg (88lb)
Distribution:	Africa and Middle East
Habitat:	Dry grassland
Diet:	Gazelles, antelopes and small deer
Status (IUCN Red List):	Vulnerable

Lion

Panthera leo

The largest cat in Africa, this species once lived across western Asia and as far east as China. All that remains of the Asian populations is a few hundred lions in the Gir Forest of India. Lions are the only social cat species, living in prides ruled by dominant males.

FACT FILE	
Length:	2.7m (8ft 9in)
Weight:	180kg (397lb)
Distribution:	Sub-Saharan Africa (plus Gir Forest)
Habitat:	Grassland
Diet:	Large herbivores
Status (IUCN Red List):	Vulnerable

Jaguar

Panthera onca

The largest cat in the Americas, the jaguar is characterized by a distinctive rosette pattern on its coat, which offers ideal camouflage amid the dappled light of the deep forest. A jaguar ambushes prey from above, leaping down from a branch vantage point. The cat's mighty jaw can crush its prey's skull.

FACT FILE	
Length:	1.9m (6ft 3in)
Weight:	158kg (348lb)
Distribution:	South and Central America
Habitat:	Forests and swamps
Diet:	Deer, peccaries and tapirs
Status (IUCN Red List):	Near threatened

Iberian Lynx

Lynx pardinus

The most endangered species of cat in the world, the Iberian lynx is a specialist rabbit hunter. Hunting and agricultural changes in Spain and Portugal have reduced the number of rabbits considerably, and so the Iberian lynx has hit serious trouble in recent decades. Fewer than 150 cats are thought to survive in the wild.

FACT FILE	
Length:	65cm (25½in)
Weight:	5kg (11lb)
Distribution:	Spanish highlands
Habitat:	Dry woodlands
Diet:	Rabbits
Status (IUCN Red List):	Critically endangered

Cougar

Puma concolor

This species goes by several names: mountain lion, puma, panther, cougar. All are testimony to this species' incredible range, which covers much of North and South America. Although of similar length to the jaguar, a cougar is considerably lighter, and, unable to roar, it is a large relation of the house cat.

FACT FILE	
Length:	2m (6ft 6in)
Weight:	100kg (220lb)
Distribution:	Southern Canada to Cape Horn
Habitat:	Any terrain
Diet:	Deer, rabbits and raccoons
Status (IUCN Red List):	Least concern

Tiger

Panthera tigris

The mightiest cat of all, the tiger is a solitary hunter that creeps unseen within a few metres of its prey, and then attacks with a burst of raw power that can knock almost any prey to the ground. Death follows soon after, as the tiger clamps its jaws around its victim's throat, severing the spinal cord and crushing the windpipe.

FACT FILE	
Length:	3m (9ft 9in)
Weight:	272kg (600lb)
Distribution:	Southern and Eastern Asia
Habitat:	Forests and swamps
Diet:	Deer, cattle and pigs
Status (IUCN Red List):	Endangered

Several subspecies of tiger exist, from the rare Sumatran tiger to the pale Siberian subspecies, which lives in the snowy forests of North Korea, northern China and eastern Russia. All subspecies are highly endangered due to poaching. At the last count, there were fewer than 5000 tigers left in the wild.

EYES
Tigers generally hunt at night; like all cats, their eyes have a mirrored surface behind the retina that reflects back any light.

NOSE
A tiger's nose is very sensitive, and is enhanced by another scent organ in the roof of the mouth. The animal pulls a frozen snarl to take the deepest sniffs.

FORELEGS
Tigers grab prey with their immense forepaws, hooking in their long claws so they can use their weight to pull victims to the ground.

STRIPES
The tiger's orange and black stripes might not look like a good disguise, but they blend in well with the tall grasses where tigers lie in wait for prey.

House Cats

No one is quite sure when wild cats became our pets. Some evidence suggests that domestic cats were living among human families more than 10,000 years ago. House cats are the descendants of the wild cat species, but have since been bred into more than 40 varieties.

Wildcat

Felis silvestris

Its scientific name means 'cat of the woods', and that is exactly where this uncommon, rarely seen but widespread species lives. Three subspecies are recognized from Europe, Asia and Africa. It is the African subspecies that is thought to be the ancestor of today's pet cats.

FACT FILE	
Length:	56cm (22in)
Weight:	4kg (8lb 13oz)
Distribution:	Europe, Asia and Africa
Habitat:	Woodland
Diet:	Mice and birds
Status (IUCN Red List):	Least concern

Russian Blue Cat

Felis catus

This breed, so named after the combined visual effect of its silver and grey hairs, is thought to have originated in Archangel, a port in the Russian Arctic. It almost always has green eyes. Its 'blue' coat is not unique; the French Chartreux variety is also a blue breed.

FACT FILE	
Length:	46cm (18in)
Weight:	4kg (8lb 13oz)
Distribution:	N/A
Habitat:	N/A
Diet:	N/A
Status (IUCN Red List):	N/A

Siamese Cat
Felis catus

One of the oldest and most well known of cat breeds, this species originated in Thailand, once known as Siam. In that region there are several home-grown varieties of cat; this one is known as the Moon Diamond breed. The breed became popular in the West in the 1950s.

FACT FILE	
Length:	46cm (18in)
Weight:	4kg (8lb 13oz)
Distribution:	N/A
Habitat:	N/A
Diet:	N/A
Status (IUCN Red List):	N/A

Exotic Shorthair Cat
Felis catus

The exotic shorthair breed was the product of several crossings between Persian cats and American shorthairs in the 1960s to reduce the length of the Persian's often unmanageable hair. Like the Persian, the exotic breed has a stocky body with a rounded face.

FACT FILE	
Length:	46cm (18in)
Weight:	4kg (8lb 13oz)
Distribution:	N/A
Habitat:	N/A
Diet:	N/A
Status (IUCN Red List):	N/A

Sphynx
Felis catus

This is a naked, or hairless, breed that originated in Canada in 1966. The genetics of the breed are still poorly understood. Even inbreeding – matings between parent and offspring, or between siblings – do not always produce hairless kittens, and many of the cats die young.

FACT FILE	
Length:	46cm (18in)
Weight:	4kg (8lb 13oz)
Distribution:	N/A
Habitat:	N/A
Diet:	N/A
Status (IUCN Red List):	N/A

Pack Dogs

Dogs make up the mammal family Canidae. Not all family members live in the same way. The lupine, or wolf-like, species live in complex family groups, or packs, whereas the foxes, and other vulpine dog species, live in less organized social units.

Grey Wolf

Canis lupus

One of the most widespread species of mammal, grey wolves are the ultimate long-distance runner. Without the bulk to bring down large prey alone, these wolves work in a team to chase victims until they are too exhausted to defend themselves. With its long legs and large lungs and heart, a wolf can run 200km (124 miles) in a single night.

FACT FILE	
Length:	1.5m (5ft)
Weight:	50kg (110lb)
Distribution:	North America, Asia, eastern Europe
Habitat:	Tundra and forest
Diet:	Deer
Status (IUCN Red List):	Least concern

Black-backed Jackal

Canis mesomelas

A jackal is a jack-of-all-trades when it comes to finding food. A pack of a dozen or so dogs work together to bring down large animals – often domestic livestock – but they also go off on their own to catch rats and lizards. Jackals are also on hand to pick clean the remains of the kills of larger hunters.

FACT FILE	
Length:	1m (3ft 3in)
Weight:	8kg (17lb 10oz))
Distribution:	Southern and eastern Africa
Habitat:	Dry grassland
Diet:	Rodents, hares and sheep
Status (IUCN Red List):	Least concern

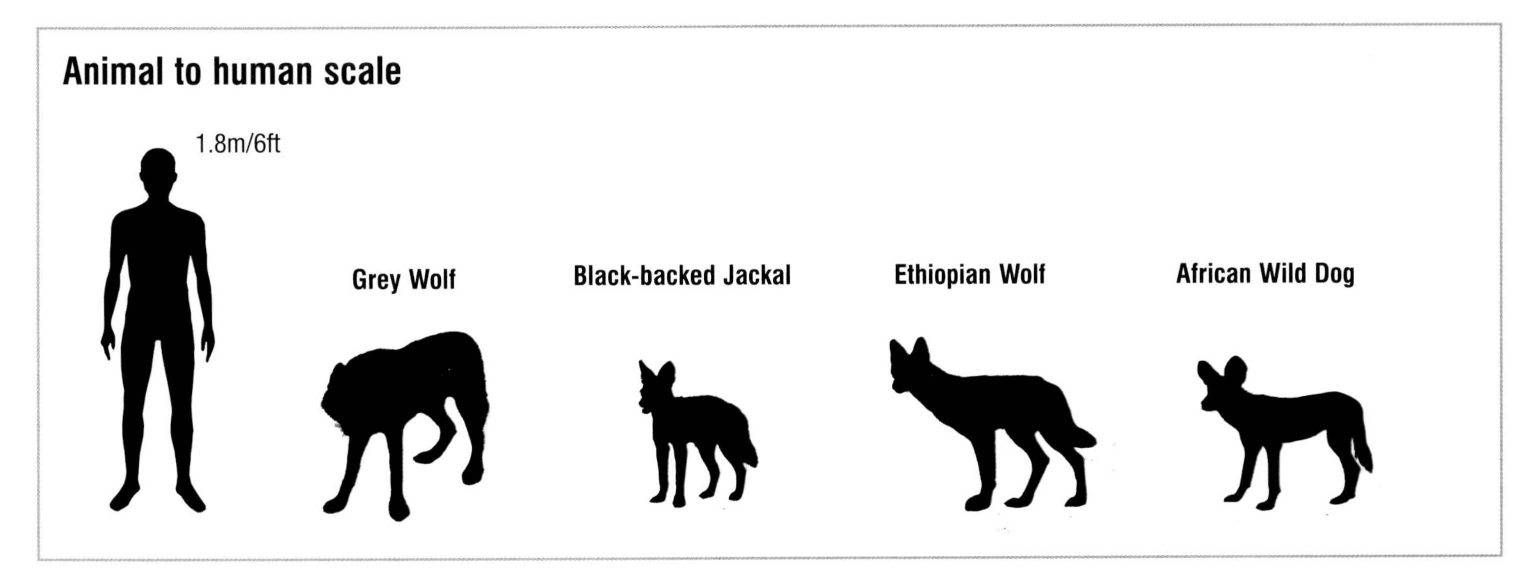

Ethiopian Wolf

Canis simensis

The most endangered species of dog in the world, this lanky wolf is found only in a few remote alpine meadows high in the Ethiopian highlands. They live in small packs but hunt alone, having evolved into specialist mole rat hunters. Diseases spread by domestic dogs threaten to wipe out the species.

FACT FILE	
Length:	1.3m (4ft 3in)
Weight:	15kg (33lb)
Distribution:	Ethiopian highlands
Habitat:	Alpine grassland
Diet:	Naked mole rats
Status (IUCN Red List):	Endangered

African Wild Dog

Lycaon pictus

Although not a close relative of the grey wolf, the wild dog is the most effective pack hunter in Africa. They live in huge packs, sometimes containing more than 100 animals. A single dog can take down a small antelope, but five or six dogs together can kill a wildebeest, repeatedly biting its muzzle to bring it to the ground.

FACT FILE	
Length:	1.1m (3ft 7in)
Weight:	36kg (79lb)
Distribution:	Southern Africa
Habitat:	Savannah
Diet:	Large herbivores
Status (IUCN Red List):	Endangered

Domestic Dogs

Man's best friends, whatever their shape, size or temperament, are all descended from grey wolves thought to have become domesticated in East Asia around 40,000 years ago. These early pets spread around the world with human migrations, which introduced dingos to Australia, and dogs were even taken to the Pacific islands.

Irish Wolfhound

Canis lupus familiaris

The Irish wolfhound is the tallest of all the world's dog breeds. Legend has it that this is the modern descendant of the Irish war dog. Ancient chroniclers said that entire battalions of soldiers went into battle with the giant dog as their main weapon. As its name suggests, the breed was also used to eradicate wild wolves from Ireland in the eighteenth century.

FACT FILE	
Height:	79cm (31in)
Weight:	54.5kg (120lb)
Distribution:	N/A
Habitat:	N/A
Diet:	N/A
Status (IUCN Red List):	N/A

Bulldog

Canis lupus familiaris

The bulldog was bred to be a tough dog for baiting bulls, perhaps as long ago as the fifteenth century. Today's bulldogs are less tough, despite their appearance, and are rated as one of the least intelligent breeds. Intensive inbreeding has resulted in many bulldogs suffering from chronic diseases.

FACT FILE	
Height :	40cm (16in)
Weight:	25kg (55lb)
Distribution:	N/A
Habitat:	N/A
Diet:	N/A
Status (IUCN Red List):	N/A

Yorkshire Terrier

Canis lupus familiaris

The Yorkshire terrier was bred in the late nineteenth century, originating in Huddersfield, England. The terrier dog was originally bred to be a tenacious pest controller, small enough to chase rabbits and badgers into their burrows. Today, the Yorkshire breed is primarily a companion dog.

FACT FILE	
Height :	20cm (8in)
Weight:	3.2kg (7lb)
Distribution:	N/A
Habitat:	N/A
Diet:	N/A
Status (IUCN Red List):	N/A

Bloodhound

Canis lupus familiaris

The bloodhound has the sharpest nose of any domestic dog. Its long muzzle contains large nasal cavities, and the loose skin around the mouth keeps the rhinarium – the cleft that connects the mouth and nostrils – moist, and thus more sensitive. A bloodhound is said to be able to smell a single skin cell several days after it was shed.

FACT FILE	
Height :	69cm (27in)
Weight:	50kg (110lb)
Distribution:	N/A
Habitat:	N/A
Diet:	N/A
Status (IUCN Red List):	N/A

English Cocker Spaniel

Canis lupus familiaris

This breed of gun dog is at least 500 years old. Its short legs made it easier for it to ride on the shoulders of a huntsman's horse. It was bred for its keen nose and intelligence. A working spaniel's job was to retrieve gamebirds or to assist in flushing out larger animals.

FACT FILE	
Height :	39cm (15½in)
Weight:	32kg (70lb 8oz)
Distribution:	N/A
Habitat:	N/A
Diet:	N/A
Status (IUCN Red List):	N/A

Small Dogs

The foxes are the largest subgroup in the wider dog family. Their lifestyle is so adaptable that they can live almost everywhere on earth, even in the heart of the Amazon rainforest. Other small members of the Canidae include the weasel-like bush dogs of South America, and the raccoon dog of Siberia.

Raccoon Dog

Nyctereutes procyonoides

Although it is a species of dog, this animal looks like a raccoon, an American member of an unrelated carnivore family. Raccoons, bears and dogs all evolved from the same group of ancient mammals. It is possible that these early ancestors resembled today's raccoon dog, and foraged for small prey on the ground and in the trees.

FACT FILE	
Length:	60cm (23½in)
Weight:	8kg (17lb 10oz)
Distribution:	Siberia and Europe
Habitat:	Damp forest
Diet:	Fish, frogs, fruits and birds
Status (IUCN Red List):	Least concern

Bat-eared Fox

Otocyon megalotis

In a family of meat-eaters, the bat-eared fox is an outsider. It uses its immense ears to listen for its favourite prey – a beetle grub munching its way out of a ball of dung. These little African foxes can be found following herds of antelope and zebra, which attract dung beetles, termites and other insects.

FACT FILE	
Length:	46cm (18in)
Weight:	8kg (17lb 10oz)
Distribution:	East and southern Africa
Habitat:	Savannah
Diet:	Rodents, birds, eggs, and fruits
Status (IUCN Red List):	Least concern

Red Fox

Vulpes vulpes

Challenging the grey wolf for the title of most widespread dog, the red fox has certainly fared better than its larger, wilder cousin. Red foxes are tough enough to survive an Arctic winter on the edge of the barren tundra, but also wily enough to make it among the bright lights of the city.

FACT FILE	
Length:	69cm (27in)
Weight:	5.5kg (12lb 2oz)
Distribution:	Northern Hemisphere and Australia
Habitat:	Tundra, desert, woodland, cities
Diet:	Voles, insects and human rubbish
Status (IUCN Red List):	Least concern

Maned Wolf

Chrysocyon brachyurus

Despite its name, this South American dog is a type of fox. Only its unusually long legs have elevated it to wolf status. The maned wolf also gets its name from the dark hair that runs down its neck; these become noticeably raised when the animal is threatened.

FACT FILE	
Length:	1.05m (3ft 5in)
Weight:	23kg (51lb)
Distribution:	Central South America
Habitat:	Swamps and grassland
Diet:	Rodents, birds and reptiles
Status (IUCN Red List):	Near threatened

Grey Fox

Urocyon cinereoargenteus

The grey fox is also known as the tree fox because it is an agile climber – a rare ability for a canid. They have longer claws than other foxes for gripping bark, and also make bold leaps between branches. The foxes raid nests and eat fruits while in the branches.

FACT FILE	
Length:	65cm (25½in)
Weight:	6kg (13lb 3oz)
Distribution:	Western US and Central America
Habitat:	Woodland
Diet:	Rabbits, mice and birds
Status (IUCN Red List):	Least concern

Bears

Containing the largest predators to live on land, the bear family Ursidae is a small one, with just eight members. The bears are a powerful adversary, capable of killing other animals with a single blow of the paw. However, most species have a quiet life, more often foraging for fruits than hunting down prey.

American Black Bear

Ursus americanus

The species credited with being the inspiration for the teddy bear, the black bear is the most common bear on earth. However, it is the weak relation in North America. It is a good tree climber, a skill that biologists think evolved as a defence tactic to escape attacks from its larger and fiercer American cousin, the brown (or grizzly) bear.

FACT FILE	
Length:	1.8m (6ft)
Weight:	270kg (595lb)
Distribution:	Canada to Mexico
Habitat:	Forest
Diet:	Fruits, insects, fish and deer
Status (IUCN Red List):	Least concern

Kodiak Bear

Ursus arctos middendorffi

Thought by most to exceed the polar bear in size and strength, this American subspecies of brown bear is confined to the island of southern Alaska, where it hunts from a plentiful supply of fish and deer. A range of other brown bear species live right across the Northern Hemisphere.

FACT FILE	
Length:	2.8m (9ft 2in)
Weight:	530kg (1168lb)
Distribution:	Kodiak Islands, Alaska
Habitat:	Forest and river meadows
Diet:	Fish, deer and fruits
Status (IUCN Red List):	Least concern

Sun Bear

Helarctos malayanus

Despite being the smallest of all bear species, the sun bear is deceptively thick-set. Its diet contains a lot of insects, and it uses its powerful jaws to crack open dead wood to reveal the grubs inside. This bear also employs its very long and rough tongue to slurp honey from bees' nests.

FACT FILE	
Length:	1.5m (5ft)
Weight:	145kg (320lb)
Distribution:	Southeast Asia
Habitat:	Tropical forest
Diet:	Honey, insects and plants
Status (IUCN Red List):	Vulnerable

Sloth Bear

Melursus ursinus

This Asian bear is a specialist termite catcher. It earns its name from its shaggy appearance and long curved claws, which are used to rip apart termite mounds, in a manner similar to the anteaters of South America. The sloth bear also eats berries and honey.

FACT FILE	
Length:	1.8m (6ft)
Weight:	190kg (420lb)
Distribution:	South Asia
Habitat:	Forests and scrubland
Diet:	Ants, termites and fruits
Status (IUCN Red List):	Endangered

Spectacled Bear

Tremarctos ornatus

Since this is the only bear species to live in South America, confined to the Andes, Paddington Bear was presumably a spectacled bear. The bear is the largest animal in the Andes, and only the Brazilian tapir beats it continent-wide. The common name is derived from the pale fur ringing the eyes.

FACT FILE	
Length:	2m (6ft 6in)
Weight:	175kg (386lb)
Distribution:	Andes Mountains south to Chile
Habitat:	Mountain forest
Diet:	Fruits, rodents and insects
Status (IUCN Red List):	Vulnerable

Giant Panda

Ailuropoda melanoleuca

Few animals share the iconic status of the giant panda. Once a little-known species hidden away in the dense bamboo forests of China, the herbivorous bear was chosen as the symbol of world conservation in the 1960s. Ever since then, those distinctive black eyes have been reminding us of the fragility of the world's wildlife.

FACT FILE	
Length:	1.8m (6ft)
Weight:	110kg (242lb)
Distribution:	China
Habitat:	Bamboo forest
Diet:	Bamboo
Status (IUCN Red List):	Endangered

Giant pandas were a rare species long before humans began to encroach on their habitat. Evolved to survive on the woody stems of bamboo, this most specialist of feeder cannot survive beyond its mountain enclave. Fewer than 2000 live in the wild, and with its very slow breeding rates, giant pandas will not recover quickly.

DIGESTIVE SYSTEM
A carnivore's stomach is ill-equipped to survive on a pure plant diet, and the panda must eat more or less constantly for 16 hours a day.

TEETH
The panda's back teeth are flatter and rougher than those of other bears, to help grind up its fibrous diet.

BLACK EYES
The dark eyes on the pale face are thought to have a defensive function, startling an enemy when it comes across a panda in the thick forest.

FOREPAW
Giant pandas have a sixth finger on their front paws. This is an extension of a wrist bone and is used like an opposable thumb to grip bamboo shoots.

Raccoons

The raccoons and its relatives occupy a mammal family called the Procyonidae. That name means 'before dogs', which alludes to their evolutionary relationship with wolves, foxes and also bears. Most procyonids have become wily opportunists, capable of eating just about anything they can get their dextrous paws on.

Red Panda

Ailurus fulgens

Despite sharing a name with the giant panda, this smaller species is a relative of the raccoons, not of the bears. The common name is due to a number of similarities between the two unconnected species: the cute mask-like facial colouring and a reliance on a bamboo diet.

FACT FILE	
Length:	64cm (25in)
Weight:	6kg (13lb 3oz)
Distribution:	South and Southeast Asia
Habitat:	Mountains forests
Diet:	Bamboo leaves and insects
Status (IUCN Red List):	Vulnerable

Bushy-tailed Olingo

Bassaricyon gabbii

The cat-like olingo lives in the trees of tropical forests. It is an agile climber, using long claws to grip the bark, and it has little need to descend to the ground. The long tail provides balance in flimsy treetops, and the nocturnal olingo makes bold leaps between branches as it searches for food.

FACT FILE	
Length:	48cm (19in)
Weight:	1.5kg (3lb 5oz)
Distribution:	Central America to south Brazil
Habitat:	Tropical forest
Diet:	Fruits, insects and rodents
Status (IUCN Red List):	Least concern

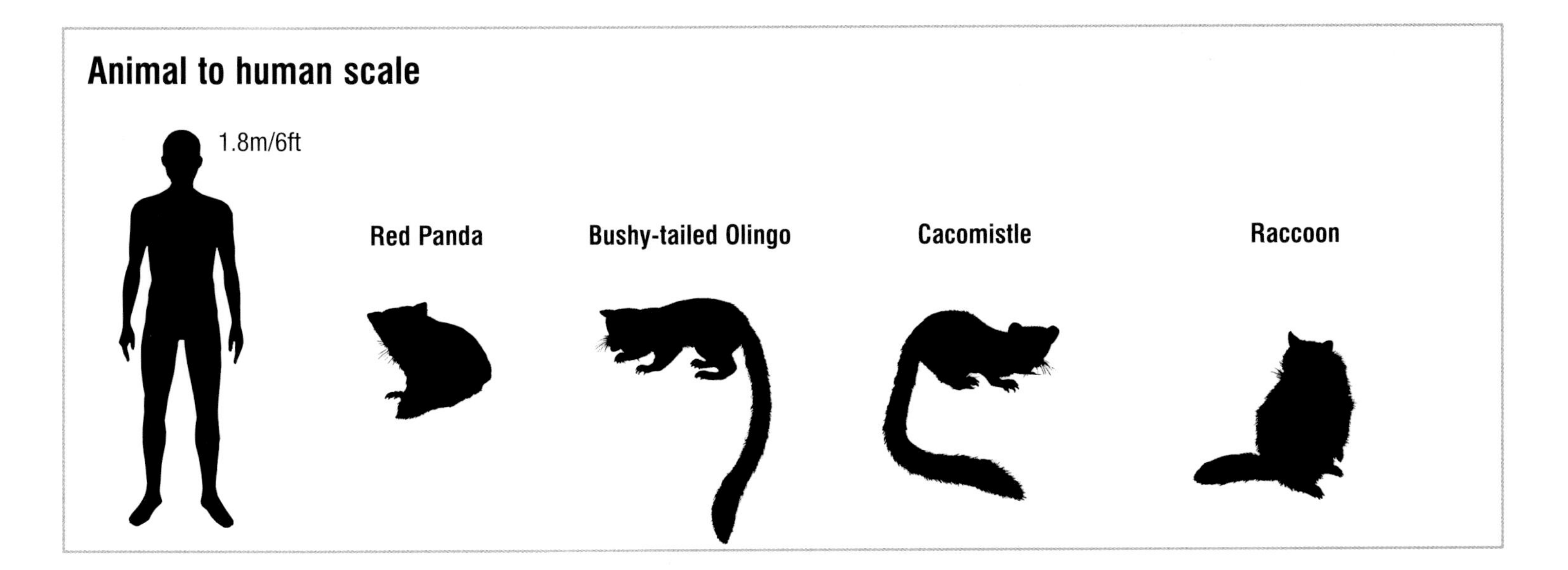

Cacomistle

Bassariscus sumichrasti

Sometimes known as the ringtail in its native Central America, the cacomistle should not be confused with a related species also named ringtail that lives in the dry canyons of the United States and Mexico. The nocturnal cacomistle is an agile climber. Its hind feet can twist around to allow the animal to climb down head first.

FACT FILE	
Length:	40cm (16in)
Weight:	1.3kg (2lb 12oz)
Distribution:	Central America
Habitat:	Rocky areas
Diet:	Insects, rodents and fruits
Status (IUCN Red List):	Least concern

Raccoon

Procyon lotor

The ultimate opportunist, the masked bandit that is the raccoon has done well out of the urbanization of its native North America. The curious creature searches high and low for titbits and is just as happy in a dustbin as a swampy thicket. Its sensitive forepaws are nimble enough to tackle any food items.

FACT FILE	
Length:	65cm (25½in)
Weight:	8kg (17lb 10oz)
Distribution:	North America
Habitat:	Woodlands, swamps and cities
Diet:	Fruits, frogs, fish, eggs, insects
Status (IUCN Red List):	Least concern

Small Carnivores

Many small, hunting mammals are grouped together in the family Mustelidae. The mustelids are all slender, inquisitive creatures with short legs that allow them to reach places that larger predators cannot. The mustelid family includes the otters, minks and martens. Skunks belong to the separate Mephitidae family.

Oriental Small-clawed Otter

Amblonyx cinereus

One of the smallest otters in the world, this species is named after the way its claws form blunt spikes on its paws. The reason for this disarmament is to increase the sensitivity and dexterity of the otter's paws, so it can find shellfish in the muddy sediments of its swampy habitat.

FACT FILE	
Length:	61cm (24in)
Weight:	5kg (11lb)
Distribution:	Southeast Asia
Habitat:	Wetlands and mangroves
Diet:	Crabs, molluscs and frogs
Status (IUCN Red List):	Vulnerable

European Otter

Lutra lutra

This species is rather misnamed, since it ranges from the west of Ireland to Manchuria and even into the fertile planes of North Africa. The otter is an expert water hunter, relying on its long whiskers to detect the swirls and eddies created in the water by its fish prey.

FACT FILE	
Length:	70cm (28in)
Weight:	10kg (22lb)
Distribution:	Europe and Asia
Habitat:	Rivers, lakes and coastlines
Diet:	Fish, frogs and eels
Status (IUCN Red List):	Near threatened

Giant Otter

Pteronura brasiliensis

The largest mustelid on earth, the giant otter lives in small groups along the banks of the slow-flowing waterways of the Amazon and other South American river systems. Unlike most mustelids, this species becomes more active in daylight. In the dry season, the otters crowd around shrinking pools, waiting for the rains.

FACT FILE	
Length:	1.4m (4ft 6in)
Weight:	32kg (70lb 8oz)
Distribution:	South America
Habitat:	Streams, riverbanks and lakes
Diet:	Fish
Status (IUCN Red List):	Endangered

Fisher

Martes pennanti

You could be easily fooled into thinking that a fisher was a water mammal, adapted for life in and around water. However, this North American marten is a forest hunter and is more likely to tackle a porcupine than a chub salmon. They can climb, but do most of their hunting on the ground.

FACT FILE	
Length:	76cm (30in)
Weight:	5kg (11lb)
Distribution:	Canada and northern US
Habitat:	Woodlands and forests
Diet:	Shrews, squirrels and chipmunks
Status (IUCN Red List):	Least concern

Molina's Hog-nosed Skunk

Conepatus chinga

The white stripes of this skunk, and others, serve a useful purpose. They are warning signs that point straight to the danger zone, the skunk's anal gland, which is primed to spray a foul mist at threats. Left well alone, the nocturnal skunk uses its fleshy pig-like snout to root out buried insects and other prey.

FACT FILE	
Length:	68cm (26in)
Weight:	3.4kg (7lb 8oz)
Distribution:	Southern South America
Habitat:	Pampas and canyons
Diet:	Spiders, insects and fruits
Status (IUCN Red List):	Least concern

Badgers

The name 'badger' is derived from the French for 'digger', and is an apt name for these muscled mustelids, which regularly dig for their food and to build dens. The American badger is such a powerful digger that it can rapidly excavate a burrow to hide in if caught out in the open by enemies.

European Badger

Meles meles

A much loved wild-wood resident, the European badger digs the most elaborate burrows of any badger species. The tunnel network, or sett, is passed down through the generations. After years of maintenance and improvements, a badger family's home contains hundreds of metres of tunnels, a dozen exits, and even a latrine.

FACT FILE	
Length:	95cm (37½in)
Weight:	12kg (26lb 8oz)
Distribution:	Europe and Asia
Habitat:	Woodlands and forests
Diet:	Insects, worms, slugs and fruits
Status (IUCN Red List):	Least concern

Teledu

Mydaus javanensis

This Southeast Asian species is also known as the Indonesian stink badger, for good reason. Like the distantly related skunk, it too squirts a noxious spray from its rear end when under attack. The teledu's toes are almost completely fused together, making them highly effective shovels.

FACT FILE	
Length:	44cm (17in)
Weight:	2.5kg (5lb 8oz)
Distribution:	Indonesia
Habitat:	Mountain forests
Diet:	Insects and worms
Status (IUCN Red List):	Least concern

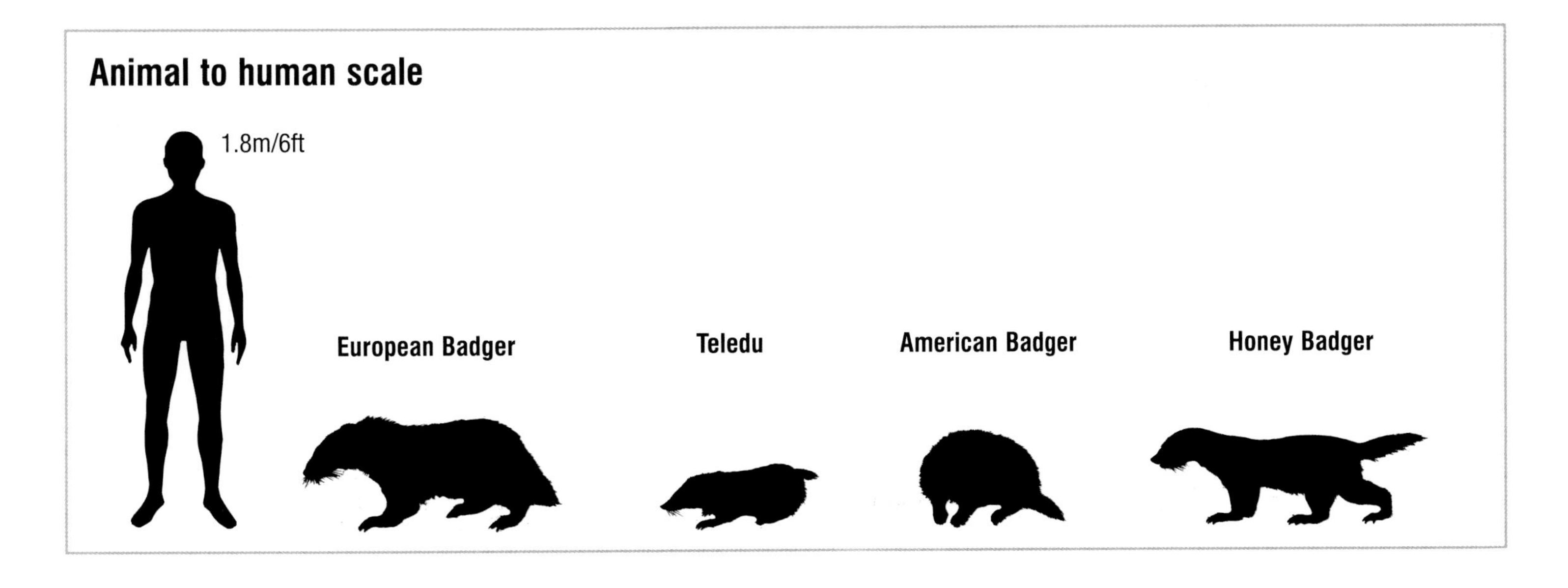

American Badger

Taxidea taxus

The American badger needs to be tough to survive in the extreme heat and cold of the Great Plains. It survives by digging out gophers and other burrowing rodents. The badger is sometimes helped in this task by coyotes, its wolfish neighbours. The dog's job is to sniff out the prey, and the badger then digs it up for the partners to share.

FACT FILE	
Length:	70cm (28in)
Weight:	12kg (26lb 8oz)
Distribution:	Southwest Canada to Mexico
Habitat:	Prairie and woodland
Diet:	Tunnelling rodents
Status (IUCN Red List):	Least concern

Honey Badger

Mellivora capensis

This creature, also known as the ratel, is one of the most stubborn scrappers in the animal kingdom, defending its food against all comers, even lions. The badger is named for its habit of following honeyguide birds to bees' nests, which it then rips apart to feast on the honey. However, its bird guide prefers the wax.

FACT FILE	
Length:	76cm (30in)
Weight:	13kg (28lb 10oz)
Distribution:	Africa, west and south Asia
Habitat:	Woodlands, savannah and forests
Diet:	Rodents, birds, frogs and honey
Status (IUCN Red List):	Least concern

Weasels and Polecats

The smallest of mammal carnivores are by no means the mildest. The weasels, polecats and minks have a fierce nature that belies their slender builds. They regularly follow prey much larger than themselves into their burrows and launch a deadly onslaught below the ground.

Stoat

Mustela erminea

Seen here in ermine, the white winter coat sported by stoats in the northern fringes of its range, the stoat is a deadly trickster. It confuses its prey by prancing before them in a deranged fashion, lulling them into a baffled reverie, unsure how to respond. Then, in an instant, the stoat's dance becomes a deadly attack.

FACT FILE	
Length:	24cm (9½in)
Weight:	100g (3½oz)
Distribution:	Northern Hemisphere
Habitat:	Grasslands and woodlands
Diet:	Rats, hares and birds
Status (IUCN Red List):	Least concern

Least Weasel

Mustela nivalis

The weasel stakes out its prey before launching an attack, gauging where its intended victim is likely to flee when battle commences. Invariably, the fight is taken underground, and the flattened head of the weasel allows it to use its small but sharp teeth to deadly effect in confined spaces.

FACT FILE	
Length:	24cm (9½in)
Weight:	100g (3½oz)
Distribution:	Northern Hemisphere
Habitat:	Grasslands and woodlands
Diet:	Rodents, rabbits and birds
Status (IUCN Red List):	Least concern

European Polecat

Mustela putorius

The wild relative of the domestic ferret, the European polecat is most active in forests and other dense habitats, but also takes to the water to catch fish and frogs. It is a perennial enemy of the chicken farmer, since it can wriggle through tiny gaps in fences and decimate the poultry.

FACT FILE	
Length:	51cm (20in)
Weight:	1.5kg (3lb 5oz)
Distribution:	Europe
Habitat:	Woodlands, riverbanks and lakes
Diet:	Birds, eggs, worms and insects
Status (IUCN Red List):	Least concern

Greater Grison

Galictis vittata

The greater grison is South America's answer to the polecat. It specializes in hunting that continent's array of chunky rodents, such as cavies and viscachas. The animal is named after the grey cape of grizzled fur (a mixture of white and black hair) on its back.

FACT FILE	
Length:	51cm (20in)
Weight:	2kg (4lb 6oz)
Distribution:	Mexico to Bolivia
Habitat:	Grasslands and rainforests
Diet:	Rodents, birds and fruits
Status (IUCN Red List):	Least concern

Ferret

Mustela putorius furo

The ferret is the domestic breed of the polecat. First domesticated at least 2500 years ago, the ferret was probably first used for hunting rabbits or other small animals. With its long, slim body and inquisitive nature, the ferret is ideal for chasing rodents out of their burrows, but this practice is illegal in several countries.

FACT FILE	
Length:	51cm (20in) including tail
Weight:	1.4kg (3lb)
Distribution:	N/A
Habitat:	N/A
Diet:	N/A
Status (IUCN Red List):	N/A

Walrus

Odobenus rosmarus

Neither a seal or a sea lion, walruses are unmistakable with their huge tusks, sported by both sexes. They live on and under the sea ice of the far north, probing the seabed for buried shellfish with their whiskered snouts. Between feeding, a walrus hauls its immense blubbery bulk onto floating islands of ice, using its tusks as grappling hooks.

FACT FILE	
Length:	Male 3.6m (11ft 9in); female 2.6m (8ft 6in)
Weight:	1.7 tonnes (1.9 tons)
Distribution:	Northern polar seas
Habitat:	Cold shallow seas with ice floes
Diet:	Clams and crustaceans
Status (IUCN Red List):	Data deficient

WHISKERS
The walrus's moustache of short whiskers forms a super-sensitive probe for seeking food on the seabed. The walrus blows great bubbles of air to blast away the sediment.

There are two subspecies of walrus, both completely isolated from one other and confined to the Atlantic and and Pacific ice packs. In summer, when the ice recedes, the walruses may gather in herds several thousand strong on land. In these crowds, males wield their tusks to assert their dominance and see off polar bears.

FLIPPER
A walrus's flippers resemble those of a sea lion more than a seal's. They are most useful for swimming, and the walrus can manage only a four-limbed shuffle on land.

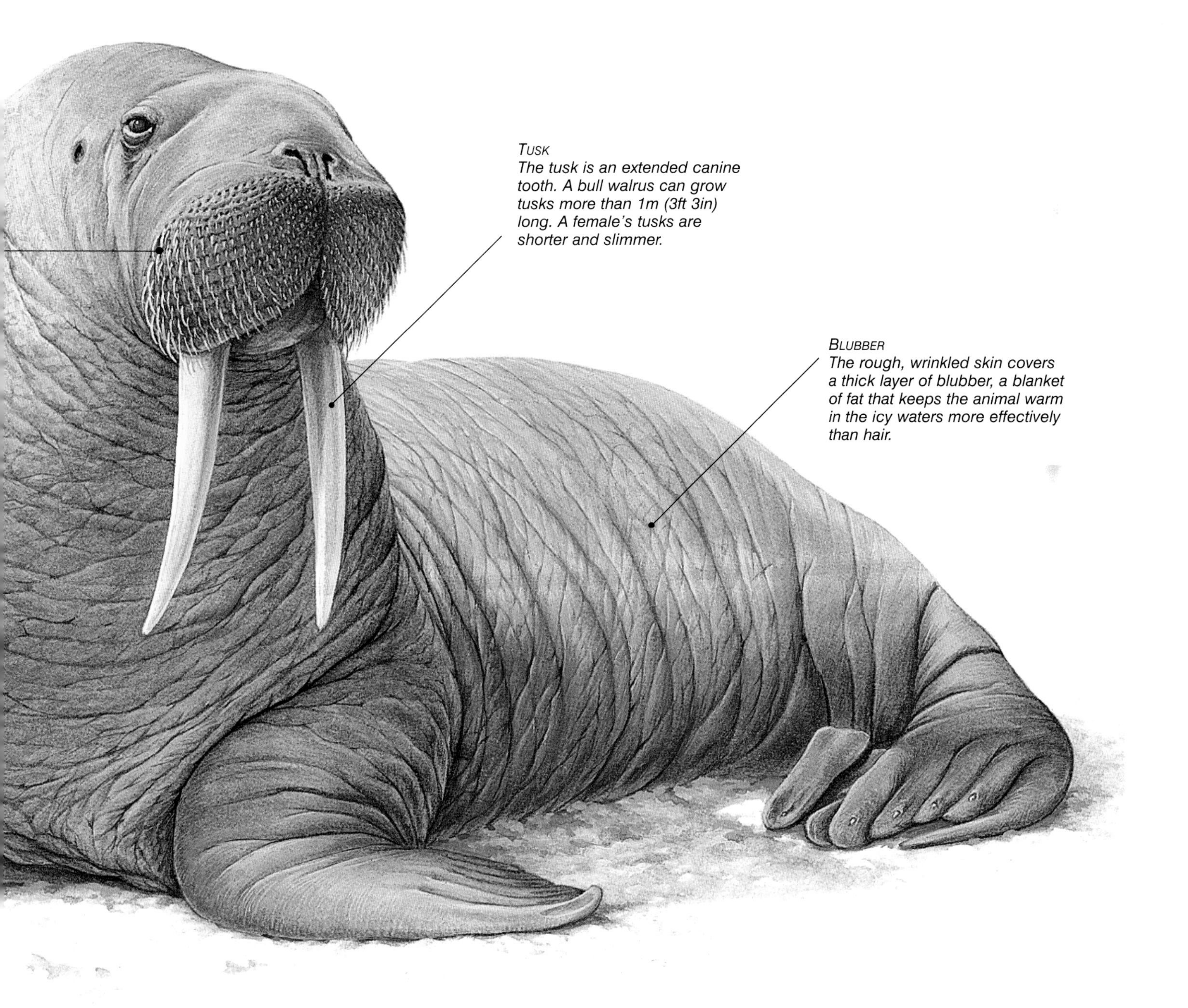
TUSK
The tusk is an extended canine tooth. A bull walrus can grow tusks more than 1m (3ft 3in) long. A female's tusks are shorter and slimmer.
BLUBBER
The rough, wrinkled skin covers a thick layer of blubber, a blanket of fat that keeps the animal warm in the icy waters more effectively than hair.

Seals and Sea Lions

The seals, sea lions and the walrus belong to a group of mammals called the pinnipeds. This name means 'feather feet' and refers to the way the sea mammals' limb bones have evolved into splayed flippers. The pinnipeds give birth and sleep out of the water, so seldom stray far from land – or thick ice.

Steller Sea Lion

Eumetopias jubatus

The biggest of the sea lions, the Steller sea lion chooses rocky beaches to rest and breed, after spending long periods hunting offshore. Breeding colonies are rough places, as each giant bull stakes out a patch of beach for his harem of females. The males are considerably larger than their mates – generally weighing twice as much.

FACT FILE	
Length:	Male 3.3m (11ft); female 2m (6ft 6in)
Weight:	Male 566kg (1245lb)
Distribution:	North Pacific rim
Habitat:	Shallow coastal waters
Diet:	Fish, squid and octopuses
Status (IUCN Red List):	Endangered

Hooded Seal

Cystophora cristata

Named after the outlandish inflatable crest used in courtship displays by the adult males, the hooded seal leads a tough life out on the ice. Polar bears are a big risk, and there is little time to stop feeding. After giving birth on the ice, a mother suckles her pup for just four days before returning to the sea – the fastest weaning of any mammal.

FACT FILE	
Length:	Male 2.6m (8ft 6in); female 2m (6ft 6in)
Weight:	300kg (660lb)
Distribution:	North Atlantic and Arctic oceans
Habitat:	Along edge of pack ice
Diet:	Fish and squid
Status (IUCN Red List):	Vulnerable

Leopard Seal

Hydrurga leptonyx

Aptly named, this Antarctic seal terrorizes penguins and smaller seals. Equipped with a wide head and a powerful streamlined body, the leopard seal swoops and swerves in relentless pursuit of its prey. Unlike other seals, this species uses its front flippers for propulsion instead of just steering.

FACT FILE	
Length:	3.2m (10ft 6in)
Weight:	590kg (1300lb)
Distribution:	Antarctica, tip of South America
Habitat:	Edge of ice shelf
Diet:	Squid, fish, seals and penguins
Status (IUCN Red List):	Least concern

Southern Elephant Seal

Mirounga leonina

The elephant seals are the largest pinnipeds of all, with some bulls reaching 4 tonnes (4½ tons), eight times the weight of a female. The short polar summer provides a small breeding window, so males rely on their might to set up a beach territory. Females are welcomed in, but any encroaching males are viciously wrestled away.

FACT FILE	
Length:	Male 6.2m (20ft 6in); female 3.7m (12ft)
Weight:	2 tonnes (2¼ tons)
Distribution:	South polar seas
Habitat:	Rocky islands
Diet:	Squid and fish
Status (IUCN Red List):	Least concern

Mediterranean Monk Seal

Monachus monachus

Once found from the Black Sea to the African Atlantic, this species of seal is now one of the most endangered animals in the world. Fewer than 500 survive in small scattered colonies.The name comes from their dark coat, said to be like a monk's robes.

FACT FILE	
Length:	2.4m (8ft)
Weight:	300kg (660lb)
Distribution:	Mediterranean and NW Africa
Habitat:	Rocky coasts and sea-caves
Diet:	Fish, squid and octopuses
Status (IUCN Red List):	Critically endangered

Baleen Whales

The largest animals ever to have lived on earth, the baleen whales are named after their unusual mouth parts. These toothless giants have great curtains of cartilage, called baleen plates or whale bone, lining the mouth. The whales feed by taking great gulps of seawater, which are then squirted back out. Any food in the water is filtered out by the baleen plates.

Bowhead Whale

Balaena mysticetus

The bowhead whale has the biggest mouth in the animal kingdom – it is said a van could drive inside. This great creature was hunted near to extinction. Its flexible baleen was a natural precursor to plastic, while its blubber was reduced to lamp oil. However, the species has recovered since the 1980s whaling ban.

FACT FILE	
Length:	20m (65ft 6in)
Weight:	100 tonnes (110 tons)
Distribution:	Arctic ocean
Habitat:	Shallow cold seas
Diet:	Krill and copepods
Status (IUCN Red List):	Least concern

Blue Whale

Balaenoptera musculus

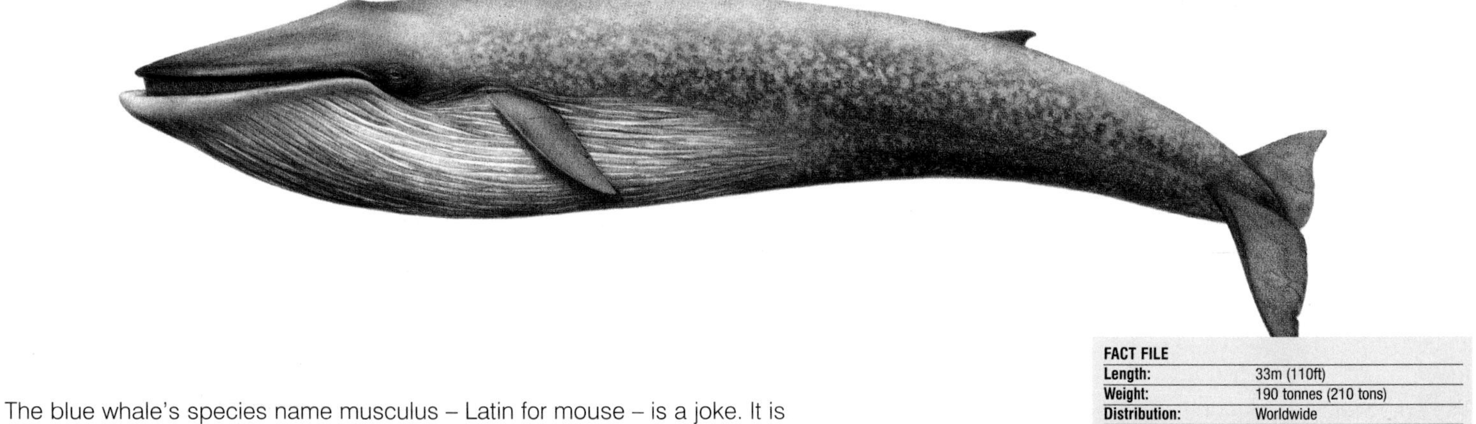

The blue whale's species name musculus – Latin for mouse – is a joke. It is earth's biggest animal – heavier, if not longer, than the largest dinosaur. Blue whales can swim at up to 25km/h (15mph). That is more than 13 knots and meant the whales were largely safe from whalers until the age of steam.

FACT FILE	
Length:	33m (110ft)
Weight:	190 tonnes (210 tons)
Distribution:	Worldwide
Habitat:	Open ocean
Diet:	Deep, cool water
Status (IUCN Red List):	Endangered

Fin Whale

Balaenoptera physalus

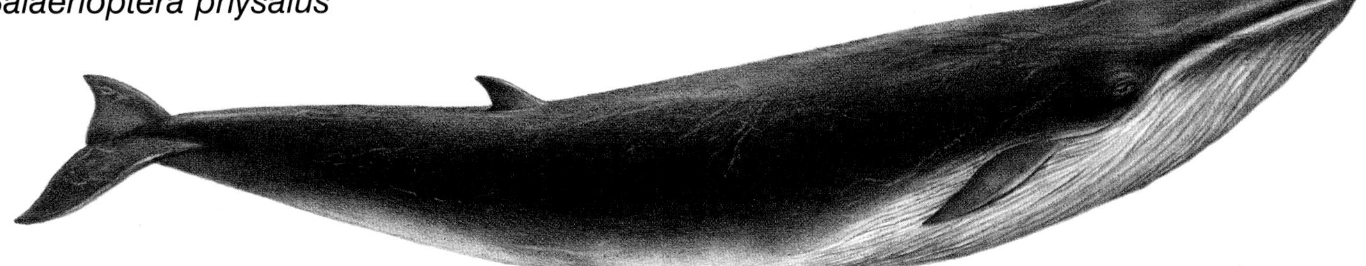

FACT FILE	
Length:	24m (78ft)
Weight:	70 tonnes (77 tons)
Distribution:	All oceans
Habitat:	Temperate and polar zones
Diet:	Small crustaceans, fish and squid
Status (IUCN Red List):	Endangered

The second largest whale, this species is also the fastest, achieving bursts of 40km/h (25mph). Dolphins that ride the bow waves of ships will do the same when a fin whale is surging past. Like the blue whale, this species has a crenellated throat that expands enormously when filled with water.

North Atlantic Right Whale

Eubalaena glacialis

FACT FILE	
Length:	17m (56ft)
Weight:	75 tonnes (83 tons)
Distribution:	Northern Hemisphere
Habitat:	Coastal waters
Diet:	Copepods, krill and euphausiids
Status (IUCN Red List):	Endangered

The right whale was very badly hit by whaling and is struggling to recover as quickly as other whale species, despite its current protected status. Its very name tells the story: it was the 'right' whale to kill, since it moved slowly, fed near the surface and floated when dead.

Humpback Whale

Megaptera novaeangliae

FACT FILE	
Length:	15m (49ft)
Weight:	30 tonnes (33 tons)
Distribution:	Worldwide
Habitat:	Winter in tropics; summer in polar areas
Diet:	Krill; small fish
Status (IUCN Red List):	Least concern

Also noted for its knobbly head, often encrusted with barnacles, and long jagged fins, the humpback whale is named after its small dorsal fin. This feature makes this slow-swimming giant easy to identify as it slides through surface water. Humpbacks blow 'nets' of bubbles to corral fish into meal-sized shoals.

Toothed Whales

The whales form the order Cetacea. The dozen or so baleen whales make up just a small proportion of this group. The 70 other cetaceans are smaller hunting mammals that clamp onto prey with powerful jaws brimming with blunt teeth. The dolphins and porpoises are perhaps the most familiar toothed whales, but they go by many other names.

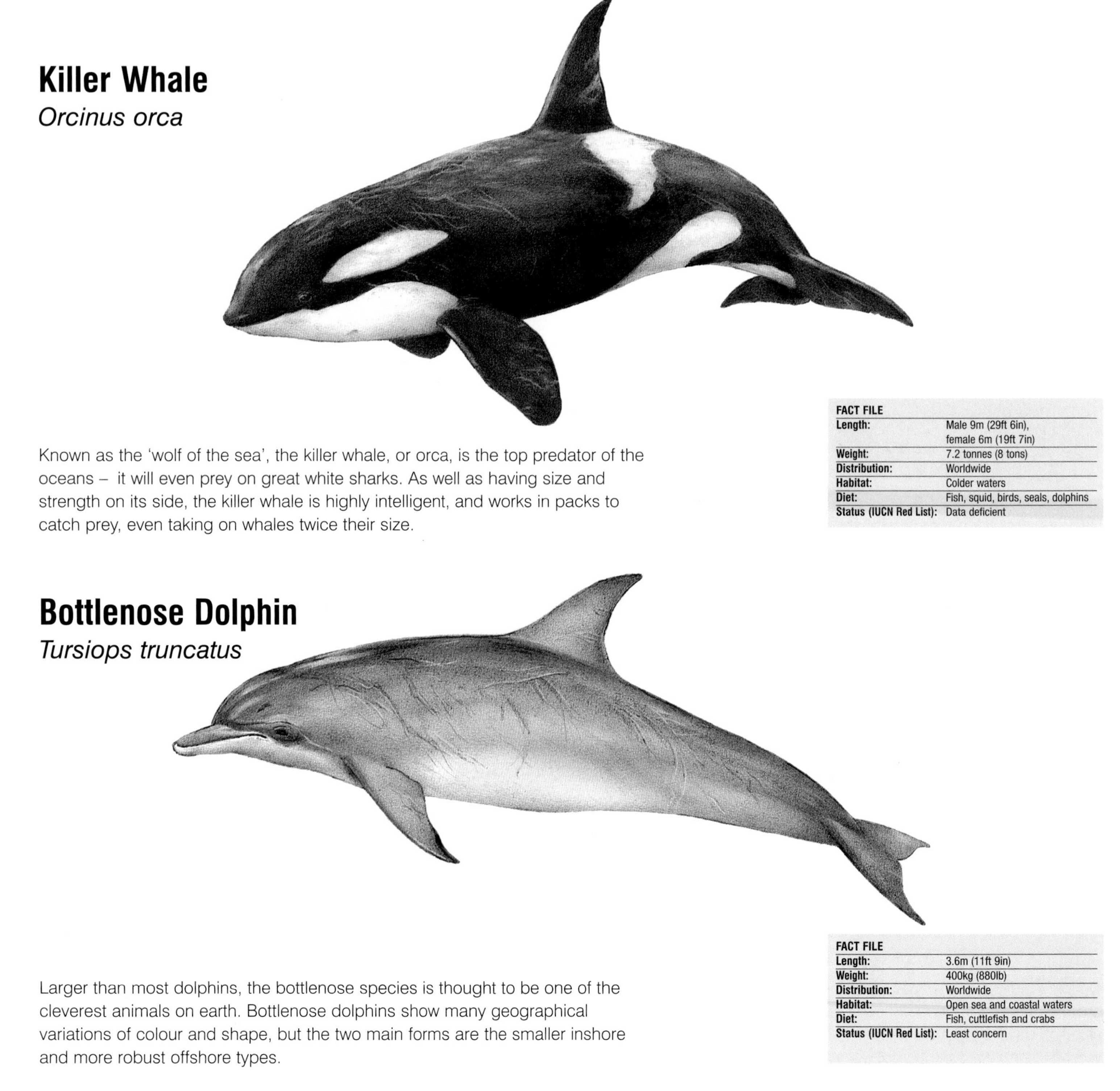

Killer Whale

Orcinus orca

Known as the 'wolf of the sea', the killer whale, or orca, is the top predator of the oceans – it will even prey on great white sharks. As well as having size and strength on its side, the killer whale is highly intelligent, and works in packs to catch prey, even taking on whales twice their size.

FACT FILE	
Length:	Male 9m (29ft 6in), female 6m (19ft 7in)
Weight:	7.2 tonnes (8 tons)
Distribution:	Worldwide
Habitat:	Colder waters
Diet:	Fish, squid, birds, seals, dolphins
Status (IUCN Red List):	Data deficient

Bottlenose Dolphin

Tursiops truncatus

Larger than most dolphins, the bottlenose species is thought to be one of the cleverest animals on earth. Bottlenose dolphins show many geographical variations of colour and shape, but the two main forms are the smaller inshore and more robust offshore types.

FACT FILE	
Length:	3.6m (11ft 9in)
Weight:	400kg (880lb)
Distribution:	Worldwide
Habitat:	Open sea and coastal waters
Diet:	Fish, cuttlefish and crabs
Status (IUCN Red List):	Least concern

Harbour Porpoise

Phocoena phocoena

Porpoises lack the long beak-shaped snouts of dolphins, and are generally smaller and less likely to make showy leaps from the water. They travel in schools of about a dozen, migrating north in summer and south in winter. They have acute hearing, and communicate by means of clicks and squeaks.

FACT FILE	
Length:	2m (6ft 6in)
Weight:	52kg (115lb)
Distribution:	Northern Hemisphere
Habitat:	Estuaries and shallow waters
Diet:	Fish and crabs
Status (IUCN Red List):	Least concern

Beluga Whale

Delphinapterus leucas

Named after the Russian word for 'white', this medium-sized whale is actually dark brown-grey at birth and becomes paler with age. The white skin offers good camouflage among the Arctic ice floes. The whale's whistling calls have earned it the alternative name of sea canary.

FACT FILE	
Length:	5m (16ft 6in)
Weight:	1.5 tonnes (1¾ tons)
Distribution:	Arctic and Northern oceans
Habitat:	Coastal waters
Diet:	Mainly crustaceans, some fish
Status (IUCN Red List):	Near threatened

Narwhal

Monodon monoceros

One of the world's stranger-looking creatures, the male narwhal has a long tusk protruding from its upper lip. This can grow up to 2m (6ft 6in) long and is an elongated twisted tooth used in dominance displays. Narwhal tusk was a valuable commodity in the Middle Ages, very often sold as the horn of a unicorn.

FACT FILE	
Length:	6m (19ft 7in) including male's tusk
Weight:	1.25 tonnes (1¼ tons)
Distribution:	North Atlantic and Arctic oceans
Habitat:	Cold Arctic waters, near pack ice
Diet:	Fish, squid, crustaceans
Status (IUCN Red List):	Near threatened

Sperm Whale

Physeter catodon

Often thought of as an aggressive killer, thanks in part to its appearance in Herman Melville's epic *Moby Dick*, the sperm whale very rarely attacks humans. It is, nevertheless, the largest predator alive today, but hunts in the deep dark ocean for giant squids. The whales often bear the scars of deep-sea combat with this mysterious prey.

FACT FILE	
Length:	Male 18m (60ft); female 10m (33ft)
Weight:	35 tonnes (38½ tons)
Distribution:	Worldwide
Habitat:	Warm, deep waters
Diet:	Giant squid
Status (IUCN Red List):	Vulnerable

Sperm whales were once hunted for their spermaceti, used as a lubricating oil. Ambergris, the waxy lining of the whale's intestines, was used as a fixative in perfume-making, while its cobble-sized teeth were sold as a form of ivory.

BLOWHOLE
As with all cetaceans, sperm whales breath air through a single nostril, or blowhole. The sperm whale's is a slit located on the left side of the head.

HEAD
The bulbous head is filled with spermaceti, a pool of waxy jelly used as a ballast tank to help the whale dive very deep.

TOOTH
The longest teeth are in the lower jaw. Reaching 20cm (8in) long, they are the largest of any animal, and are used to stab in struggling prey.

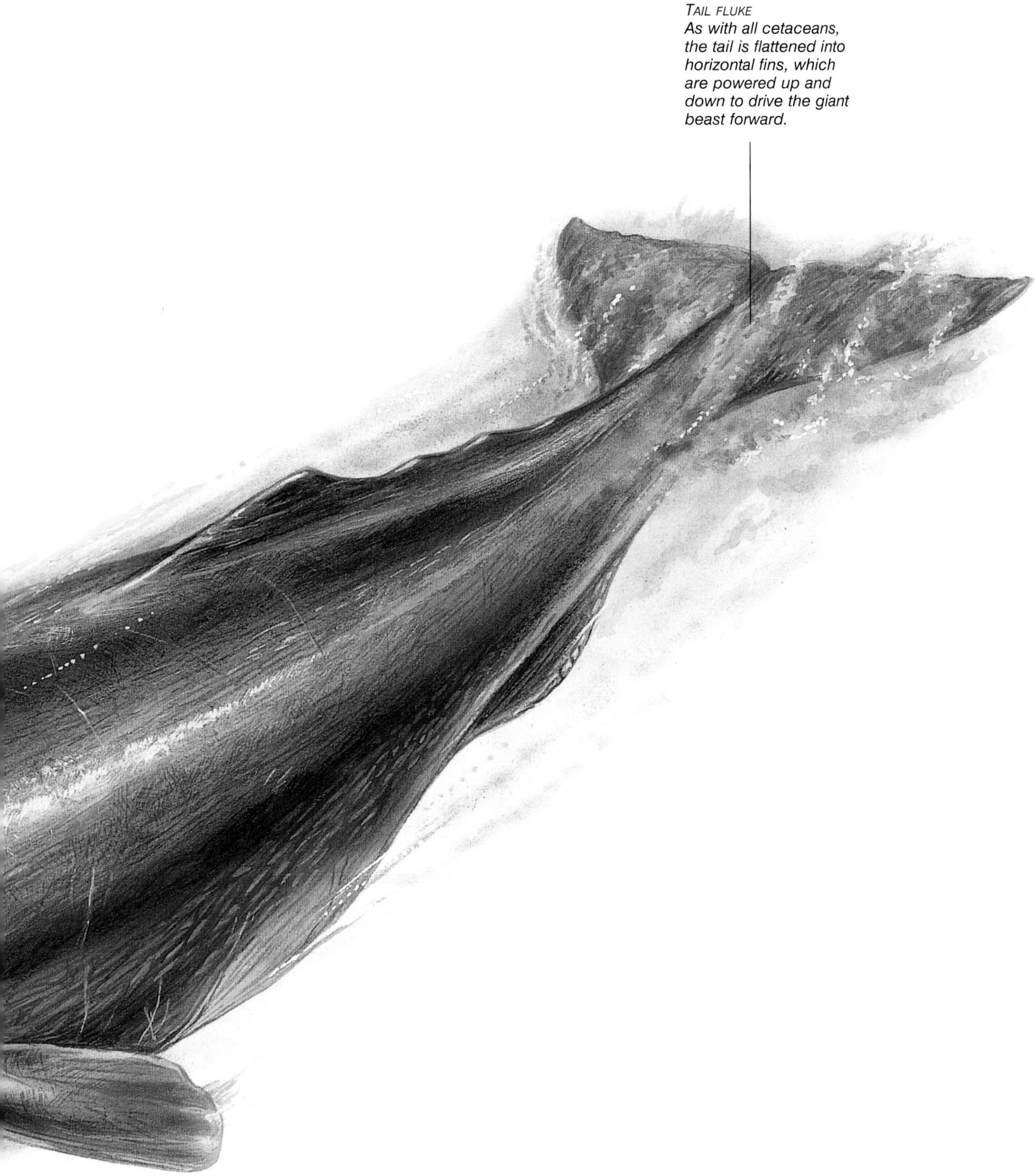

TAIL FLUKE
As with all cetaceans, the tail is flattened into horizontal fins, which are powered up and down to drive the giant beast forward.

Wild Hogs

The wild relatives of domestic pigs form a family of hoofed mammals called Suidae. The members all share the familiar blunt snout of the farm animals, an adaptation to a life spent rooting through leaf litter and soil for tubers and mushrooms. Most wild hogs are also armed with formidable tusks.

Giant Forest Hog

Hylochoerus meinertzhageni

As its name suggests, this is the largest of the wild pigs – and few domestic animals achieve its great size. More of a grazer than its relatives, this great forest beast roots for food only occasionally. It is normally seen eating grass in small groups, known as sounders.

FACT FILE	
Length:	2.1m (6ft 10in)
Weight:	275kg (606lb)
Distribution:	West, Central and East Africa
Habitat:	Forest
Diet:	Grass and leaves
Status (IUCN Red List):	Least concern

Desert Warthog

Phacochoerus aethiopicus

A smaller cousin of the common warthog of the great plains further south, this species is also equipped with four ungainly tusks. Males have longer tusks than females and more distinctive wart-like lumps on the face. The hogs do not let good grazing go to waste – they kneel down to crop even the shortest grass.

FACT FILE	
Length:	1.25m (4ft 1in)
Weight:	75kg (165lb)
Distribution:	Horn of Africa
Habitat:	Dry savannah
Diet:	Grass and roots
Status (IUCN Red List):	Least concern

African Bushpig

Potamochoerus porcus

Also known as the red river hog, this species has a characteristic white beard of tufted hair. The hog lives in large sounders, or groups, ruled over by a dominant male. With the fall of leopard numbers in Africa, bushpig numbers have boomed, and the animal has become a pest, wreaking havoc in fields of crops.

FACT FILE	
Length:	1.5m (5ft)
Weight:	130kg (286lb)
Distribution:	West and Central Africa
Habitat:	Woodland
Diet:	Fruits, roots, eggs and carrion
Status (IUCN Red List):	Least concern

Philippine Warty Pig

Sus philippensis

This small pig lives on the main islands of the Philippines. Only the males have large tusks, but both sexes have four warty protrusions on their faces. The warty pig is nocturnal, like most of its relatives, and spends the day hidden in thickets. Females build cosy nests in quiet spots before giving birth to a litter.

FACT FILE	
Length:	1.1m (3ft 7in)
Weight:	35kg (77lb 1oz)
Distribution:	Philippines
Habitat:	Grassy areas
Diet:	Roots and leaves
Status (IUCN Red List):	Vulnerable

Collared Peccary

Pecari tajacu

It looks like a pig, but the collared peccary belongs to a completely different mammal family, the Tayassuidae. Peccaries are restricted to the Americas and appear to have evolved the hog-like snout independently. This particular species is also known as the javelina, because of its sharp, pointed tusks.

FACT FILE	
Length:	1m (3ft 3in)
Weight:	30kg (66lb)
Distribution:	South America and southwest US
Habitat:	Woodland and scrub
Diet:	Fruits, roots and small animals
Status (IUCN Red List):	Least concern

Pig Breeds

All domestic breeds of pig are descended from wild boars. Pigs were among the first livestock animals, known to be reared by farmers in the Tigris Basin 14,000 years ago. Few domestic pigs grow to full size. Porkers are slaughtered at about 50kg (110lb), while baconers are left a little longer, and slaughtered at 80kg (176lb).

Wild Boar

Sus scrofa

The wild ancestor of domestic pigs became locally extinct in many parts of Europe and Asia, where it was hunted for sport as well as food. There have been several reintroduction programmes in forested regions of western Europe, but this shy creature is still a rare sight.

FACT FILE	
Length:	1.8m (6ft)
Weight:	200kg (440lb)
Distribution:	Europe, Asia, North Africa
Habitat:	Forests, woodlands and marsh
Diet:	Grass, roots and fungus
Status (IUCN Red List):	Least concern

Gloucester Old Spot Pig

Sus scrofa domesticus

The old spot is a well-loved although quite rare breed of pig. Once commonly raised by English smallholders, who left them to clean up the windfalls in orchards, the breed proved unsuited to intensive farming techniques. The good-natured pigs are popular with hobby farmers because they happily forage for themselves in woodland.

FACT FILE	
Length:	2m (6ft 6in)
Weight:	136kg (300lb)
Distribution:	N/A
Habitat:	N/A
Diet:	N/A
Status (IUCN Red List):	N/A

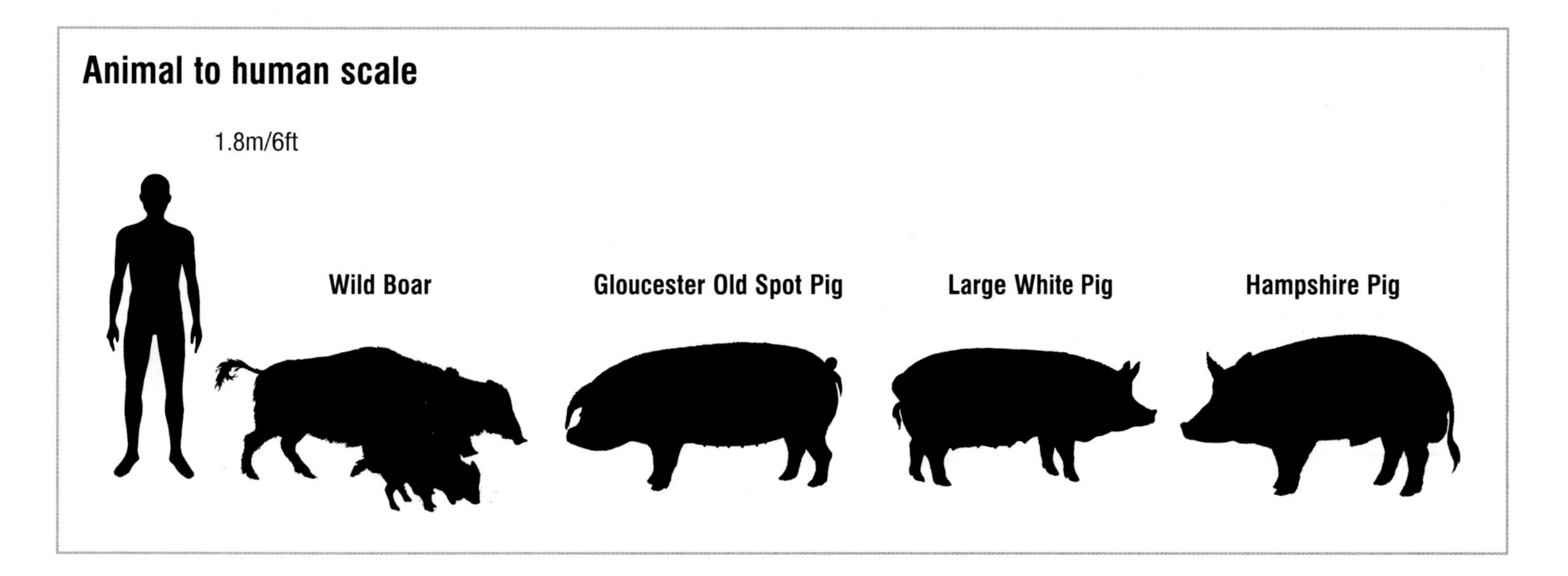

Large White Pig

Sus scrofa domesticus

Also known as the Yorkshire pig outside the UK, this breed is the ultimate porker, raised in their millions in farms across the Americas, Australia and Europe. This is also the pig of storybooks, with its clear pink skin and short, curly tail – a feature adopted by breeders to make it harder for crowded pigs to bite each other's tails off.

FACT FILE	
Length:	2m (6ft 6in)
Weight:	225kg (496lb)
Distribution:	N/A
Habitat:	N/A
Diet:	N/A
Status (IUCN Red List):	N/A

Hampshire Pig

Sus scrofa domesticus

A relatively unusual breed that retains pointed ears and a long tail, this pig originated in the UK but is now more prevalent in North America. The UK breed has since been developed into the Wessex Saddleback. Hampshires provide good meat, but do not grow as fast as Large Whites.

FACT FILE	
Length:	1.8m (6ft)
Weight:	200kg (440lb)
Distribution:	N/A
Habitat:	N/A
Diet:	N/A
Status (IUCN Red List):	N/A

Hippopotamus

Hippopotamus amphibius

An immense hoofed animal, living in and around Africa's rivers and lakes, the hippopotamus is one of the most iconic species in the world. Despite its great bulk, it is a skilled swimmer, although it spends most of its time walking through the water. Its name is a combination of the Greek words for 'horse' and 'river'.

FACT FILE	
Length:	3m (9ft 9in)
Weight:	2 tonnes (2¼ tons)
Distribution:	Sub-Saharan Africa
Habitat:	Ponds, rivers and grasslands
Diet:	Grass
Status (IUCN Red List):	Vulnerable

Despite being so closely associated with water, hippos always feed on land, grazing on grasses in the cool of the night before returning to the water to cool off during daylight. If spooked, a grazing herd charges back into the water, trampling any unfortunates in their path.

FEET
A hippo's broad feet act as paddles when in water. They also spread the hippo's enormous weight to avoid it sinking when walking in soft sediment.

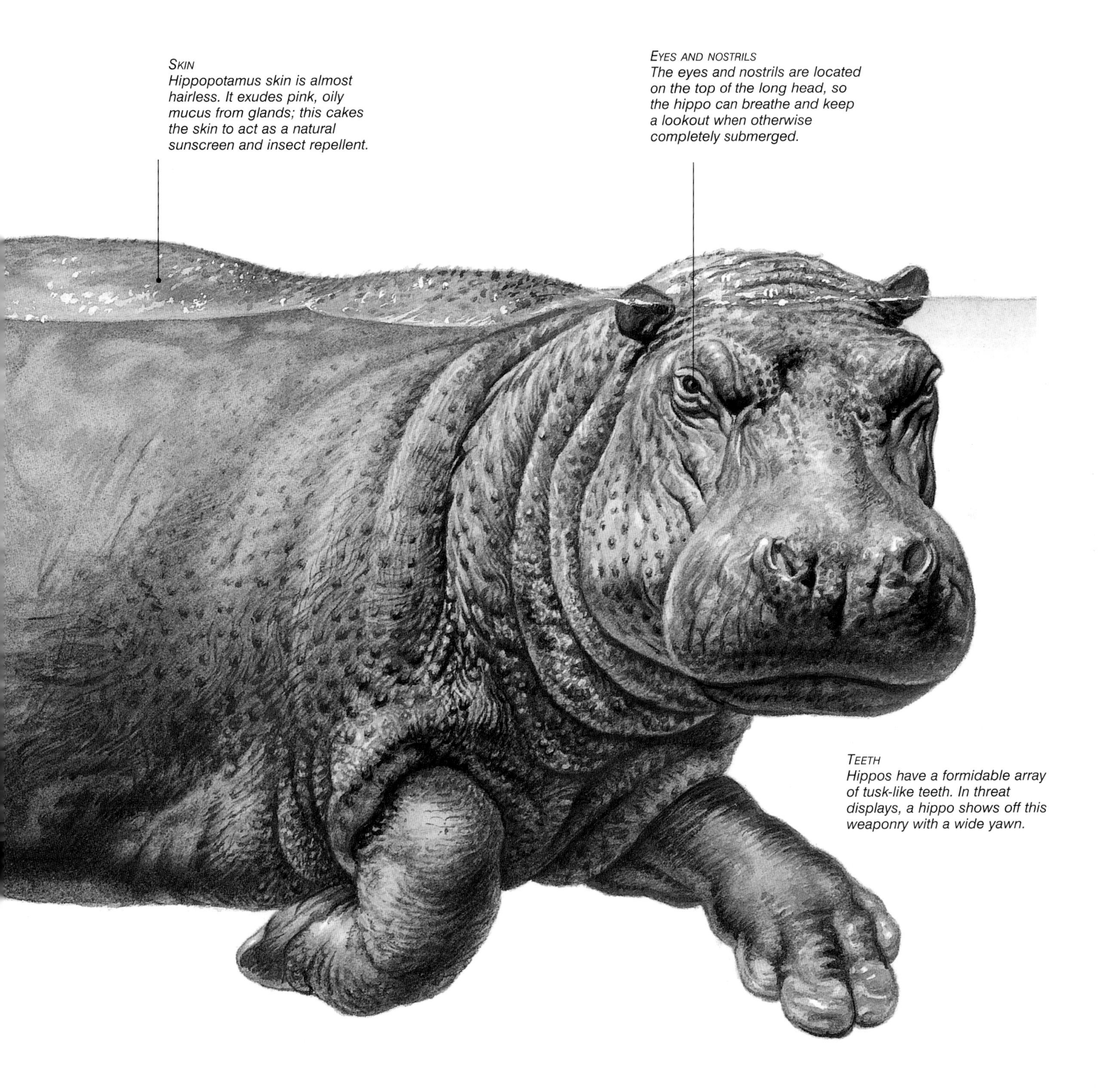
SKIN
Hippopotamus skin is almost hairless. It exudes pink, oily mucus from glands; this cakes the skin to act as a natural sunscreen and insect repellent.
EYES AND NOSTRILS
The eyes and nostrils are located on the top of the long head, so the hippo can breathe and keep a lookout when otherwise completely submerged.
TEETH
Hippos have a formidable array of tusk-like teeth. In threat displays, a hippo shows off this weaponry with a wide yawn.

Deer

Forming the family Cervidae, the deer live across the world, though the red deer is the only African species, where antelopes dominate. Deer do not have horns, but males have antlers – long bones covered in velvet, a soft skin. The antlers are shed and regrown each year, often gaining a new branch, or tine, with each regrowth.

Thorold's Deer

Przewalskium albirostris

This Asian species has a thick coat to withstand the cold winters of the high Tibetan Plateau. Its broad cloven hooves spread under the animal's weight, creating a wide cleft in the middle that grips the rugged rocky land underfoot. In summer, the deer graze in high meadows; in winter they climb into sheltered valleys.

FACT FILE	
Length:	1.95m (6ft 4in)
Weight:	135kg (297lb)
Distribution:	Tibetan Plateau
Habitat:	Mountain forest and meadows
Diet:	Grasses and herbs
Status (IUCN Red List):	Vulnerable

Visayan Spotted Deer

Rusa alfredi

Although small for a deer, this species is the largest animal native to the Visayan Islands of central Philippines. The deer live in small groups and forage at night, plucking fresh leaves and buds from shrubs. During the December breeding season, male deer roar to mates through the thick forest.

FACT FILE	
Length:	1.3m (4ft 3in)
Weight:	47kg (104lb)
Distribution:	Visayan Islands, Philippines
Habitat:	Forest
Diet:	Leaves, grass and fruits
Status (IUCN Red List):	Endangered

Roe Deer

Capreolus capreolus

The smallest deer in Europe, the roe deer lives alone or in small herds. It lives in all types of woodland, can survive well enough in farmland, and may even stray into the suburbs of cities. Unusually for large herbivores, this species seems to have increased in number since the advent of intensive agriculture in the last few centuries.

FACT FILE	
Length:	1.5m (5ft)
Weight:	50kg (110lb)
Distribution:	Europe
Habitat:	Forests and farmland
Diet:	Grass and leaves
Status (IUCN Red List):	Least concern

White-tailed Deer

Odocoileus virginianus

Known as the Virginia deer in North America, this species has one of the largest ranges of any deer, outdone only by the likes of reindeer and red deer. The white tail is a defensive mechanism, raised when the deer is alarmed to expose a wide white rump. This signal warns other deer nearby to be alert to danger.

FACT FILE	
Length:	2.1m (6ft 10in)
Weight:	200kg (440lb)
Distribution:	Southern Canada to Brazil
Habitat:	Woodland and shrubs
Diet:	Grass, leaves and twigs
Status (IUCN Red List):	Least concern

Huemel

Hippocamelus bisulcus

Also known as the South Andean deer, this species lives on the steep slopes of the Andes at the far south of the range. They have very short legs to provide stability on the slopes and look as if they are almost crouching when standing tall.

FACT FILE	
Length:	1.65m (5ft 5in)
Weight:	65kg (143lb)
Distribution:	Chile and Argentina
Habitat:	Steep forested slopes
Diet:	Leaves, fruits and bark
Status (IUCN Red List):	Endangered

Camels and Relatives

Camels are well known as pack animals, criss-crossing the stifling desert, spending weeks without food and days without a drink. The other members of the Camilidae family live in dry, but also cold, places: the guanaco and vicuña live in the High Andes, while the bactrian camel withstands the cold winters of Central Asia.

Dromedary

Camelus dromedarius

The camel with only one hump has no truly wild populations. Ironically, it is only in Australia, where imported dromedaries escaped from captivity, that the animals behave in a wild fashion. In its native range of western Asia and North Africa, all dromedaries have a human owner, after being domesticated at least 3500 years ago.

FACT FILE	
Length:	3.3m (11ft)
Weight:	635kg (1400lb)
Distribution:	North Africa, Middle East, Australia
Habitat:	Desert
Diet:	Grass
Status (IUCN Red List):	N/A

Bishari Camel

Camelus dromedarius

This breed of camel from northern Sudan is bred as a mount, to be ridden – and raced – by people rather than as a pack animal. The Bishari people, after which the breed is named, are thought to be the descendants of the ancient Egyptians and Nubians. They sometimes slaughter the dromedary for its meat.

FACT FILE	
Length:	3.3m (11ft)
Weight:	635kg (1400lb)
Distribution:	Sudan and Egypt
Habitat:	Desert
Diet:	Grass
Status (IUCN Red List):	N/A

Rashaida Camel

Camelus dromedarius

The Rashaida tribe of Sudan breeds two types of camel: the Anafi breed, the thoroughbred racers of the camel world, and the smaller, darker Rashaida breed, which is more like a dairy cow. Camel milk is a key ingredient in the diet of the pastoralist Rashaida, being their only regular source of fat and protein.

FACT FILE	
Length:	3.3m (11ft)
Weight:	635kg (1400lb)
Distribution:	Sudan
Habitat:	Desert
Diet:	Grass
Status (IUCN Red List):	N/A

Llama

Lama glama

The llama is one of the domestic breeds of the guanaco; another is the alpaca. The latter was bred for its fine wool, while the llama is a pack animal – perhaps not as strong as the Old World's horses and oxen, but certainly sure-footed.

FACT FILE	
Length:	1.2m (4ft)
Weight:	65kg (143lb)
Distribution:	Andes Mountains
Habitat:	Mountains
Diet:	Grass
Status (IUCN Red List):	N/A

Giraffe

Giraffa camelopardalis

Another icon of the animal world, the giraffe is the tallest animal on earth, exceeding 5m (16ft 6in) in height. The purpose of its long neck is to pluck the freshest leaves from the tops of trees with its flexible 40cm (16in) tongue, beyond the reach of other browsers. The useful neck also causes problems. For example, lowering the head to drink is a laborious process.

FACT FILE	
Length:	4.7m (15ft 5in)
Weight:	1930kg (4255lb)
Distribution:	Sub-Saharan Africa
Habitat:	Woodland and savannah
Diet:	Leaves
Status (IUCN Red List):	Least concern

One species of giraffe lives across Africa, although it exists in several subspecies, including the reticulated giraffe (shown here) of northern Kenya. The species is a member of the Giraffidae family along with the okapi, a rare forest browser from the Congo with a neck 1m (3ft 3in) long.

HOOVES
The giraffe's chief defence tactic is a kick from its long back legs. The force of a well-placed blow is enough to break the jaw of an attacking lion – condemning it to death.

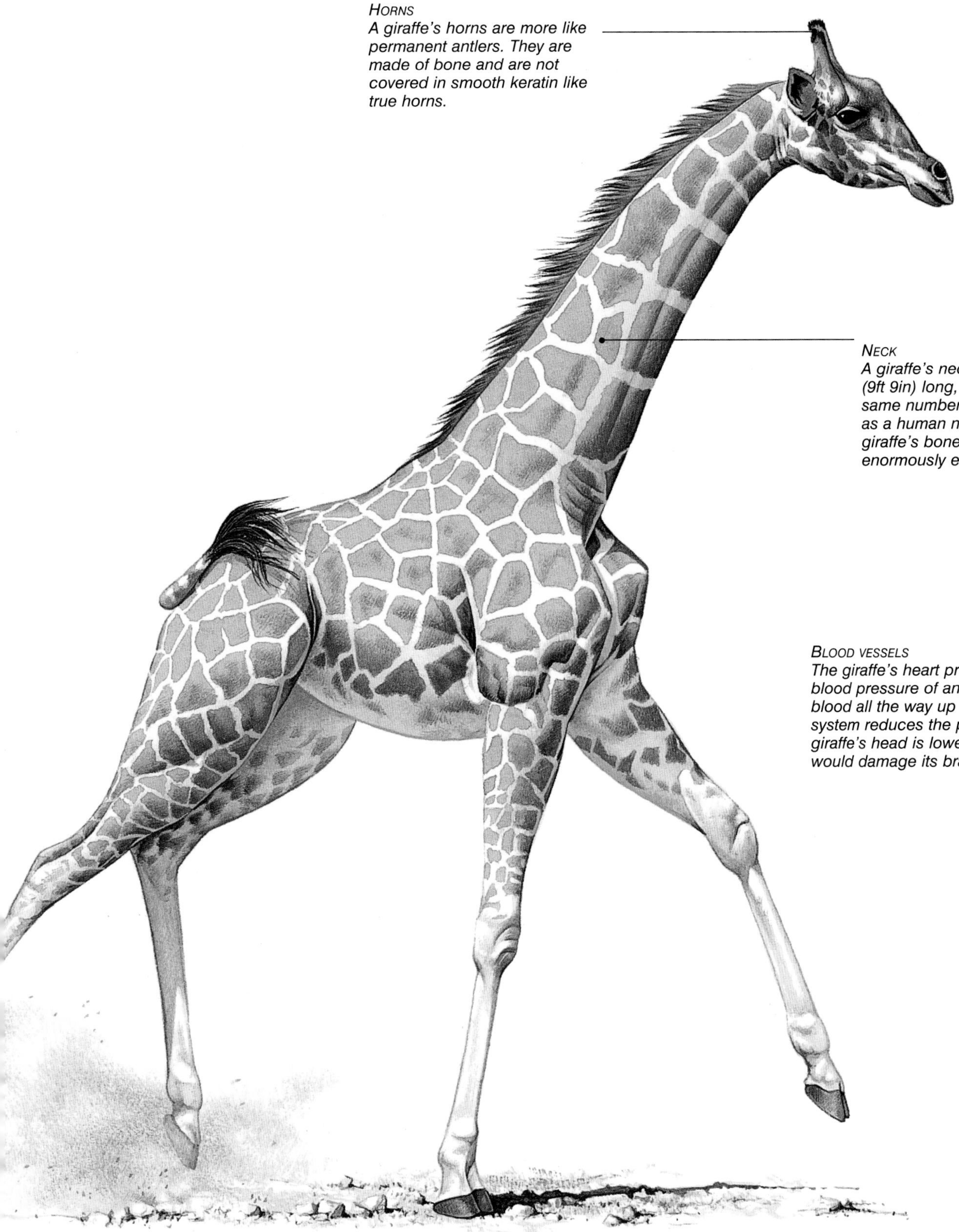

HORNS
A giraffe's horns are more like permanent antlers. They are made of bone and are not covered in smooth keratin like true horns.

NECK
A giraffe's neck may be 3m (9ft 9in) long, but it has the same number of vertebrae as a human neck. The giraffe's bones are just enormously elongated.

BLOOD VESSELS
The giraffe's heart produces the highest blood pressure of any animal to pump blood all the way up to its head. A valve system reduces the pressure when the giraffe's head is lowered – full pressure would damage its brain.

Grazing Antelopes

The antelopes are medium-sized herbivores in the Bovidae family, and thus closely related to cattle and sheep. They dominate in Africa, with only a few species found in Asia. Grazing antelopes form three tribes: the Alcelaphani live in woodlands, the Reduncini feed in wetlands, and the horse-like Hippotragini graze the open plains.

Bontebok

Damaliscus pygargus

A small member of the Alcelaphani tribe, the bontebok was once common across southern Africa, but is now restricted to a small part of South Africa's Cape Province. It is closely related to the blesbok, which is found to the east and north, and they were once thought to be one species. However, the blesbok has redder fur than the bontebok's dark brown.

FACT FILE	
Length:	1.6m (5ft 2in)
Weight:	80kg (176lb)
Distribution:	Cape Province, South Africa
Habitat:	Grassland
Diet:	Grass
Status (IUCN Red List):	Least concern

Hartebeest

Alcelaphus buselaphus

Hartebeest have an unusual look to their horns. Both lyre-shaped adornments grow from a single bony plate on the forehead. The antelopes live in large herds that browse on bushes in dry woodlands; they also venture out onto the grassy savannah.

FACT FILE	
Length:	2.15m (7ft)
Weight:	218kg (480lb)
Distribution:	Eastern and southern Africa
Habitat:	Grassland and woodland
Diet:	Grass
Status (IUCN Red List):	Least concern

Sable Antelope

Hippotragus niger

A member of the Hippotragini tribe, the sable cuts a fine figure on the savannah with is long curved horns. The adult males also grow an impressive jet-black coat. The antelope, which is also known as the mbarapi, often grazes along the edges of woodlands.

FACT FILE	
Length:	2.1m (6ft 10in)
Weight:	230kg (507lb)
Distribution:	East and southern Africa
Habitat:	Savannah
Diet:	Grass
Status (IUCN Red List):	Least concern

Reedbuck

Redunca redunca

Many antelopes mark their territories with scented secretions from facial and hoof glands. However, scent is less effective in the tall reedbeds where reedbucks often stake out a patch. Instead, they warn intruders to stay away by giving a whistle. The same sound is used to raise the alarm when predators appear.

FACT FILE	
Length:	1.5m (5ft)
Weight:	45kg (99lb)
Distribution:	Southern Africa
Habitat:	Marsh and riverbanks
Diet:	Grass
Status (IUCN Red List):	Least concern

Kob

Kobus kob

The kob is closely associated with water and can be seen feeding on the lush plants along riverbanks and around watering-holes. The antelope forages mostly in the morning and evening. They live in single-sex herds. Only the males grow horns.

FACT FILE	
Length:	1.8m (6ft)
Weight:	105kg (231lb)
Distribution:	West and Central Africa
Habitat:	Riverbanks and water-holes
Diet:	Grass and reeds
Status (IUCN Red List):	Least concern

Saiga

Saiga tatarica

This unusual, goofy-looking species shares similarities with both gazelles and goats, but is not quite either one. The species once lived in immense herds that criss-crossed the steppes of Central Asia, but natural climate changes shrunk its habitat and later human hunters killed them in their thousands.

FACT FILE	
Length:	1.4m (4ft 6in)
Weight:	70kg (154lb)
Distribution:	Central Asia
Habitat:	Arid grassland
Diet:	Grass
Status (IUCN Red List):	Critically endangered

The saiga is one of the most endangered antelope species. At last count there were perhaps 50,000 left in the wild, but this has fallen from 120,000 in the 1970s. Although hunting the saiga is illegal, its isolated populations are barely protected from poachers.

Nose
Both sexes have enlarged nostrils, although they are more pronounced in the males. The big noses filter out dust in summer and warm up cold breaths in winter.

COAT
The coat is thick to protect against the cold winters. At that time of year, the hairs become paler, providing a degree of camouflage.

HORNS
Only males grow the pointed horns, which are ringed by ridges. The saiga is hunted for its horn, which is believed to have therapeutic value in Chinese medicine.

LEGS
The saiga has sturdy legs and can walk 120km (75 miles) a day. It can run at 80km/h (50mph) when under attack.

Gazelles and Dwarf Antelopes

Smaller antelopes are often called gazelles. The term is generally reserved for the Antilopini tribe; similarly delicate species (largely the Neotragini tribe) are termed dwarf antelopes. Big-eyed and slender-legged, gazelles spread into western Asia, from where the word 'antelope' is thought to originate, meaning 'beautiful eyes'.

Blackbuck

Antilope cervicapra

Blackbucks live in large herds, numbering up to 50 individuals. These large groups are generally organized into several harems, each controlled by a single male who watches over four or five females and their young. When a blackbuck sees danger, it bounds away, quickly followed by the rest of the herd.

FACT FILE	
Length:	1.2m (4ft)
Weight:	37kg (81lb 8oz)
Distribution:	South Asia
Habitat:	Woodlands and semi-desert
Diet:	Grass and crops
Status (IUCN Red List):	Near threatened

Oribi

Ourebia ourebi

The oribi antelope mates for life. Pairs control a feeding territory, smearing gooey scent markings produced by preorbital glands – modified tear ducts – onto tree trunks and tall grasses. The oribi eats a wide range of leaves and grasses and is a regular visitor to salt licks.

FACT FILE	
Length:	1.1m (3ft 7in)
Weight:	24kg (53lb)
Distribution:	Central and southern Africa
Habitat:	Grasslands
Diet:	Grass and leaves
Status (IUCN Red List):	Least concern

Thomson's Gazelle

Gazella thomsonii

The Thomson's gazelle lives in large herds on the dry grasslands of East Africa. They can survive in areas too hot and arid for many other herd antelopes. They keep cool using a mesh of blood vessels in the head that works like a heat pump, extracting excess heat from blood arriving from elsewhere in the body.

FACT FILE	
Length:	1m (3ft 3in)
Weight:	29kg (64lb)
Distribution:	Tanzania and Kenya
Habitat:	Savannah
Diet:	Short grass
Status (IUCN Red List):	Near threatened

Dama Gazelle

Gazella dama

The dama gazelle is a resident of the Sahel region, the transitional grassland zone between the Sahara's sea of sand and the tropical forests of Central Asia. (The word sahel means 'shore' in Arabic.) The people of this impoverished region have hunted the gazelles for food, and there are now fewer than 500 truly wild individuals.

FACT FILE	
Length:	1.65m (5ft 5in)
Weight:	75kg (165lb)
Distribution:	Chad, Mali and Niger
Habitat:	Arid grassland
Diet:	Grasses
Status (IUCN Red List):	Critically endangered

Mongolian Gazelle

Procapra gutturosa

This hardy gazelle, also known as the zeren, lives on the high and dry grasslands of the eastern Asia. It is a stocky species that looks more like a goat than its slender African relatives. In the winter breeding season, males develop a swollen throat as a sign of dominance.

FACT FILE	
Length:	1.5m (5ft)
Weight:	39kg (86lb)
Distribution:	Mongolia
Habitat:	Steppe
Diet:	Grass
Status (IUCN Red List):	Least concern

Large Antelopes

The biggest antelopes are more closely related to cattle and buffalo than the smaller grazing species and gazelles. Their large size is an adaptation to the poor nutritional value of their plant foods – large bodies are more efficient to run. These big beasts are also known as the spiral-horned antelopes.

Giant Eland

Tragelaphus derbianus

The giant eland is the largest species of antelope, and only marginally smaller than the mighty bisons and buffalo. Elands resemble cattle in many ways and have been hunted for their meat. As a result, the population has become fragmented across West and Central Africa.

FACT FILE	
Length:	3.4m (11ft 3in)
Weight:	1 tonne (1 ton)
Distribution:	From Senegal to Sudan
Habitat:	Grasslands
Diet:	Grass
Status (IUCN Red List):	Least concern

Bongo

Tragelaphus eurycerus

Bongos are forest antelopes. They use their horns to pull down leafy branches. The antelopes also have shorter, sturdier legs than their fleet-of-foot grassland cousins. However, unlike most forest browsers, bongos do not forage alone but stick together in herds of about six.

FACT FILE	
Length:	2.5m (8ft 3in)
Weight:	220kg (485lb)
Distribution:	West and Central Africa
Habitat:	Forest
Diet:	Leaves, fruits and flowers
Status (IUCN Red List):	Near threatened

Greater Kudu

Tragelaphus strepsiceros

The greater kudu is one of the tallest antelopes, with bulls attaining a shoulder height of 1.5m (5ft). Their horns, which often grow to more than 1m (3ft 3in) long, are the longest horns of the large antelopes. Southern populations have darker coats than those in the north.

FACT FILE	
Length:	2.5m (8ft 3in)
Weight:	315kg (694lb)
Distribution:	Southern and eastern Africa
Habitat:	Woodlands and shrubs
Diet:	Leaves and grass
Status (IUCN Red List):	Least concern

Nyala

Tragelaphus angasii

A herd of nyalas seldom strays far from the lush grasses and thickets of riverbanks and watering-holes. They feed at night, avoiding any nastiness when large predators come to drink. Both sexes have a tufted crest of hairs along their backs. Males raise this crest during courtship.

FACT FILE	
Length:	2.1m (6ft 10in)
Weight:	126kg (278lb)
Distribution:	Southeast Africa
Habitat:	Thick grasses
Diet:	Grass
Status (IUCN Red List):	Least concern

Saola

Pseudoryx nghetinhensis

The saola was unknown until the 1990s. It was identified as a new species from horns brought out of the rugged Indochinese forests by hunters, and the first live specimen was obtained in 1994. Its relationships are unclear, but it is thought to be a small cattle species rather than a spiral-horned antelope.

FACT FILE	
Length:	2m (6ft 6in)
Weight:	100kg (220lb)
Distribution:	Laos and Vietnam
Habitat:	Mountain forest
Diet:	Leaves and fruits
Status (IUCN Red List):	Critically endangered

Wild Cattle

With domestic cattle farmed in their millions across six continents, it is no surprise that many of their wild cousins have been driven out of their habitats and are now endangered. The wild cattle species form the Bovini tribe within the large Bovidae family, which they share with antelopes, sheep and goats.

Wild Yak

Bos mutus

There are an estimated 13 million domestic yaks living in the eastern half of Asia. Along with water buffalo, they were one of the first pack animals. The yaks of the Nepalese Himalayas are the highest living mammals, after humans. However, it is estimated that there are barely 10,000 yaks living wild in their natural mountain habitat.

FACT FILE	
Length:	3.3m (11ft)
Weight:	525kg (1157lb)
Distribution:	South and southeast Asia
Habitat:	Mountain meadows and valleys
Diet:	Grass and lichens
Status (IUCN Red List):	Vulnerable

Kouprey

Bos sauveli

This forest species was discovered by scientists in 1937. Its dense jungle home is almost impossible to survey, but it is feared that the animal could be extinct outside of its Cambodian heartland. Male horns form curved hooks, while females sport lyre-shaped headgear.

FACT FILE	
Length:	2.1m (6ft 10in)
Weight:	955kg (2105lb)
Distribution:	Thailand and Indochina
Habitat:	Woodland and grasslands
Diet:	Grass and bamboo
Status (IUCN Red List):	Critically endangered

American Bison
Bison bison

This iconic American grazer once swept across the Great Plains in herds numbering more than a million. They entered a steady decline when horse-based Native groups arrived on the prairies and began to hunt them. European settlers almost wiped out the bison in the nineteenth century.

FACT FILE	
Length:	3.5m (11ft 5in)
Weight:	1 tonne (1 ton)
Distribution:	North America
Habitat:	Woodlands and prairie
Diet:	Grass and sedge
Status (IUCN Red List):	Near threatened

Mountain Anoa
Bubalus quarlesi

This small cattle species is confined to the Indonesian island of Sulawesi, which it shares with a lowland anoa species. Anoa are very secretive and flee long before humans can approach through thick jungle. However, if trapped, the anoa will charge.

FACT FILE	
Length:	1.7m (5ft 6in)
Weight:	300kg (660lb)
Distribution:	Sulawesi, Indonesia
Habitat:	Mountain forest
Diet:	Leaves
Status (IUCN Red List):	Endangered

African Buffalo
Syncerus caffer

Perhaps the most numerous and widespread of the truly wild cattle, the African buffalo is a tough animal. They are one of the most dangerous animals in Africa because their herds stampede frequently. Both sexes have horns connected by a boss on the forehead, but this is much thicker in the bulls.

FACT FILE	
Length:	3.4m (11ft 3in)
Weight:	900kg (1984lb)
Distribution:	Sub-Saharan Africa
Habitat:	Grasslands and woodlands
Diet:	Grasses
Status (IUCN Red List):	Least concern

Cattle Breeds

Today's domestic cattle are the descendants of the auroch, a large grazer that lived across North Africa, Europe and Asia. The last wild herd died out in the forests of Poland in the 1620s. Humped cattle, or zebus, of South Asia and Africa originate from Indian aurochs, while the western breeds relate to the European subspecies.

Gaur

Bos gaurus

Herds of wild gaur live in the Indian forests, but a domestic breed, known as the gayal, is also farmed in that region. The gaur is the largest bovid of all, larger even than the African buffalo. Domestic gaur herds are probably hybridized with ordinary cattle breeds.

FACT FILE	
Length:	3.6m (11ft 9in)
Weight:	1.5 tonnes (1¾ tons)
Distribution:	Northeast India
Habitat:	Forest
Diet:	Leaves and grass
Status (IUCN Red List):	Vulnerable

Texas Longhorn

Bos taurus

This aptly named breed has horns up to 2m (6ft 6in) across. The breed originates from feral cattle herds living in northern Mexico generations after being brought over from Spain. These animals were bred with cattle from the eastern United States, themselves originating from northern Europe.

FACT FILE	
Length:	3m (9ft 9in)
Weight:	900kg (1984lb)
Distribution:	N/A
Habitat:	N/A
Diet:	N/A
Status (IUCN Red List):	N/A

Holstein

Bos taurus

This black and white cattle is very familiar in western Europe and colder parts of North America. It is a highly productive dairy breed and also produces good meat. The breed is also known as the Friesian, and it originated in the northern part of the Netherlands.

FACT FILE	
Length:	3m (9ft 9in)
Weight:	580kg (1278lb)
Distribution:	N/A
Habitat:	N/A
Diet:	N/A
Status (IUCN Red List):	N/A

Highland Cattle

Bos taurus

With its thick woolly fur to keep out the cold wind and persistent rain, the Highland cow is an ancient Scottish breed. Its meat is so highly prized that the breed has been exported to many other parts of the world. Groups of Highland cattle are known as folds rather than herds.

FACT FILE	
Length:	3m (9ft 9in)
Weight:	600kg (1322lb)
Distribution:	N/A
Habitat:	N/A
Diet:	N/A
Status (IUCN Red List):	N/A

Hereford Cattle

Bos taurus

Originally from Herefordshire in central England, this cow was bred for its meat. There are now thought to be more than five million Herefords grazing around the world. The breed does best in damp climates; too much bright sunlight can cause eye cancer.

FACT FILE	
Length:	3m (9ft 9in)
Weight:	1 tonne (1 ton)
Distribution:	N/A
Habitat:	N/A
Diet:	N/A
Status (IUCN Red List):	N/A

Muskox

Ovibos moschatus

A muskox might look like a hairy species of cattle, but it is in fact a relative of the goat and sheep. Its large size is given a boost by the thick hair that covers its body. Muskoxen are named after the strong smells produced by the males during the breeding season, which is carried by the wind to attract females.

FACT FILE	
Length:	2.3m (7ft 6in)
Weight:	440kg (970lb)
Distribution:	Arctic Canada, Siberia, Greenland
Habitat:	Tundra
Diet:	Grass and sedge
Status (IUCN Red List):	Least concern

Muskoxen live on the Arctic tundra. They do not venture on to the pack ice because none of their grass food grows there. They scrape away the snow with their hooves to get at food, or brave the coldest hillsides where the winds blow the snow away.

HORNS
A male's horns grow over the head to form a boss, while the females lack this feature. When threatened by a polar bear, the muskoxen form a circle to face down the hunter.

COAT
The long shaggy coat forms a curtain against the wind. The muskox stands face first into the wind to get the benefit. The thick hair also keep off flies in summer.

OVES
muskox has wide hooves
do not sink too much in soft
w. The inner edges between
h hoof are sharp and grip ice
ocks on hard ground.

HAIRY FEET
The exposed feet are insulated by 'socks' of thick and fine hairs.

Goats and Relatives

There is no firm zoological distinction between wild goats and sheep. Together they form a subfamily called the caprids. Caprids known as goats tend to have beards and a more distinct cleft between lips and nose. Both sexes of a goat species generally have horns; these are often spiralled or raised high off the head.

Arabian Tahr

Hemitragus jayakari

The Arabian tahr is the smallest of the tahr species, a group of primitive goats living across southern Asia. This species is very rare and is confined to the dry slopes of the Hajar Mountains overlooking the Straits of Hormuz. They climb the rocky cliffs to reach food, but climb into valleys to find water.

FACT FILE	
Length:	1m (3ft 3in)
Weight:	40kg (88lb)
Distribution:	UAE and Oman
Habitat:	Mountains
Diet:	Grass, bark and leaves
Status (IUCN Red List):	Endangered

Takin

Budorcas taxicolor

The closest relative to the muskox, this large caprid also lives in cold and icy conditions, although not to the same extremes as the Arctic muskox. In summer, herds of up to 300 gather on the high pastures. In winter, the herd fragments as the takins climb into sheltered valleys.

FACT FILE	
Length:	2.2m (7ft 2in)
Weight:	275kg (606lb)
Distribution:	Himalayas
Habitat:	Mountains
Diet:	Leaves and grass
Status (IUCN Red List):	Vulnerable

Chamois

Rupicapra rupicapra

The chamois has leant its name to a soft leather, originally made from its hide. Like many other caprids, the chamois is a sure-footed mountain grazer. The females and kids live in flocks, while males like to be alone. The chamois will whistle and stamp its feet when danger is near.

FACT FILE	
Length:	1.3m (4ft 3in)
Weight:	50kg (110lb)
Distribution:	Europe and western Asia
Habitat:	Mountains pasture
Diet:	Grass, lichens, moss and twigs
Status (IUCN Red List):	Least concern

Japanese Serow

Capricornis crispus

The Japanese serow lives on the main Japanese islands of Honshu and the smaller ones to the south. However, its range does not extend into the cold climate of Hokkaido. The serows marks out territories in the forested slopes using scent. They can be found feeding both day and night.

FACT FILE	
Length:	1.3m (4ft 3in)
Weight:	37kg (81lb 8oz)
Distribution:	Japan
Habitat:	Mountain forests
Diet:	Leaves and buds
Status (IUCN Red List):	Least concern

Markhor

Capra falconeri

Markhors are the largest species of goat. Both the male and females have horns; the males' grow to about 1.6m (5ft 2in) long and feature a characteristic spiral that makes them highly prized as hunting trophies. In winter, the goats grow hairy 'pantaloons' to the knees to keep out the cold.

FACT FILE	
Length:	1.8m (6ft)
Weight:	110kg (242lb)
Distribution:	Central Asia
Habitat:	Mountains
Diet:	Grass, leaves and twigs
Status (IUCN Red List):	Endangered

Mountain Goat

Oreamnos americanus

This white-coated species is the only goat native to the Americas. It is a sure-footed grazer and can be seen leaping from tiny ledge to precipitous peak during the summer months in search of the merest tufts of grass. Winter ice makes the high mountains too slippery even for mountain goats, and they climb down to the shelter – and better grazing – of valleys.

FACT FILE	
Length:	1.6m (5ft 2in)
Weight:	140kg (308lb)
Distribution:	Western North America
Habitat:	Mountains
Diet:	Grass, lichens, moss and twigs
Status (IUCN Red List):	Least concern

Mountain goats are related to the chamois and serows. The males are about 30 per cent larger than the females. During the spring breeding season, males do not butt heads like many other caprids; instead, rivals stand side by side and jab each other with their horns.

TOES
The pale woolly fur helps keep the goat hidden among the snow and grey mountain slopes. The fur grows longer in winter.

ORNS
oth sexes have horns, although
e males' are longer, reaching
0cm (12in) long.

RUMP
Males have extra-thick skin on their rumps to protect them from the worst damage of the yearly fights over mates.

HOOVES
The sharp hooves provide good grip. When placed on the ground the toes spread slightly, grabbing onto rough terrain. The soles are soft and leathery to prevent slipping.

Wild Sheep

Most of the eight or nine sheep species belong to the genus Ovis. The horns – especially those of the males – form wide loops or even coils. Occasionally, the females of a few sheep populations do not grow horns. Like goats, sheep are adapted to life on steep mountains.

Barbary Sheep

Ammotragus lervia

This species is endemic to the Barbary Coast, the plain that runs between the Atlas Mountains and the sea in northwest Africa. Today, the sheep is found in small flocks mainly on the slopes of the Atlas and further south along the edges of the Sahara Desert.

FACT FILE	
Length:	1.5m (5ft)
Weight:	145kg (320lb)
Distribution:	Northwest Africa
Habitat:	Deserts, canyons and mountains
Diet:	Grasses and leaves
Status (IUCN Red List):	Vulnerable

Bighorn Sheep

Ovis canadensis

The most common wild sheep in North America, the bighorn sheep lives up in the Rockies and the Great Basin. Flocks of up to 100 climb to high grazing spots in summer, but as autumn arrives the flock follows traditional trails to wintering grounds lower down.

FACT FILE	
Length:	1.8m (6ft)
Weight:	125kg (275lb)
Distribution:	Western North America
Habitat:	Mountain slopes
Diet:	Grass, lichens, moss and twigs
Status (IUCN Red List):	Least concern

Thinhorn Sheep

Ovis dalli

Often going by the name dall sheep, this species' other name of thinhorn is a comparison with its southern neighbour, which has bigger, thicker horns. The thinhorn's covering of keratin can be almost transparent. Males court females by doing a stiff-legged crouch and sticking out their tongues.

FACT FILE	
Length:	1.8m (6ft)
Weight:	113kg (249lb)
Distribution:	Western Canada and Alaska
Habitat:	Alpine pastures
Diet:	Grass
Status (IUCN Red List):	Least concern

Argali

Ovis ammon

Argalis are the world's largest species of sheep. Like domestic sheep, these wild animals like to stick together in a flock, and they instinctively follow each other. The benefits are obvious: together they are more likely to spot danger and, if a predator does attack, the odds are that it will kill another member of the flock.

FACT FILE	
Length:	1.8m (6ft)
Weight:	160kg (352lb)
Distribution:	Tibet and Siberia
Habitat:	Grassland and woodlands
Diet:	Leaves and grass
Status (IUCN Red List):	Near threatened

Himalayan Blue Sheep

Pseudois nayaur

Also known as the bharal, the blue sheep have to cope with one of the most extreme climates on earth, with searingly hot summers and sub-zero winters. They normally graze close to steep cliffs and climb up high ledges for safety if attacked.

FACT FILE	
Length:	1.3m (4ft 3in)
Weight:	55kg (121lb)
Distribution:	Tibetan Plateau
Habitat:	Mountains
Diet:	Grasses
Status (IUCN Red List):	Least concern

Domestic Sheep and Goats

Domestic sheep are descended from the urial, a wild species that still lives in the mountains of central and western Asia. Domestic breeds normally lack horns, as such weaponry is not helpful on the farm. However, sheep retain their wild instincts. Just like their mountaineering cousins, flocks of sheep run up hill when spooked.

Mouflon

Ovis orientalis musimon

The mouflon is a European subspecies of the urial. Today, small semi-wild herds live in the mountains of the largest Mediterranean islands. It is likely that some domestic breeds originate from this subspecies. It is the smallest wild sheep, just a third of the size of the mighty argali.

FACT FILE	
Length:	1.3m (4ft 3in)
Weight:	55kg (121lb)
Distribution:	Sardinia, Corsica and Cyprus
Habitat:	Steep woodlands
Diet:	Grass
Status (IUCN Red List):	Vulnerable

Wild Goat

Capra aegagrus

Domestic goats are descended from the wild goat of Central Asia. (It is a close relative of the larger ibex.) Most goat breeds retain the sexual dimorphism of wild individuals. The bearded males are larger than the less hirsute she-goats and have longer, thicker horns.

FACT FILE	
Length:	1.1m (3ft 7in)
Weight:	45kg (99lb)
Distribution:	Central Asia
Habitat:	Dry grasslands
Diet:	Grass and leaves
Status (IUCN Red List):	Vulnerable

Texel Sheep

Ovis aries

Hailing from the largest of the Frisian Islands, the Texel is the result of multiple crosses with older English breeds. This white-faced variety was bred for both meat and wool. The fleece does not grow below the knees, and the meat is prized for being low in fat.

FACT FILE	
Length:	1.5m (5ft)
Weight:	75kg (165lb)
Distribution:	N/A
Habitat:	N/A
Diet:	N/A
Status (IUCN Red List):	N/A

Jacob Sheep

Ovis aries

This very unusual breed has four, and sometimes six, horns. Rarely bred by modern farmers, the sheep is thought to have descended from an ancient Middle Eastern breed. The horns were probably selected by breeders as a means of self-defence during wolf attacks on the fold.

FACT FILE	
Length:	1.5m (5ft)
Weight:	80kg (176lb)
Distribution:	N/A
Habitat:	N/A
Diet:	N/A
Status (IUCN Red List):	N/A

Anglo-Nubian Goat

Capra hircus

This common breed is the result of a cross between English milking goats and breeds from the Middle East. The result was a goat with floppy ears and a distinctive bump on the forehead. Anglo-Nubians can withstand hot conditions and still provide a good supply of milk.

FACT FILE	
Length:	1.2m (4ft)
Weight:	79kg (175lb)
Distribution:	N/A
Habitat:	N/A
Diet:	N/A
Status (IUCN Red List):	N/A

Black Rhinoceros

Diceros bicornis

This species is the smaller and more endangered of Africa's two rhino species. The word rhinoceros means 'nose horn' and the iconic horns have been the species' downfall. Poaching reduced the population to fewer than 1000 in the 1980s. It has tripled since then, but the species is far from secure.

FACT FILE	
Length:	3.75m (12ft)
Weight:	1.4 tonnes (1½ tons)
Distribution:	Sub-Saharan Africa
Habitat:	Woody savannah
Diet:	Leaves
Status (IUCN Red List):	Critically endangered

HORN
Unlike the horns of other animals, rhinoceros horns do not have a bone core; they are made from solid keratin, the same protein in hair and fingernails.

LIPS
The black rhino has sensitive, highly mobile lips used to pluck leaves from bushes.

EYES
Rhinos have poor vision and will charge at anything moving that they judge to be a threat, from a campfire to a train.

Black rhinos are browsers; they do not crop grass but pluck leaves from bushes. Their horn is used in traditional Yemeni ornaments, and is powdered into a Chinese aphrodisiac. However, recent research has shown that swallowing powdered buffalo horn had more of the desired effect than the real-deal rhino powder.

Skin
The skin is thickened into an armoured pad. Without sweat glands, the animal takes regular cooling dust baths.

Toes
Rhinos have three toes. The wide middle toe takes most of the animal's immense weight.

Odd-toed Hoofed Animals

An ungulate is an animal with hooves in place of the claws or fingernails of other mammals. Not all the ungulates are related. The deer, bovids and pigs belong to the Artiodactyla, also known as the even-toed ungulates. The minority form the Perissodactyla, the odd-toed ungulates, and include rhinos, horses and tapirs.

Malayan Tapir

Tapirus indicus

Despite its trunk-like nose, this species is not related to elephants. In fact, its closest living relatives are the horse and other equids. It is a forest animal and the flexible snout is used to sniff out food and rip off leaves. The black and white colouring provides camouflage in the dappled sunlight of the deep forest.

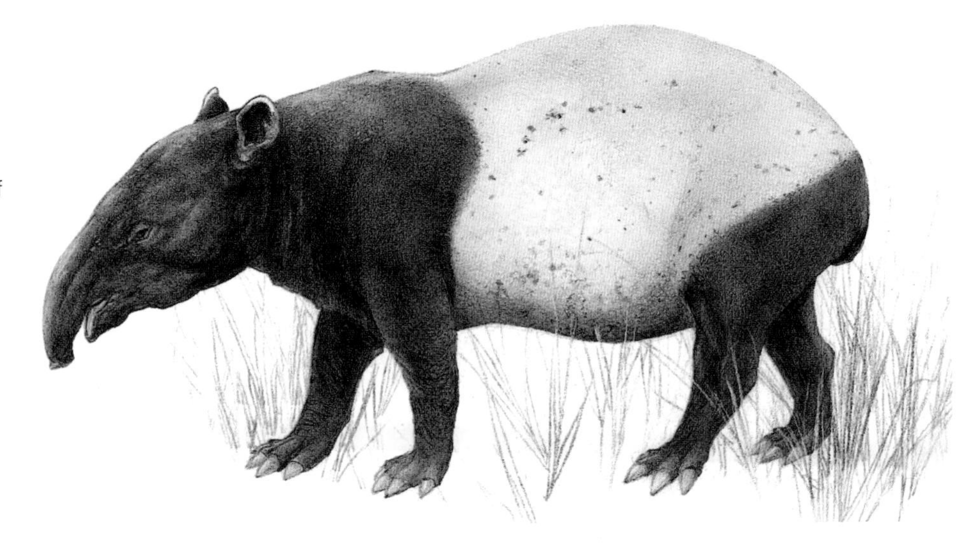

FACT FILE	
Length:	2.5m (8ft 3in)
Weight:	540kg (1190lb)
Distribution:	Southeast Asia
Habitat:	Forests
Diet:	Leaves
Status (IUCN Red List):	Endangered

Brazilian Tapir

Tapirus terrestris

Only rivalled by the spectacled bear, this is the largest mammal in South America. It lives in swampy forests and takes frequent dips. Zoo keepers have found that tapirs kept in enclosures without deep water tend to become constipated. The tapir's wedge-shaped body, wider at the rump, allows it to charge through dense foliage at speed.

FACT FILE	
Length:	2m (6ft 6in)
Weight:	250kg (551lb)
Distribution:	Northern and central S. America
Habitat:	Forests and swamps
Diet:	Water plants
Status (IUCN Red List):	Vulnerable

White Rhinoceros

Ceratotherium simum

Despite being paler than its African relative, the black rhino, this species' name is derived not from its colouring but from the Dutch word for 'wide'. This is in reference to the rhino's squared lips, which are an adaptation to grazing, efficiently cropping mouthfuls of short grass.

FACT FILE	
Length:	4m (13ft 1in)
Weight:	2.5 tonnes (2¾ tons)
Distribution:	Sub-Saharan Africa
Habitat:	Grassy savannah
Diet:	Grass
Status (IUCN Red List):	Near threatened

Sumatran Rhinoceros

Dicerorhinus sumatrensis

This Asian rhino is one of the rarest mammals on earth. It has been brought close to extinction by centuries of poaching, followed by rapid habitat loss in more recent years. The species is a solitary browser, and each rhino needs 40 square km (15 square miles) of forest to itself.

FACT FILE	
Length:	3.2m (10ft 6in)
Weight:	950kg (2094lb)
Distribution:	Southeast Asia and Indonesia
Habitat:	Forests
Diet:	Leave, fruits and twigs
Status (IUCN Red List):	Critically endangered

Javan Rhinoceros

Rhinoceros sondaicus

A leading contender as an inspiration for the unicorn – along with the Indian rhino and, more bizarrely, the narwhal – this rhino species has just one horn, and a rather small one. Despite its name, the animal's natural range covers much of southeast Asia; like its cousins, it is now extremely rare.

FACT FILE	
Length:	3.75m (12ft)
Weight:	1.4 tonnes (1½ tons)
Distribution:	Java and Vietnam
Habitat:	Rainforest
Diet:	Leaves, shoots and twigs
Status (IUCN Red List):	Critically endangered

Horses and Relatives

The Equidae family could have remained a rather obscure branch of the Perissodactyla (odd-toed hoofed mammals), if the horse and donkey had not become the world's most widely used pack animals. Today, Africa's zebras are the only equids that live wild in large numbers.

Thoroughbred Horse

Equus caballus

Despite the name suggesting otherwise, the thoroughbred horse – the main racing breed – is in fact the result of crosses between tough English mares with fast and high-spirited Arabian stallions in the seventeenth century. The result is a horse that loves the chase and is equipped with long legs and neck, but also a brawny body and a deep chest.

FACT FILE	
Height:	1.7m (5ft 6in)
Weight:	590kg (1300lb)
Distribution:	N/A
Habitat:	N/A
Diet:	Grass
Status (IUCN Red List):	N/A

Plains Zebra

Equus quagga

Also known as Burchell's zebra, this is the most common wild equid, living in large herds on savannah and open woodlands of Africa. A family group of zebras is dominated by a stallion, who rules over several mares and their foals. Zebras cover large distances in search of grazing and can smell water from miles away.

FACT FILE	
Length:	2.5m (8ft 3in)
Weight:	260kg (573lb)
Distribution:	East and southern Africa
Habitat:	Savannah
Diet:	Grasses
Status (IUCN Red List):	Least concern

African Wild Ass

Equus africanus

The wild relative of today's donkeys, the African wild ass is a highly endangered species with just a few hundred living in the dry grasslands along the African coast of the Red Sea. More graceful than its domestic cousins, the wild ass can run at speeds of 50km/h (31mph).

FACT FILE	
Length:	2.3m (7ft 6in)
Weight:	230kg (507lb)
Distribution:	East Africa
Habitat:	Arid regions
Diet:	Grasses
Status (IUCN Red List):	Critically endangered

Kulan

Equus hemionus kulan

This equid is the Central Asian subspecies of the Asian wild ass, sometimes referred to as the onager. Slightly larger than the donkey, the kulan is named after a district of northern Afghanistan. Its natural range is now in Turkmenistan, although it has recently been reintroduced to neighbouring states.

FACT FILE	
Length:	2.1m (6ft 10in)
Weight:	290kg (639lb)
Distribution:	Central Asia
Habitat:	Grassland
Diet:	Grasses
Status (IUCN Red List):	Endangered

Kiang

Equus kiang

Sometimes regarded as another subspecies of the Asian wild ass, the kiang is the largest wild equid after the zebras. The bulky animal grows a long shaggy coat to withstand the highland winters. Unlike zebras, females rule the herds, while bachelor males live alone or in small groups.

FACT FILE	
Height:	2.1m (6ft 10in)
Weight:	440kg (970lb)
Distribution:	Tibetan Plateau
Habitat:	High grasslands
Diet:	Grass
Status (IUCN Red List):	Least concern

Beaver

Castor fiber

The largest rodent in North America, the beaver is the engineer of the animal world. Beavers dam rivers with a lattice of logs and mud to create a large, calm pond, where they store their food. The residents also build a domed den, known as a lodge, on the dam or bank. Most lodges have a hidden underwater entrance.

FACT FILE	
Length:	88cm (34½in)
Weight:	26kg (57lb)
Distribution:	North American
Habitat:	Rivers and lakes
Diet:	Grasses and wood pulp
Status (IUCN Red List):	Least concern

A beaver eats the lush plants that grow around the pond as well as wood pulp harvested from the forest. Using its large upper incisors, the chunky water rodent fells small trees and cuts the trunks into smaller logs. These are then floated into the beaver's pond and left to soften in the water, before being eaten.

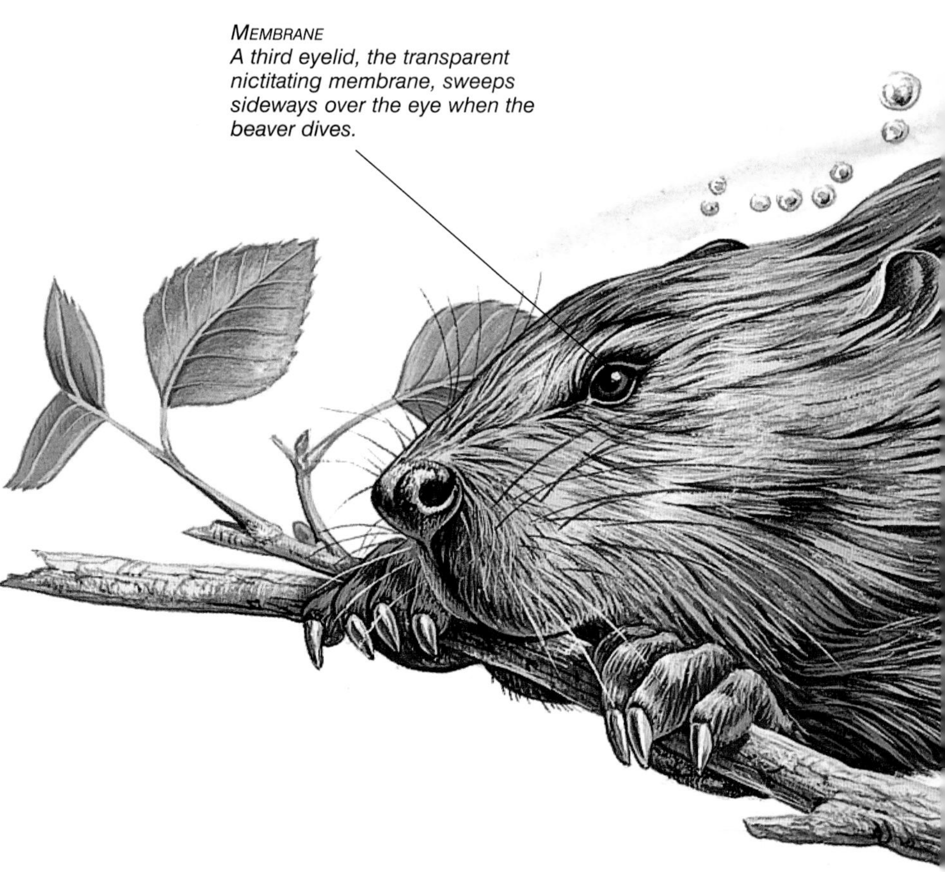

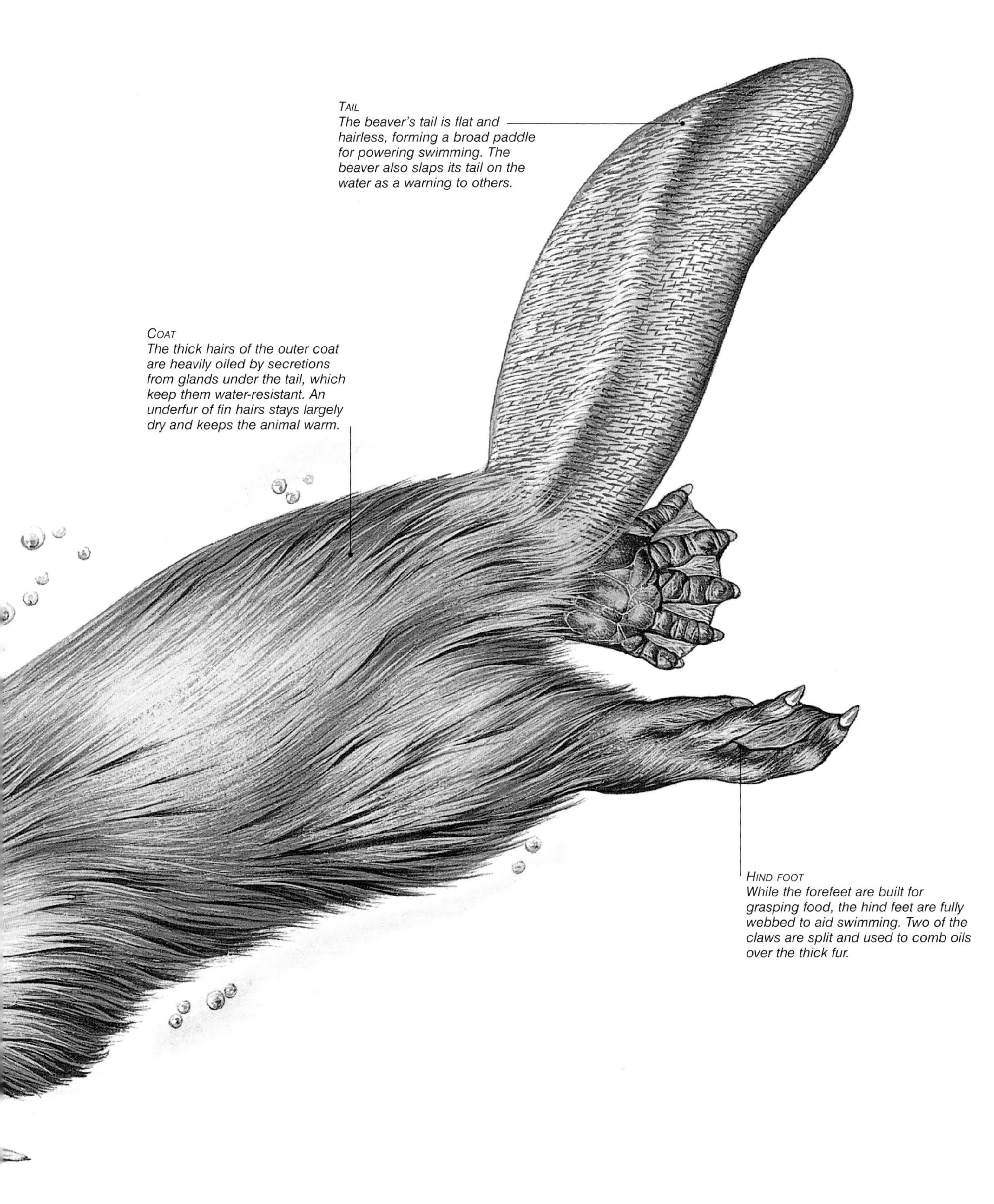
TAIL
The beaver's tail is flat and hairless, forming a broad paddle for powering swimming. The beaver also slaps its tail on the water as a warning to others.
COAT
The thick hairs of the outer coat are heavily oiled by secretions from glands under the tail, which keep them water-resistant. An underfur of fin hairs stays largely dry and keeps the animal warm.
HIND FOOT
While the forefeet are built for grasping food, the hind feet are fully webbed to aid swimming. Two of the claws are split and used to comb oils over the thick fur.

Old World Squirrels

The squirrels belong to a suborder of rodents, known as the sciuromorphs (literally squirrel forms). There are about 275 squirrel species worldwide, including in the so-called Old World – Africa, Europe and Asia. Squirrels are primarily seed eaters and many are adapted to life in trees.

Alpine Marmot

Marmota marmota

Marmots are large ground squirrels most associated with cold regions, such as the sub-Arctic region and mountain ranges. This species is heavily built to aid digging burrows in frozen mountain soils with its heavily clawed feet. Alpine marmots hibernate in winter and forage in groups of about 20 during warmer periods.

FACT FILE	
Length:	18cm (7in)
Weight:	8kg (17lb 10oz)
Distribution:	Southern to eastern Europe
Habitat:	Mountain grasslands
Diet:	Grasses, leaves seeds and bulbs
Status (IUCN Red List):	Least concern

European Ground Squirrel

Spermophilus citellus

Also known as the souslik, this species of squirrel is most common in dry habitats, where there is plenty of open country and shrubs. They avoid dense woodlands. They sleep in burrows, which are blocked up during hibernation. They forage by day but slip into thickets and shrubs when disturbed.

FACT FILE	
Length:	20cm (8in)
Weight:	220g (7¾oz)
Distribution:	Central and eastern Europe
Habitat:	Grassland and woodlands
Diet:	Nuts and seeds
Status (IUCN Red List):	Vulnerable

Red Squirrel

Sciurus vulgaris

Once the most common squirrel in Europe's woodlands, the red squirrel's tufted ears are an increasingly rare sight in the broad-leaved forests of western Europe, where the grey squirrel, an American import, has muscled them out. However, this species still out-competes its rival in the pine forests of colder regions.

FACT FILE	
Length:	25cm (10in)
Weight:	475g (16¾oz)
Distribution:	Europe and northern Asia
Habitat:	Forests
Diet:	Seeds and nuts
Status (IUCN Red List):	Least concern

Indian Giant Squirrel

Ratufa indica

The world's largest species of tree squirrel, with a combined head-to-tail length of nearly 1m (3ft 3in), the Indian giant squirrel is nevertheless an agile mover. Breeding pairs build large ball-shaped nests in the high treetops, where the female rears her young.

FACT FILE	
Length:	46cm (18in)
Weight:	3kg (6lb 10oz)
Distribution:	India
Habitat:	Forests
Diet:	Fruit, nuts, insects and eggs
Status (IUCN Red List):	Least concern

Springhare

Pedetes capensis

The springhare is an African rodent related to the scaly-tailed squirrels. This family of unusual gliding rodents uses a scaly pad to anchor themselves to tree trunks when landing. The springhare lives an altogether different life, bounding across dry grassland on its rabbit feet at speeds of 40km/h (25mph).

FACT FILE	
Length:	45cm (17¾in)
Weight:	4kg (8lb 13oz)
Distribution:	East and southern Africa
Habitat:	Sandy grasslands
Diet:	Grasses and bulbs
Status (IUCN Red List):	Least concern

New World Squirrels

The squirrels of North and South America do not differ greatly from their Old World cousins – they all belong to the same family, the Sciuridae. However, American squirrels often go by different names, such as chipmunk, ground hog and woodchuck. This last species is the largest squirrel of all, weighing in at 5kg (11lb).

Eastern Chipmunk

Tamias striatus

The root of the name chipmunk is uncertain, but it seems likely that this little squirrel is named after its squeaky, 'chip chip' calls. They often gather in groups to sing when not foraging on the ground for seeds. They retire to shallow burrows at night, and sleep through much of the winter, occasionally emerging to feed on cached food.

FACT FILE	
Length:	16.5cm (6½in)
Weight:	130g (4½oz)
Distribution:	Eastern North America
Habitat:	Woodlands and forests
Diet:	Seeds
Status (IUCN Red List):	Least concern

Southern Flying Squirrel

Glaucomys volans

Despite its name, this squirrel cannot fly, only glide. When running along a branch it looks like any other tree squirrel, but when it leaps into the air, it spreads its limbs to unfurl a patagium – a wing-like skin membrane strung between the legs. The tail is used as a rudder, which the squirrel steers to land on a distant tree trunk.

FACT FILE	
Length:	15cm (6in)
Weight:	85g (3oz)
Distribution:	North and Central America
Habitat:	Woodlands
Diet:	Insects, fruits, nuts and bark
Status (IUCN Red List):	Least concern

American Red Squirrel

Tamiasciurus hudsonicus

Like its Old World cousin, the American red squirrel has its stronghold in the needle-leaf forests of the chilly north. It lacks the ear tufts of the Eurasian red, and its coat is more of a russet, especially in the winter. The squirrel often dens in abandoned bird holes, but descends into underground burrows in cold areas to escape the frosts.

FACT FILE	
Length:	23cm (9in)
Weight:	250g (8¾oz)
Distribution:	Canada and northern US
Habitat:	Forest
Diet:	Seeds, fruits and nuts
Status (IUCN Red List):	Least concern

Thirteen-lined Ground Squirrel

Spermophilus tridecemlineatus

The genus name for this species, Spermophilus, means 'seed lover', but the thirteen-lined ground squirrel does not have the luxury of being able to forage at leisure for seeds. With attacks from snakes, coyotes and eagles an ever-present danger, the squirrels snatch meals of any kind before heading back to the safety of their burrows.

FACT FILE	
Length:	25cm (10in)
Weight:	140g (5oz)
Distribution:	Central North America
Habitat:	Short grasses
Diet:	Seeds, eggs, insects and carrion
Status (IUCN Red List):	Least concern

Rats and Mice

The rats and mice make up about three-quarters of the entire rodent order. The suborder Myomorpha contains around 1300 species. The myomorphs make the most of the main rodent feature – gnawing teeth. The four front incisors never stop growing, and are self-sharpening as the mice and rats chew their way through life.

House Mouse

Mus musculus

The little house mouse has followed human migrations since the dawn of history. They even stow away on research trips to Antarctica, but this ice continent is too cold for a permanent population. However, the mouse is resident everywhere else on earth, gnawing through wood and plastic to reach food supplies.

FACT FILE	
Length:	10cm (4in)
Weight:	35g (1¼oz)
Distribution:	Worldwide, except polar regions
Habitat:	Human habitats
Diet:	Seeds, insects, rubbish
Status (IUCN Red List):	Least concern

Maned Rat

Lophiomys imhausi

Also known as the crested rat, this largish rodent hides out in rock crevices by day, and then creeps through the dark in search of food. It does not dash for cover if spooked. Instead, it raises its mane to give the impression of a much larger animal. It then squirts a foul spray from its rear end, sending attackers running.

FACT FILE	
Length:	36cm (14in)
Weight:	750g (26½oz)
Distribution:	Eastern Africa
Habitat:	Forests and woodlands
Diet:	Fruits and roots
Status (IUCN Red List):	Least concern

Wood Mouse

Apodemus sylvaticus

Alternatively known as the long-tailed field mouse, this is the country mouse to *Mus musculus's* town mouse. It lives across Europe, Asia and North Africa, although it avoids the coldest regions, and can make do in most habitats and climates. It digs a deep burrow and lines it with leaves. Most feeding is done at night.

FACT FILE	
Length:	15cm (6in)
Weight:	23g (¾oz)
Distribution:	Europe, N. Africa and N. Asia
Habitat:	Meadows and woodlands
Diet:	Fruits, roots and seeds
Status (IUCN Red List):	Least concern

Lab Rat

Rattus novegicus

A domesticated variety of the brown rat, these inquisitive creatures can make good pets, and can even be trained to use a litter box. However, most people prefer pets with a better reputation, and most domestic rats live and die in the science lab, where they are used for everything from drug tests to genetic research.

FACT FILE	
Length:	25cm (10in)
Weight:	350g (12½oz)
Distribution:	All continents except Antarctica; Canada and New Zealand have restrictions on rat ownership
Habitat:	Wherever humans live, particularly urban areas
Diet:	Omnivore, with a high cereal intake
Status (IUCN Red List):	N/A

Arctic Lemming

Dicrostonyx torquatus

Lemmings do not commit suicide, but they do leave overcrowded habitats. On occasion, these trekking lemmings are forced together again by natural geographic features. That increases the impulse to get away ever more, leading the lemmings to flee in panic – and perhaps fall over a cliff in the process.

FACT FILE	
Length:	14cm (5½in)
Weight:	40g (1½oz)
Distribution:	Arctic land region
Habitat:	Tundra
Diet:	Twigs and shoots
Status (IUCN Red List):	Least concern

Black Rat

Rattus rattus

Originating in southern Asia, the black rat is now found worldwide, but is more common in warmer areas than the closely related brown rat. The black rat's spread around the world was given a boost as global trade routes became established between east and west. The rodent is often known as the ship rat because it is a regular unwanted passenger on board sea vessels.

FACT FILE	
Length:	24cm (9½in)
Weight:	250g (8¾oz)
Distribution:	Global except for polar regions
Habitat:	Cities, ships, grasslands
Diet:	Carrion, insects and rubbish
Status (IUCN Red List):	Least concern

The black rat was responsible for spreading the Black Death, the bubonic plague epidemics that ravaged Europe, Africa and Asia in the fourteenth century, killing more than 75 million people in just six years. The rats are immune to the plague bacteria, which is carried by its fleas. Humans can develop the disease if bitten by the infected rat fleas.

TOOTH GAP
There is a gap, or diastema, between the incisors and the rest of the rat's teeth. As the rat gnaws with its front teeth, its lips fold into the gap, stopping non-food debris from getting into the mouth.

PAWS
The forepaws have four toes, while the hind feet have five toes. These feet are good at everything from holding food to climbing a ship's anchor chain.

WHISKERS
Black rats often live in total darkness and use their whiskers as feelers. If the whiskers fit through a hole without being overly bent, the rat knows that the rest of its body will fit as well.

TAIL
The hairless tail is longer than the length of the head and body combined. It is used as a feeler, especially as an early-warning system of an attack from the rear.

Dormice and Jumping Mice

The names 'mouse' and 'rat' are applied to most small rodents, but they are not all closely related, or indeed members of the Myomorpha suborder. Dormice are actually related to squirrels, while jumping mice – equipped with long back feet for hopping – fall into two groups, the Old World's jerboas and American kangaroo rats.

Desert Kangaroo Rat

Dipodomys deserti

This little rodent lives in some of the hottest and driest places on earth, including California's Death Valley. It inhabits wind-blown sand dunes, digging complex burrow systems. The rats come to the surface at night to look for food. They do not need to drink, but can extract all the water they need from their food.

FACT FILE	
Length:	16cm (6¼in)
Weight:	135g (4¾oz)
Distribution:	Southwest US and Mexico
Habitat:	Sand dunes
Diet:	Seeds and dried leaves
Status (IUCN Red List):	Least concern

Long-eared Jerboa

Euchoreutes naso

The giant outer ears of this jerboa probably have multiple functions. First, they are heat dumps, radiating unwanted heat from the blood that flow through them. Second, jerboas are burrowing animals and the ears are thought to pick up sounds and vibrations transmitted through tunnels by other animals.

FACT FILE	
Length:	9cm (3½in)
Weight:	50g (1¾oz)
Distribution:	Mongolia and northern China
Habitat:	Sandy valleys and scrub
Diet:	Insects
Status (IUCN Red List):	Least concern

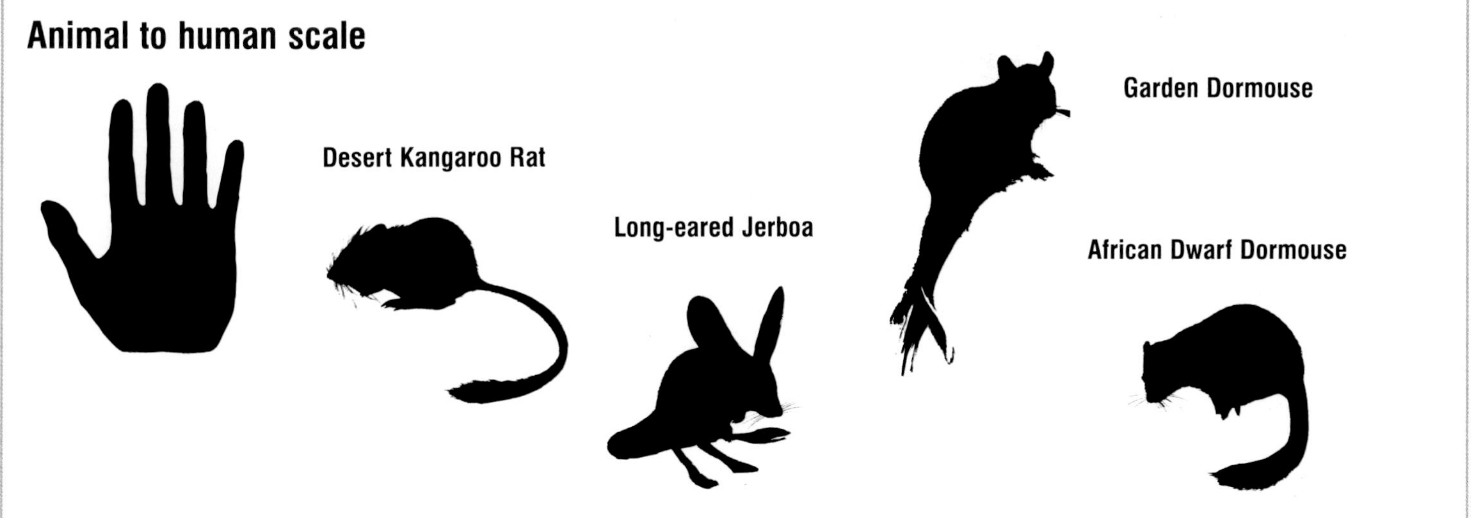

Garden Dormouse

Eliomys quercinus

With the widest range of any dormouse species, the common name of this species is somewhat misleading. It does come into gardens and fields, but lives in just about any tree habitat. In some parts of the world it turns up in marshy areas. This species was introduced to Britain by the Romans, possibly as a food animal.

FACT FILE	
Length:	17cm (6¾in)
Weight:	85g (3oz)
Distribution:	Europe, Asia and N. Africa
Habitat:	Forests, swamps and gardens
Diet:	Nuts, insects, chicks and snails
Status (IUCN Red List):	Near threatened

African Dwarf Dormouse

Graphiurus murinus

This little creatures hides out by day in crevices under bark or in abandoned nest holes. As with many rodents, the tail is used as a signal flag and puts the dormouse at a disadvantage if lost in an attack. However, this species has the unique ability to regrow a tufty stump as a partial replacement.

FACT FILE	
Length:	8cm (3in)
Weight:	23g (¾oz)
Distribution:	South Africa
Habitat:	Montane and river forest
Diet:	Grass seeds and insects
Status (IUCN Red List):	Least concern

Hamsters and Gerbils

These plump and fluffy rodents are popular pets because they are easy to keep in small cages. Hamsters hail from the Middle East, but are close relatives of American mice. Gerbils are Asian animals and are banned from some U.S. states because they would wreak havoc among native species if they escaped to the wild.

European Hamster

Cricetus cricetus

Also known as the black-bellied hamster, this species is considerably larger than pet hamsters,although they still have the cheek pouches that give pet hamsters their cute round-faced look. The European hamster uses the pouches to transport food to its burrow and stockpiles it there for the winter.

FACT FILE	
Length:	27cm (10½in)
Weight:	500g (17½oz)
Distribution:	Eastern Europe and Siberia
Habitat:	Grasslands and fields
Diet:	Seeds, roots and insect larvae
Status (IUCN Red List):	Least concern

Dzungarian Dwarf Hamster

Phodopus sungorus

Dzungarian hamsters live wild on the steppes of Mongolia and Manchuria, where their fluffy coats keep out the biting cold. In winter, the brown coat turns white to provide camouflage in the snow. Dzungarian hamsters make good pets and can be kept in small single-sex groups.

FACT FILE	
Length:	10cm (4in)
Weight:	23g (¾oz)
Distribution:	Central and eastern Asia
Habitat:	Asian steppes
Diet:	Seeds
Status (IUCN Red List):	Least concern

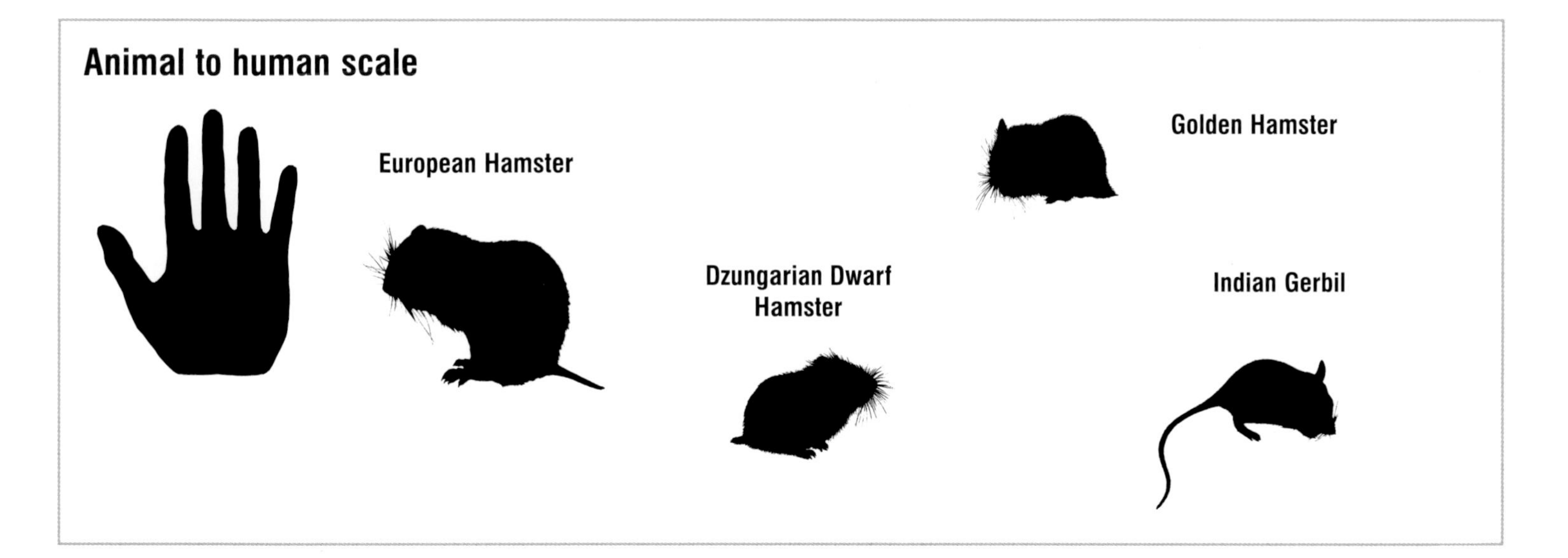

Golden Hamster

Mesocricetus auratus

This species is the now-rare wild ancestor of most pet hamsters. It is named after the flecks of gold on its fur. Like other hamsters, this species is crepuscular – most active at dusk and dawn – which people with a hamster cage in their bedroom will already know.

FACT FILE	
Length:	18cm (7in)
Weight:	200g (7oz)
Distribution:	Syria
Habitat:	Desert borders, scrub
Diet:	Seeds
Status (IUCN Red List):	Vulnerable

Indian Gerbil

Tatera indica

This species can be a damaging pest if it gets into grain stores. Like all gerbils, it is a desert animal and extracts valuable water from its faeces, leaving dry pellets, a bonus for any pet owner. Most captive gerbils are Mongolian jirds (*Meriones unguiculatus*), which were first kept as pets in the 1960s.

FACT FILE	
Length:	17cm (6¾in)
Weight:	225g (8oz)
Distribution:	Western and south Asia
Habitat:	Sandy grasslands, fields
Diet:	Leaves, seeds and roots
Status (IUCN Red List):	Least concern

Muskrat

Ondatra zibethicus

The muskrat is a water rodent that is actually a giant vole, often growing to the size of a rabbit. It lives in marshes and on riverbanks, where it builds a nest lined with dry leaves in burrows or inside a mound of twigs and mud. The nest's chamber is above the water line, but its entrance is always under the water.

FACT FILE	
Length:	35cm (13¾in)
Weight:	2kg (4lb 6oz)
Distribution:	North America
Habitat:	Lakes and rivers
Diet:	Water plants, fish and frogs
Status (IUCN Red List):	Least concern

Muskrats have short legs and are not fast over land, but they come into their own in water. They swim blind – with their eyes shut tight – and can seal their mouths around their ungainly incisors to keep water out of their mouths. A muskrat can stay under water for about 15 minutes.

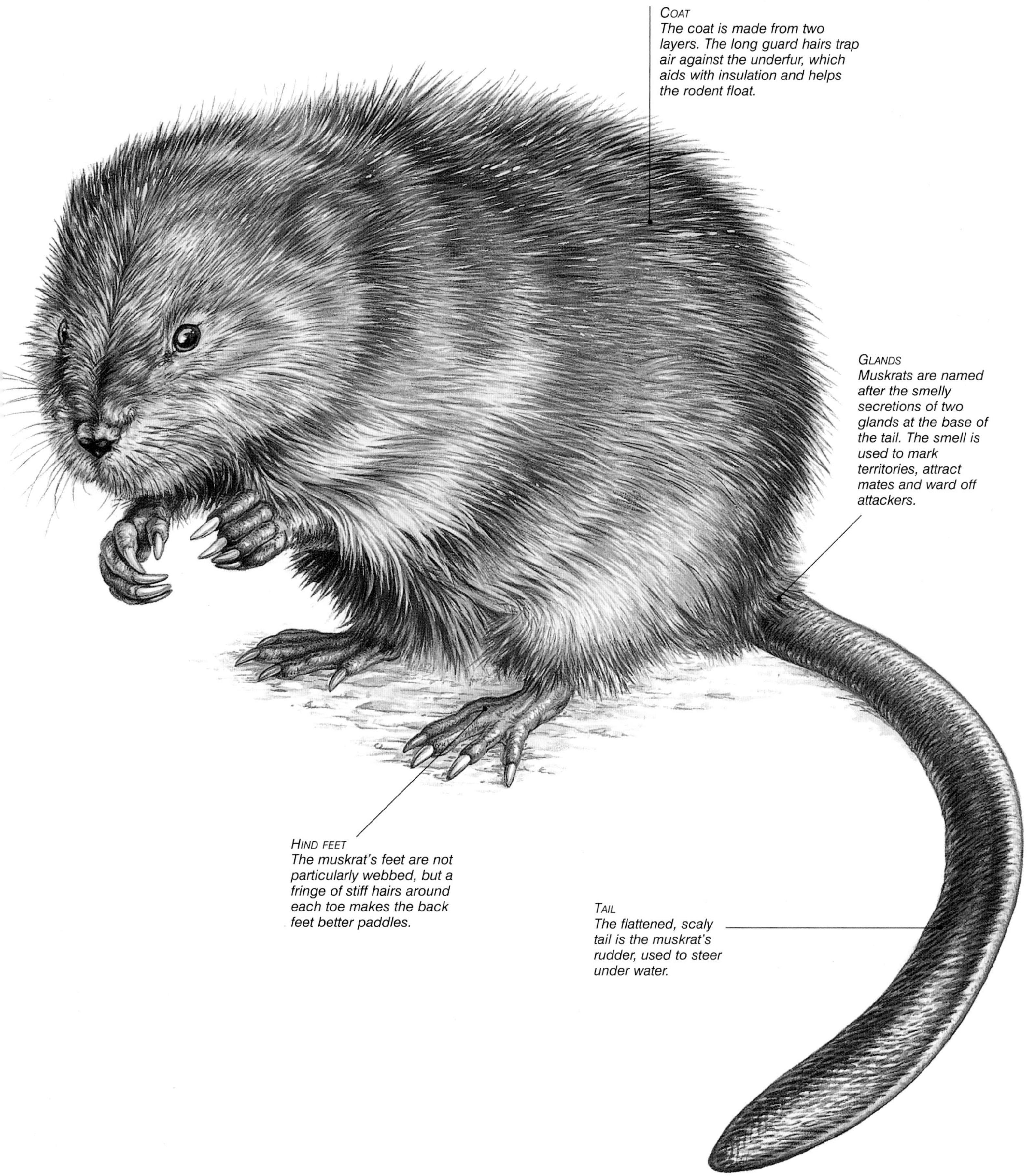

COAT
The coat is made from two layers. The long guard hairs trap air against the underfur, which aids with insulation and helps the rodent float.

GLANDS
Muskrats are named after the smelly secretions of two glands at the base of the tail. The smell is used to mark territories, attract mates and ward off attackers.

HIND FEET
The muskrat's feet are not particularly webbed, but a fringe of stiff hairs around each toe makes the back feet better paddles.

TAIL
The flattened, scaly tail is the muskrat's rudder, used to steer under water.

Guinea Pigs and Allies

The hystricognaths form the third suborder of rodents, the most familiar members of which are guinea pigs. Its relatives share the same square-jawed skull, as opposed to the pinched, mouse-like features of other rodents. Hystricognaths are found across the Americas, but are more restricted to tropical parts of the Old World.

Capybara

Hydrochaeris hydrochaeris

The largest hystricognath and the largest rodent of all, the capybara is also known as the water pig. Groups of this rodent are quite rightly called herds, and comprise about 20 capybara. Herd members graze near the edge of slow-flowing rivers or wetlands, and when threatened will gallop into the water and hide among water plants.

FACT FILE	
Length:	1.3m (4ft 3in)
Weight:	66kg (145lb)
Distribution:	South America
Habitat:	Wetlands and rivers
Diet:	Grasses and bark
Status (IUCN Red List):	Least concern

Guinea Pig

Cavia aperea

Known as the cavy in the wild, the guinea pig was domesticated about 7000 years ago. Back then it was bred for its oily meat, and guinea pig still appears on menus in the Andes. Guinea pig pets should be kept in small groups to prevent loneliness.

FACT FILE	
Length:	25cm (10in)
Weight:	900g (32oz)
Distribution:	Worldwide in captivity
Habitat:	Grassy plains in the wild
Diet:	Fresh grass
Status (IUCN Red List):	Least concern

Mara

Dolichotis patagonum

This long-legged cavy looks more like a little deer than a rodent. The mara lives on the pampas grasslands of Argentina, and grazes out in the open during the day. They are vulnerable to attack from cats and eagles, and use their long legs to sprint out of danger at speeds of 45km/h (28mph).

FACT FILE	
Length:	79cm (31in)
Weight:	2kg (4lb 6oz)
Distribution:	Southern South America
Habitat:	Grassland and bushlands
Diet:	Grass
Status (IUCN Red List):	Near threatened

Coypu

Myocastor coypus

Also known as the nutria, the coypu is one of South America's most successful emigrés. The water rodent has been introduced to North America, Europe and Asia as stock for fur farms, and has since become feral in many places. The big omnivores dwarf many of the native rodent species in their new homes.

FACT FILE	
Length:	58cm (23in)
Weight:	6.5kg (14lb 4oz)
Distribution:	Americas, Europe and Asia
Habitat:	Aquatic environments
Diet:	Water plants and shellfish
Status (IUCN Red List):	Least concern

Cuban Hutia

Capromys pilorides

While several of Cuba's endemic species are now endangered by the environmental pressures of sharing the island with humans, the hutia has done rather well. The cat-sized rodent waddles around most of the island's habitats and is hunted for its meat.

FACT FILE	
Length:	60cm (23½in)
Weight:	7kg (15lb 8oz)
Distribution:	Cuba
Habitat:	Forests, scrubs, swamps
Diet:	Leaves, fruits and lizards
Status (IUCN Red List):	Least concern

South American Rodents

There is more to the Hystricognathi suborder than guinea pigs. The group includes the bizarre naked mole rats of Africa and the porcupines. However, South America is home to the widest range of these rodents, including the agouti, which now lends its name to any fur that shows the same characteristic bands of light and dark pigment.

Long-tailed Chinchilla

Chinchilla lanigera

Their popularity as a pet has been bad news for wild chinchilla populations. The animals were collected from the wild for sale, and now there are just a few dozen colonies left in their rocky mountain habitat. Chinchillas have incredibly thick fur, with up to 60 hair shafts growing from every single follicle.

FACT FILE	
Length:	23cm (9in) excluding tail
Weight:	500g (17½oz)
Distribution:	Northern Chile
Habitat:	Barren mountain slopes
Diet:	Seeds
Status (IUCN Red List):	Critically endangered

Northern Viscacha

Lagidium peruanum

They may look like rabbits, but viscachas are close relatives of chinchillas. They live along the edge of the tree line and forage in large groups among the rocks up to the snow line. Nothing much grows in this cold and dry environment, and the viscacha grazes on small and hardy alpine plants and fungus.

FACT FILE	
Length:	45cm (17¾in)
Weight:	1.6kg (3lb 8oz)
Distribution:	Peruvian Andes
Habitat:	Rocky areas
Diet:	Grass, moss and lichen
Status (IUCN Red List):	Least concern

Colburn's Tuco-tuco

Ctenomys colburni

The tuco-tucos are a poorly understood group of rodents. They live in the same way as gophers do in North America, burrowing through soft soils. They use their enormous front teeth as shovels and to cut through the roots in their way. Tuco-tucos emerge at night to feed on the surface.

FACT FILE	
Length:	25cm (10in)
Weight:	700g (25oz)
Distribution:	Argentina
Habitat:	Grasslands
Diet:	Roots, grasses and seeds
Status (IUCN Red List):	Data deficient

Tuft-tailed Spiny Tree Rat

Lonchothrix emiliae

The spiny rats resemble the rodents of the Old World a little more than most other hystricognaths. They are named after the thickened hairs on the back that form stiff spines. A spiny rat's tail will also detach if grabbed by a predator, giving it valuable time to escape. The tail does not grow back.

FACT FILE	
Length:	15cm (6in)
Weight:	550g (19½oz)
Distribution:	Brazil
Habitat:	Forests
Diet:	Leaves and fruits
Status (IUCN Red List):	Least concern

Brazilian Porcupine

Coendou prehensilis

This large rodent is also known as the prehensile-tailed porcupine. Its long tail – easily longer than the rest of its body – is used as a fifth limb to grip branches as the animal climbs through trees. The tail is spineless and the quills that cover the rest of the body are shorter than in other porcupine species.

FACT FILE	
Length:	60cm (23½in)
Weight:	5kg (11lb)
Distribution:	Tropical South America
Habitat:	Forests
Diet:	Leaves, fruits and flowers
Status (IUCN Red List):	Endangered

North American Porcupine

Erethizon dorsatum

This species of porcupine is one of the largest rodents in North America, second only in size to the beaver. It is a close relative of other New World porcupines living in South America and Central America, but despite a superficial similarity, it belongs to a separate family from the Old World porcupines.

FACT FILE	
Length:	80cm (32in)
Weight:	7kg (15lb 8oz)
Distribution:	North America
Habitat:	Forests, grasslands and desert
Diet:	Fruits, leaves and seeds
Status (IUCN Red List):	Least concern

The North American porcupine is not a hurried animal, safe in the knowledge that few predators will attempt to attack its spiked body. It raises its quills when under threat, and adds a further warning by chattering its teeth. One hunter that does kill porcupines is the fisher, which attacks from the front, where there are fewer spines.

SENSES
Porcupines cannot see very well, but they use their keen senses of smell and touch to find foods in the dark while foraging at night.

FEET
Equipped with long claws for gripping bark, the porcupine's paws also have soft pads, a bit like a primate's hands, which help to grip small branches.

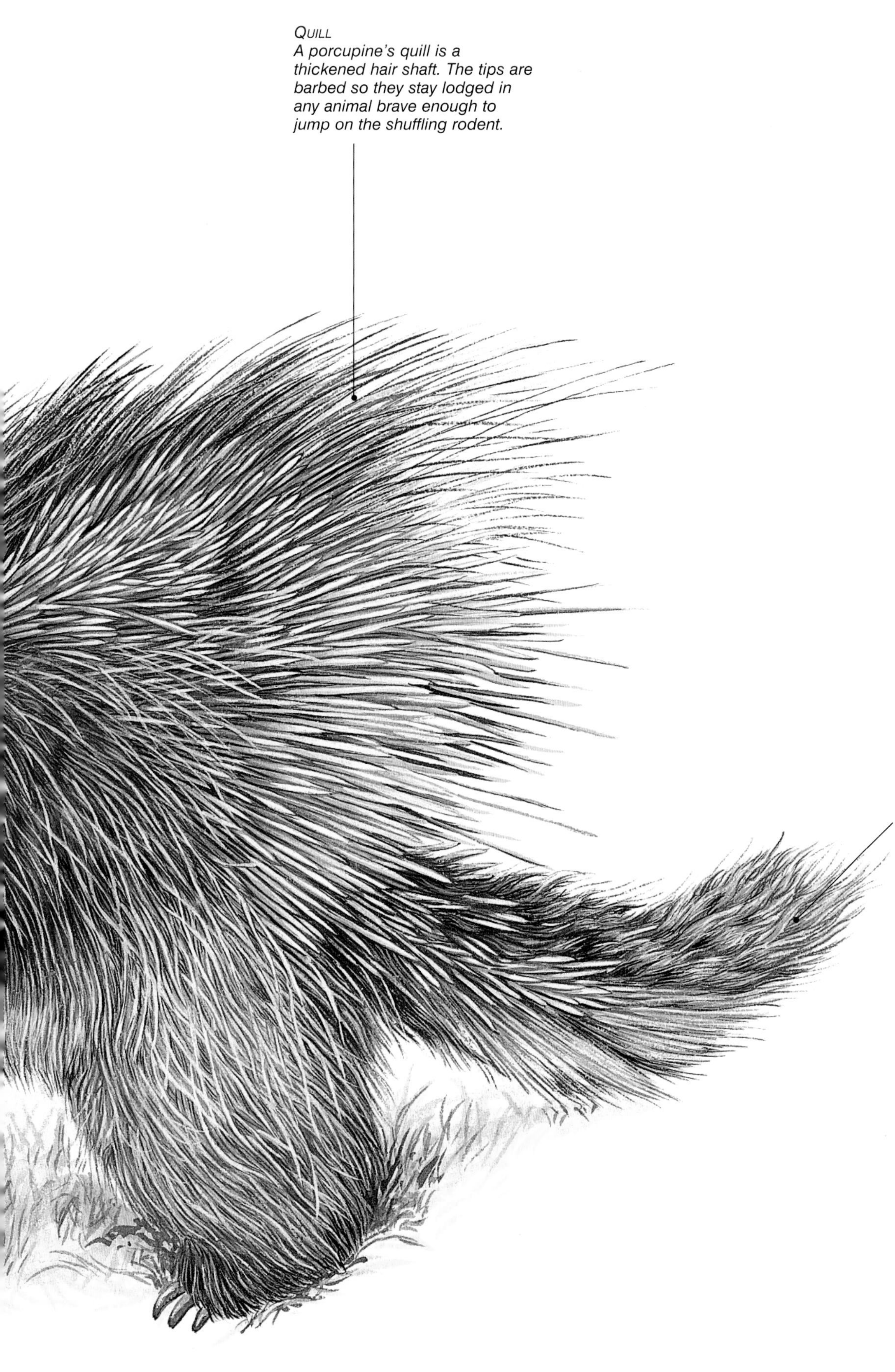
QUILL
A porcupine's quill is a thickened hair shaft. The tips are barbed so they stay lodged in any animal brave enough to jump on the shuffling rodent.
TAIL
The porcupine's tail is armed with quills and used to whack attackers. It also helps the rodent grip bark while climbing.

Rabbits and Hares

Rabbits, hares and pikas belong to the order Lagomorpha. They occur on all continents and are most associated with drier, open habitats. The difference between a rabbit and a hare is not that distinct. Generally, hares belong to the genus Lepus, and all other species are known as rabbits.

Royle's Pika

Ochotona roylei

Pikas look rather different to other lagomorphs. They have rounded bodies and lack the pointed ears and long, hopping hind feet of their relatives. Like other pikas, this species lives in the cold and dry rock fields of mountain slopes. They dry piles of grass into hay during summer to feed on when winter snow covers the ground.

FACT FILE	
Length:	20cm (8in)
Weight:	500g (17½oz)
Distribution:	Himalayas and Tibet
Habitat:	Mountain scree
Diet:	Grass and sedge
Status (IUCN Red List):	Least concern

Black-tailed Jackrabbit

Lepus californicus

The most common jackrabbit in North America, this species is actually a type of hare. It is built to speed across open country to escape coyote and cougar attacks. Unlike other hares, this jackrabbit lives in a burrow. It does not dig one but enlarges the abandoned den of a desert tortoise.

FACT FILE	
Length:	63cm (24¾in)
Weight:	3.5kg (7lb 11oz)
Distribution:	United States and Mexico
Habitat:	Dry grassland and scrub
Diet:	Grasses and bark
Status (IUCN Red List):	Least concern

Brown Hare

Lepus europaeus

These lagomorphs live alongside rabbits across Eurasia, but are larger and lankier. They do not live in burrows, but scrape out depressions, or forms, in grassy fields. The hare is the inspiration for the Easter bunny, because it becomes most conspicuous in early spring as the males chase females across the landscape.

FACT FILE	
Length:	70cm (28in)
Weight:	5kg (11lb)
Distribution:	Europe and northern Asia
Habitat:	Grasslands and fields
Diet:	Grass and herbs
Status (IUCN Red List):	Least concern

Riverine Rabbit

Bunolagus monticularis

One of the rarest mammals in the world, the riverine rabbit survives on salty desert plants growing along the seasonal, and largely dry, riverbeds in the arid Karoo region of South Africa's Cape Province. There are fewer than 500 adults left in the wild.

FACT FILE	
Length:	44cm (17in)
Weight:	1.65kg (3lb 12oz)
Distribution:	Karoo region of South Africa
Habitat:	Riverside scrub
Diet:	Salty plants
Status (IUCN Red List):	Critically endangered

Sumatran Short-eared Rabbit

Nesolagus netscheri

The Sumatran short-eared rabbit lives only in the highland forests of the Barisan Mountains in western Sumatra, Indonesia. There are few sightings in the wild, and, as one would expect of an animal with such a limited range, the species is threatened because of habitat loss.

FACT FILE	
Length:	40cm (16in)
Weight:	1.5kg (3lb 5oz)
Distribution:	Western Sumatra
Habitat:	Highland forest
Diet:	Leaves and stalks
Status (IUCN Red List):	Vulnerable

Domestic Rabbits

Domestic rabbits are the descendants of the European species that originated in the dry woodlands of Iberia. The animals are known for their prolific breeding, and spread across the continent as farmed rabbits escaped to the wild. In 1859, 24 European rabbits were introduced to Australia; 90 years later there were 600 million.

European Rabbit

Oryctolagus cuniculus

The European rabbit was introduced to Britain, much of Europe and possibly North Africa by the Romans, for whom the animal was a regular source of meat. Since then, the rabbit has been bred into dozens of pet breeds, and an albino breed is used in laboratories for testing cosmetics and drugs and other research.

FACT FILE	
Length:	51cm (20in)
Weight:	2.5kg (5lb 8oz)
Distribution:	Europe, North Africa, Australia
Habitat:	Grasslands, woodlands
Diet:	Grass, leaves and twigs
Status (IUCN Red List):	Least concern

Alaska Rabbit

Oryctolagus cuniculus

Despite its name, the Alaska rabbit originated in Germany in the 1920s. Bred originally for its fur, this rabbit's silky, jet-black coat is its most notable feature. The rabbits sometimes have white hairs interspersed through their coats. The Alaskan's body is well muscled and stocky, with almost no neck.

FACT FILE	
Length:	60cm (23½in)
Weight:	4kg (8lb 13oz)
Distribution:	N/A
Habitat:	N/A
Diet:	N/A
Status (IUCN Red List):	N/A

Rhinelander

Oryctolagus cuniculus

As its name suggests, the Rhinelander was developed in Germany, at the turn of the twentieth century. The Rhinelander is one of the few tricoloured rabbits: it has a white body with black and bright orange spots. This is an arched breed; its body arches from the shoulders through to the hips, giving it a graceful appearance.

FACT FILE	
Length:	60cm (23½in)
Weight:	4.5kg (10lb)
Distribution:	N/A
Habitat:	N/A
Diet:	N/A
Status (IUCN Red List):	N/A

Japanese Harlequin Rabbit

Oryctolagus cuniculus

Japanese harlequins are orange and black in a split pattern down the front of the face and body. The ears should be of different colours, and each side of the face should be the colour of the opposite ear. The feet are also of alternating colours.

FACT FILE	
Length:	51cm (20in)
Weight:	3.6kg (8lb)
Distribution:	N/A
Habitat:	N/A
Diet:	N/A
Status (IUCN Red List):	N/A

Angora Rabbit

Oryctolagus cuniculus

Angora rabbits originated in central Turkey, around the city now known as Ankara. They are known for their long, soft hair. Angoras are coated with wool rather than fur, since they have no guard hairs. They are often bred commercially for their wool, which is removed by shearing or combing.

FACT FILE	
Length:	48cm (19in)
Weight:	3.4kg (7lb 8oz)
Distribution:	N/A
Habitat:	N/A
Diet:	N/A
Status (IUCN Red List):	N/A

Prosimians

Many people will have heard of the primates, a mammal order that includes monkeys, apes and, of course, humans. However, this group also contains a number of less familiar tree-living species, sometimes known as the prosimians (meaning 'before monkeys').

Needle-clawed Galago

Euoticus elegantulus

Primates do not have claws on their fingertips, but flatter nails. In this species, however, the distinction is blurred as the nails form points to help the galago grip on to bark while climbing. A long 'toilet claw' on the second digit is used for grooming the fur.

FACT FILE	
Length:	23cm (9in)
Weight:	360g (12¾oz)
Distribution:	Western and Central Africa
Habitat:	Tropical forest
Diet:	Gums, sap and fruits
Status (IUCN Red List):	Least concern

Northern Bushbaby

Galago senegalensis

Also known as the lesser galago, this species has the widest range of any African prosimian. They are sluggish by day but display more agility at night. They urinate on their hands and feet in order to leave a scent-marked trail through the dark, all the way back to their den.

FACT FILE	
Length:	21cm (8¼in)
Weight:	300g (10½oz)
Distribution:	Sub-Saharan Africa
Habitat:	Woodlands
Diet:	Insects, eggs and fruits
Status (IUCN Red List):	Least concern

Slender Loris

Loris tardigradus

The loris is Asia's answer to the galagos – the most obvious difference is the lack of tail. The slender loris is named after the species' long limbs. The animal moves very deliberately through the trees, always keeping three anchor points gripping the branches.

FACT FILE	
Length:	26cm (10¼in)
Weight:	350g (12⅓oz)
Distribution:	Southern India and Sri Lanka
Habitat:	Forests
Diet:	Insects, leaves, eggs and fruits
Status (IUCN Red List):	Least concern

Slow Loris

Nycticebus coucang

Some animals rely on camouflage to stay hidden. Others use a burst of speed to escape danger or catch prey. The slow loris has a different strategy. It creeps very slowly through the trees so it does not disturb its prey. It grips mainly with its strong hind feet, leaving its hands free to grab food.

FACT FILE	
Length:	38cm (15in)
Weight:	2kg (4lb 6oz)
Distribution:	South and southeast Asia
Habitat:	Tropical forest
Diet:	Insects, chicks and fruits
Status (IUCN Red List):	Vulnerable

Potto

Perodicticus potto

Pottos are prosimians related to the lorises that live in Africa. They are active during the night and have large sensitive eyes that help them find food in the dark. If threatened, the animal lowers its head between its arms, so it is protected by the shoulder blades.

FACT FILE	
Length:	39cm (15½in)
Weight:	1.6kg (3lb 8oz)
Distribution:	West, Central and East Africa
Habitat:	Tropical forest
Diet:	Fruits. insects and lizards
Status (IUCN Red List):	Least concern

Ring-tailed Lemur

Lemur catta

One of the most common lemurs, the ring-tailed lemur lives in forests but spends much of its time foraging on the ground for fallen fruits and nuts. During drought periods, the lemurs turn to insects and supplement their diet with the seed pods of the kily tree, a type of tamarind plant.

FACT FILE	
Length:	46cm (18in)
Weight:	3.5kg (7lb 11oz)
Distribution:	Madagascar
Habitat:	Forests and bushland
Diet:	Fruits, leaves, sap and flowers
Status (IUCN Red List):	Near threatened

Ring-tailed lemurs live in bands of about 20 individuals. The bands have a complex social hierarchy dominated by the females. Fights are very common. Females fight over feeding space – often while their infants are clinging to their backs – while the males jostle with each other for access to mates.

TAIL
The tail is used in fights, so-called stink battles in which the combatants do not touch, but waft pongs towards each other with their bushy tails.

EYE
The eye has a tapetum lucidum behind the retina. This mirror layer helps the lemur see in the dark and creates eye shine, like that of a cat's eye.

NOSE
Like all lemurs (and other prosimians), this species has a rhinarium, a damp cleft that connects the nose to the lips. This 'wet nose' enhances the sense of smell.

FOOT PADS
The lemur's fleshy palms are tough enough to withstand walking on rough ground, but also dextrous enough to handle food.

SCENT GLANDS
The lemur has scent glands on its wrists and near its genitals. They are used to mark tree trunks and other landmarks in the territory.

Lemurs

The island of Madagascar, divided from East Africa by a deep ocean channel, is the home of a unique group of primates called the lemurs. They are prosimians, like mainland bushbabies, but have diversified into about 30 species adapted to life in Madagascar's many, varied and often outlandish habitats.

Brown Mouse Lemur

Microcebus rufus

The brown mouse lemur is one of the smallest primates, being about the same size as a hamster. This lemur sleeps by day in tree holes and forages at night in a small personal territory. A male mouse lemur's territory overlaps with those of its harem, typically made up of three or four females.

FACT FILE	
Length:	12cm (4¾in)
Weight:	50g (1¾oz)
Distribution:	North and eastern Madagascar
Habitat:	Tropical forest
Diet:	Fruits
Status (IUCN Red List):	Least concern

Weasel Sportive Lemur

Lepilemur mustelinus

Nineteenth-century naturalists were reminded of a boxer when they saw the defensive posture of these lemurs, hence the name 'sportive'. However, this name is not very apt. This lemur is one of the smallest mammals to survive on a diet of leaves, and as such it spends a lot of time just sitting around, digesting its tough meals.

FACT FILE	
Length:	30cm (12in)
Weight:	900g (32oz)
Distribution:	Western Madagascar
Habitat:	Forest
Diet:	Leaves
Status (IUCN Red List):	Data deficient

Red Ruffed Lemur

Varecia rubra

This strikingly coloured lemur is one of the biggest of the true lemurs. It spends a lot of its time caring for its fur, combing it with two extra-long claws on its hind feet and with its lower incisors, which poke out of the mouth for this purpose.

FACT FILE	
Length:	56cm (22in)
Weight:	3.5kg (7lb 11oz)
Distribution:	Masoala Peninsula, Madagascar
Habitat:	Tropical forest
Diet:	Fruits
Status (IUCN Red List):	Endangered

Eastern Woolly Lemur

Avahi laniger

Sometimes known simply as the avahi, the woolly lemur gets its name from its curly fur. Woolly lemurs cling to vertical trunks and make leaps between trees. They cannot walk – their feet do not stand flat on the ground – so the lemurs hop along on the sides of their feet.

FACT FILE	
Length:	37cm (14½in)
Weight:	950g (33½oz)
Distribution:	Eastern and NW Madagascar
Habitat:	Forest
Diet:	Leaves
Status (IUCN Red List):	Least concern

Indri

Indri indri

The largest of all prosimians, the indri belongs to a family of larger lemurs that also includes woolly lemurs and sifakas. It is diurnal and lives in small family groups, which defend a small territory marked with scent. Sometimes a family of indris will sing together. Their calls can be heard 2km (1¼ miles) away.

FACT FILE	
Length:	90cm (35in)
Weight:	10kg (22lb)
Distribution:	Eastern Madagascar
Habitat:	Rainforest
Diet:	Leaves, flowers, fruits
Status (IUCN Red List):	Endangered

Tarsier

Tarsius bancanus

The tarsier is not a monkey, but nor is it a prosimian. It lacks the 'wet-nose' rhinarium of the primitive primates, which puts it into the Haplorrhini suborder of dry-nosed monkeys, apes and humans. It is not certain, but the tarsiers could be an example of what our distant ancestors looked like.

FACT FILE	
Length:	16cm (6¼in)
Weight:	165g (5¾oz)
Distribution:	Sumatra and Borneo
Habitat:	Forests, mangroves, scrubland
Diet:	Insects, snakes and bats
Status (IUCN Red List):	Vulnerable

EYES
Tarsiers have enorm eyes – they take up head space than its brain.

Tarsiers are insect eaters, although they will snatch bats, frogs and snakes too. They scan the forest for food before leaping to attack. The tarsiers grab their victims in their long-fingered hands and kill them with a bite to the neck.

HEAD
The eyes can barely move in their huge sockets. Instead, the head turns to scan the forest, and the neck can swivel almost 180 degrees, so the tarsier can look behind it.

TAIL
The long tail is used as a balancing rudder as the tarsier sails through the air.

LEGS
The tarsier moves by leaping from branch to branch. Its elongated back legs and feet form coiled springs ready to push the animal on its way.

New World Monkeys

Just under half of the world's monkeys live in the Americas, mostly the tropical regions of Central and South America. These New World monkeys fall into two families: the callitrichids (including the marmosets and tamarins), and the cebids (the capuchins, squirrel monkeys and howlers, among many others).

Common Marmoset

Callithrix jacchus

For obvious reasons, this species is also known as the white-tufted-ear marmoset. Despite its 'common' status, the species is under pressure from the reduction of its forest habitat in northern Brazil. Common marmosets are polyandrous – each female mates with two or three males, all of which help with childcare.

FACT FILE	
Length:	15cm (6in)
Weight:	360g (12¾oz)
Distribution:	Northeastern Brazil
Habitat:	Forest edges
Diet:	Sap, insects and flowers
Status (IUCN Red List):	Least concern

Pygmy Marmoset

Cebuella pygmaea

The smallest monkey species in the world, a pygmy marmoset is light enough to perch on a blade of grass. The little marmosets clamber around in the low bushes on the forest floor. They live in nuclear families with a mother, fathers and half a dozen offspring.

FACT FILE	
Length:	13cm (5in)
Weight:	140g (5oz)
Distribution:	Upper Amazon Basin
Habitat:	Rainforest
Diet:	Fruits, buds, insects and sap
Status (IUCN Red List):	Least concern

Red-handed Tamarin

Saguinus midas

This species is also known as the Midas tamarin. Its striking ginger hands and feet reminded naturalists of King Midas, the ancient monarch who turned everything he touched into gold. The main difference between a tamarin and a marmoset is that the former has longer, almost tusk-like, canine teeth.

FACT FILE	
Length:	20cm (8in)
Weight:	475g (16¾oz)
Distribution:	Northeastern South America
Habitat:	Treetops
Diet:	Insects, ripe fruit and sap
Status (IUCN Red List):	Least concern

Northern Owl Monkey

Aotus trivirgatus

This is one of just two species of nocturnal monkey, the other being the southern owl monkey. In the Old World, no monkeys, only prosimians and tarsiers, are active at night. The owl monkey has large eyes that provide excellent night vision. However, unlike other monkeys, this species can see only in black and white.

FACT FILE	
Length:	47cm (18½in)
Weight:	1.3kg (2lb 12oz)
Distribution:	Panama to northern Argentina
Habitat:	Forests
Diet:	Insects, ripe fruit and sap
Status (IUCN Red List):	Least concern

Common Squirrel Monkey

Saimiri sciureus

Squirrel monkeys are small and agile creatures that gather in large groups of up to 300 individuals. Such groups frequently disband and reform, and the males are in a constant battle for supremacy over their rivals. Scuffles are common, and only the dominant males can breed with the females.

FACT FILE	
Length:	32cm (12½in)
Weight:	925g (33oz)
Distribution:	Tropical South America
Habitat:	Forest
Diet:	Fruits
Status (IUCN Red List):	Least concern

Titis, Sakis and Uakaris

The Cebidae family of New World monkeys contains 48 species. There are several subgroups, or genera, which include the titi monkeys, sakis and uakaris. These are medium-sized species. The sakis live at the tops of tall trees; the sakis live nearer to the ground; and the uakaris prefer swampy, flooded forests.

Masked Titi

Callicebus personatus

There are five subspecies of masked titi, each one sporting a different colour of coat, although they mostly retain the 'mask' of darkened forehead and sideburns. The masked titis live in Brazil's Atlantic forest, a rugged coastal jungle that is cut off from the larger Amazon forest.

FACT FILE	
Length:	42cm (16½in)
Weight:	1.65kg (3lb 12oz)
Distribution:	Coast of Brazil
Habitat:	Atlantic forest
Diet:	Fruits, insects and eggs
Status (IUCN Red List):	Vulnerable

Black-headed Uakari

Cacajao hosomi

This species of uakari has only recently been recognized as separate from the similar black uakari. It lives along the upper reaches of the Negro and Marauiá rivers, both large tributaries of the Amazon. It is often found in flooded forests, where the river water covers most of the ground.

FACT FILE	
Length:	50cm (19½in)
Weight:	4kg (8lb 13oz)
Distribution:	Northwest Amazonia
Habitat:	Flooded forest
Diet:	Seeds and unripe fruits
Status (IUCN Red List):	Vulnerable

Bald Uakari

Cacajao calvus

Local people called the bald uakari the 'English monkey', due to its bright pink face and often gingery hair. Unlike its namesake, the pink visage is not caused by sunburn and perhaps too many afternoon drinks, but serves as a visual signal to other group members in the thick forests.

FACT FILE	
Length:	70cm (28in)
Weight:	4kg (8lb 13oz)
Distribution:	Peru and Colombia
Habitat:	Flooded rainforest
Diet:	Fruits, seeds and insects
Status (IUCN Red List):	Vulnerable

Monk Saki

Pithecia monachus

Monk sakis get their name from their mop-top hairstyles. Not much is known about these little monkeys because they live at the very tops of the forest's tallest trees, which makes observing them very difficult. Like other sakis, the tail is very bulky compared to the rest of the body and is used for balance.

FACT FILE	
Length:	50cm (19½in)
Weight:	2kg (4lb 6oz)
Distribution:	Northern South America
Habitat:	Forest
Diet:	Fruit, seeds, nuts and insects
Status (IUCN Red List):	Least concern

White-faced Saki

Pithecia pithecia

Only male white-faced sakis actually have white faces; the females have a less conspicuous brown colouring. All sakis have wide, rounded faces – a look that is aided by thick hair – but this species is especially moon-faced. Unusually for a saki, this species lives in the middle layer of the forest.

FACT FILE	
Length:	70cm (28in)
Weight:	1.65kg (3lb 12oz)
Distribution:	Venezuela and northern Brazil
Habitat:	Tropical forest
Diet:	Fruits, honey, leaves and mice
Status (IUCN Red List):	Least concern

Capuchin Monkey

Cebus apella

Capuchins are among the most intelligent of all monkeys. They use their cognitive abilities and innate inquisitiveness to exploit a wide range of habitats. They are, of course, at home in the rainforest, but also do well along the seashore, feeding on shellfish, and in suburbs. Capuchins make easy pets and learn tricks. They were often the species accompanying 'organ grinder' street performers.

FACT FILE	
Length:	55cm (21½in)
Weight:	4.5kg (10lb)
Distribution:	Tropical South America
Habitat:	Rainforest
Diet:	Fruits, seeds, insects and birds
Status (IUCN Red List):	Least concern

Capuchins are one of the few animals to use tools. They crush hard nuts by pounding them with stones. They are also the most playful of the New World monkeys, spending a lot of time playing with and grooming group members. The group communicates through rapid chatters and squeaks.

Hair
The black cap of hair reminded European discoverers of the hats worn by an Italian sect of friars, known as capuchins.

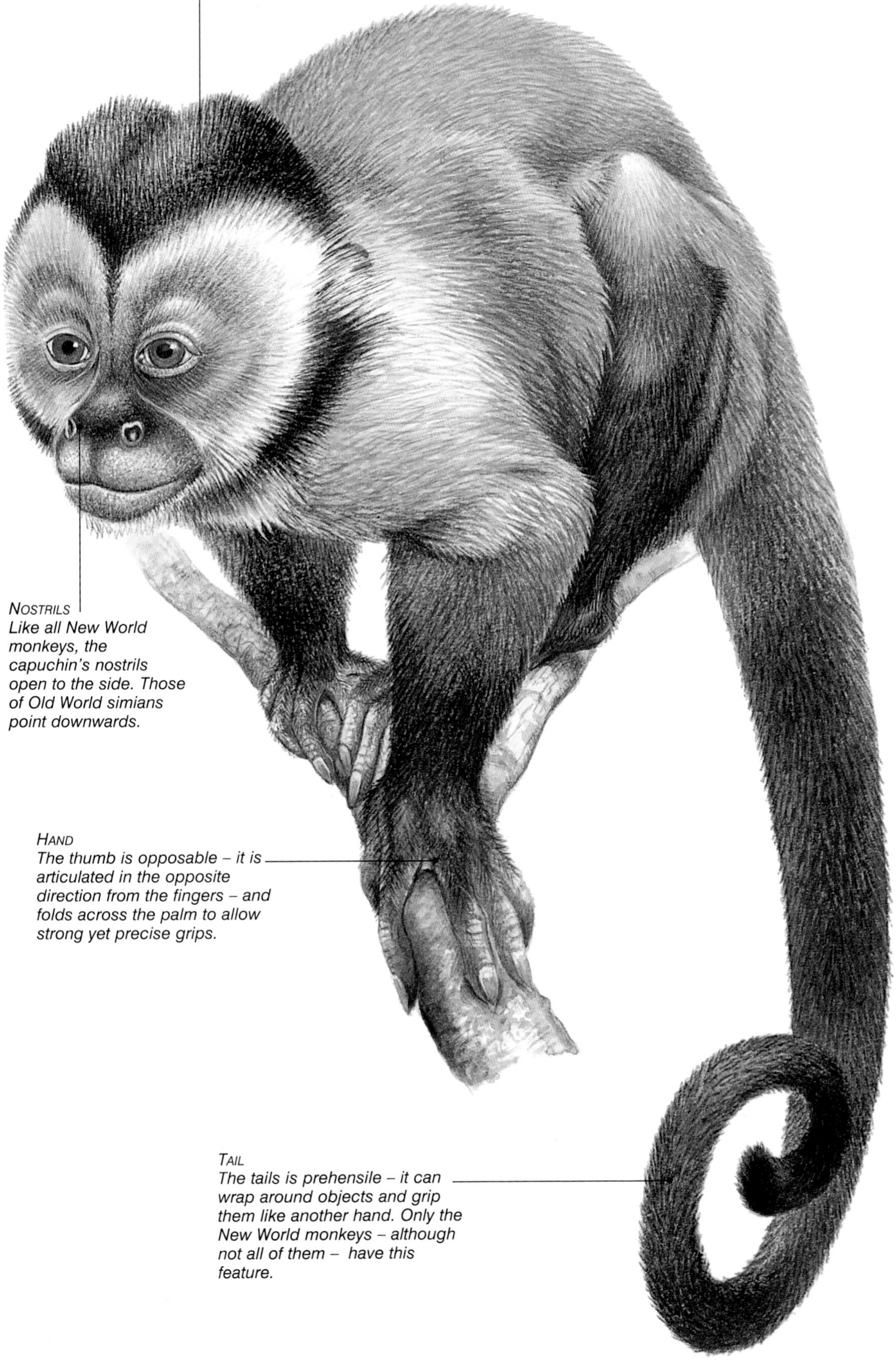

Nostrils
Like all New World monkeys, the capuchin's nostrils open to the side. Those of Old World simians point downwards.

Hand
The thumb is opposable – it is articulated in the opposite direction from the fingers – and folds across the palm to allow strong yet precise grips.

Tail
The tails is prehensile – it can wrap around objects and grip them like another hand. Only the New World monkeys – although not all of them – have this feature.

Howler and Spider Monkeys

The biggest – and noisiest – monkeys in South America are the howlers and spider monkeys. Both groups have highly prehensile tails, which are used as a fifth limb, wrapping around branches to provide support. Perhaps surprisingly for such a recognizable monkey characteristic, fewer than 20 species have these flexible tails.

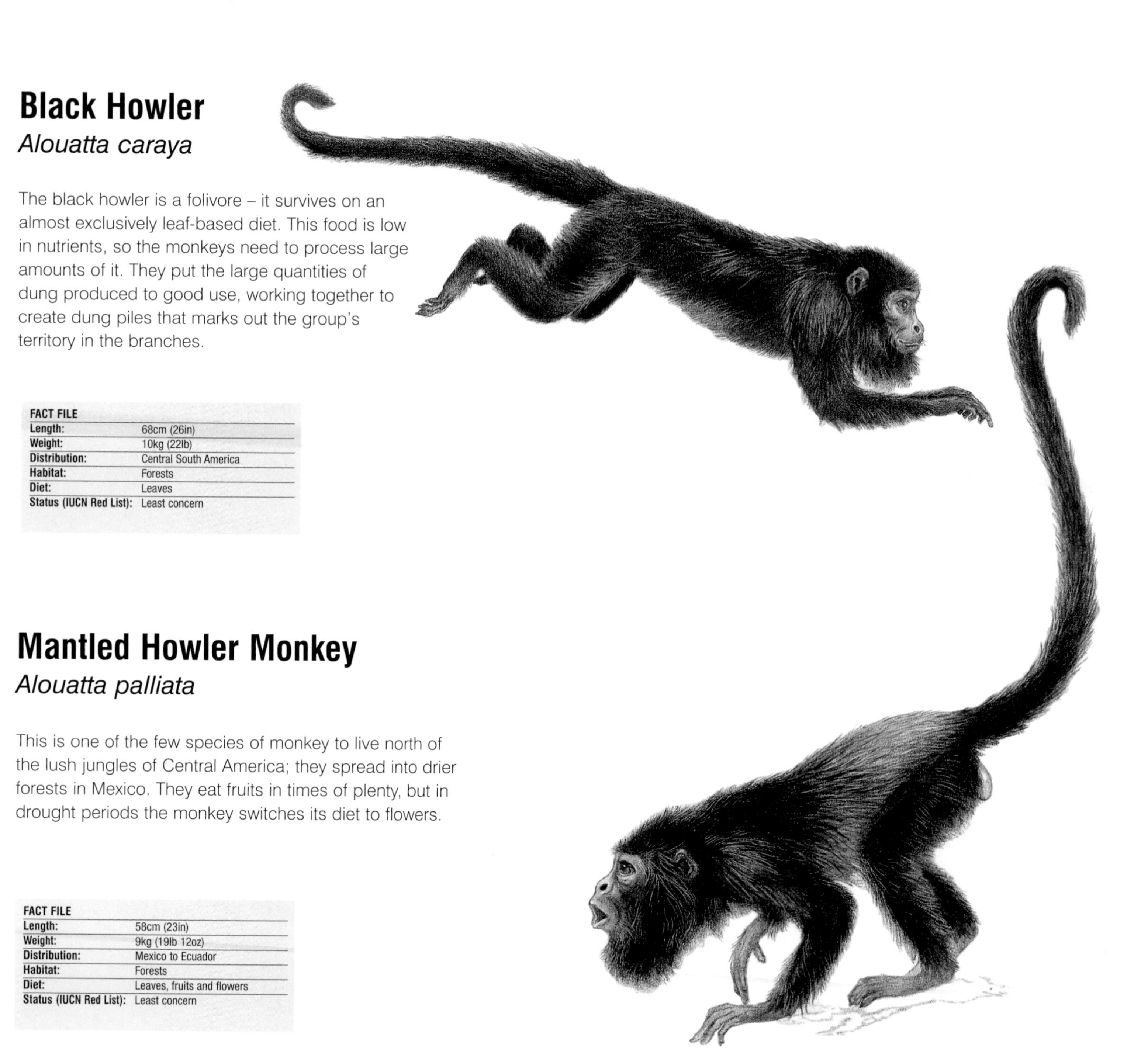

Black Howler

Alouatta caraya

The black howler is a folivore – it survives on an almost exclusively leaf-based diet. This food is low in nutrients, so the monkeys need to process large amounts of it. They put the large quantities of dung produced to good use, working together to create dung piles that marks out the group's territory in the branches.

FACT FILE	
Length:	68cm (26in)
Weight:	10kg (22lb)
Distribution:	Central South America
Habitat:	Forests
Diet:	Leaves
Status (IUCN Red List):	Least concern

Mantled Howler Monkey

Alouatta palliata

This is one of the few species of monkey to live north of the lush jungles of Central America; they spread into drier forests in Mexico. They eat fruits in times of plenty, but in drought periods the monkey switches its diet to flowers.

FACT FILE	
Length:	58cm (23in)
Weight:	9kg (19lb 12oz)
Distribution:	Mexico to Ecuador
Habitat:	Forests
Diet:	Leaves, fruits and flowers
Status (IUCN Red List):	Least concern

Red Howler Monkey

Alouatta seniculus

This is the biggest and loudest of the howler monkeys, and both sexes of red howler make roaring calls at dusk and dawn. The calls are amplified by an enlarged throat sac. Like other howlers, the red's prehensile tail has a patch of naked rough skin on the underside to aid with grip.

FACT FILE	
Length:	72cm (28¼in)
Weight:	9kg (19lb 12oz)
Distribution:	Peru and Colombia
Habitat:	Northern South America
Diet:	Leaves and fruits
Status (IUCN Red List):	Least concern

Black-handed Spider Monkey

Ateles geoffroyi

Spider monkeys are the most agile of the New World monkeys, leaping through the treetops with their long, rangy limbs. The prehensile tail is strong enough to hold the monkey's relatively lightweight frame, so the animal can dangle upside down to pick hard-to-reach fruits.

FACT FILE	
Length:	63cm (24¾in)
Weight:	8kg (17lb 10oz)
Distribution:	Mexico to Colombia
Habitat:	Tropical forest
Diet:	Fruits, seeds, insects and eggs
Status (IUCN Red List):	Endangered

Muriqui

Brachyteles arachnoides

The largest of the American monkeys is by no means slow-moving. It swings through the trees, hanging from long fingers, which form a hook. The thumb is so small as to be useless. The muriqui is also known as the woolly spider monkey.

FACT FILE	
Length:	65cm (25½in)
Weight:	15kg (33lb)
Distribution:	Southeastern Brazil
Habitat:	Coastal forest
Diet:	Fruits, leaves, flowers and seeds
Status (IUCN Red List):	Endangered

Leaf Monkeys

The leaf monkeys form a subfamily of Old World Monkeys called the Colobinae. This group lives in tropical Africa and across southern Asia from the Himalayas to Borneo. Almost all of its members are folivorous species – relatively large monkeys that have adopted a diet of leaves only.

Hanuman Langur

Semnopithecus hector

Named after the Hindu deity Hanuman, who is often depicted as a monkey, this species is one of several that go by that name. It is also known as the grey langur. This particular species lives in the high forests of Nepal and the Himalayas.

FACT FILE	
Length:	79cm (31in)
Weight:	23.5kg (52lb)
Distribution:	South Asia
Habitat:	Forests, savannah and scrub
Diet:	Leaves, flowers and fruits
Status (IUCN Red List):	Near threatened

Tonkin Snub-nosed Langur

Rhinopithecus avunculus

This most striking of Asian monkeys was presumed to be extinct until it was rediscovered in 1989. It is Vietnam's largest primate and remains one of the most endangered mammals in the world. Other snub-nosed monkey species live in equally rugged, but colder, habitats in East Asia.

FACT FILE	
Length:	65cm (25½in)
Weight:	14kg (30lb 14oz)
Distribution:	Northern Vietnam
Habitat:	Forest
Diet:	Leaves, fruits, flowers and seeds
Status (IUCN Red List):	Critically endangered

Red-shanked Douc Monkey

Pygathrix nemaeus

With an orange face so striking it looks as if it could have been painted on, the douc langur lives in dense jungles of Cambodia, Laos and Vietnam. Its bold markings form flashes of colour as it moves through branches, helping group members keep tabs on each other's location.

FACT FILE	
Length:	76cm (30in)
Weight:	10kg (22lb)
Distribution:	Indochina
Habitat:	Forest
Diet:	Leaves, fruit, buds and bamboo
Status (IUCN Red List):	Endangered

Guereza

Colobus guereza

This species is a large example of a colobus monkey, an African leaf-eating monkey. Its most striking feature is a shaggy cape with a V-shape of white tassels. The guereza has a three-chambered stomach, which stews its leafy food to extract as many nutrients as possible.

FACT FILE	
Length:	72cm (28¼in)
Weight:	14kg (30lb 14oz)
Distribution:	Central and eastern Africa
Habitat:	Forest and woodland
Diet:	Leaves
Status (IUCN Red List):	Least concern

Western Red Colobus

Procolobus badius

This species' diet consists mainly of petioles, the stalks that attach broad leaves to branches. To digest such fibrous meals, the colobus has a four-chambered stomach. Gut bacteria in the chambers ferment the fibres into a sugary soup for the monkey.

FACT FILE	
Length:	69cm (27in)
Weight:	11kg (24lb 4oz)
Distribution:	Central and Western Africa
Habitat:	Forests and grasslands
Diet:	Leaves
Status (IUCN Red List):	Endangered

Proboscis Monkey

Nasalis larvatus

With their strange, bulbous noses, proboscis monkeys have a unique appearance. They live in mangrove forests that grow out of water. The monkeys rarely move more than a few hundred metres on land, and take shortcuts between trees by making great leaps. They also swim across rivers and paddle in the shallows.

FACT FILE	
Length:	68cm (26in)
Weight:	16kg (35lb)
Distribution:	Borneo
Habitat:	Mangrove forest
Diet:	Leaves, fruit, flowers and seeds
Status (IUCN Red List):	Endangered

Proboscis monkeys live in a sexually charged society. The adult males live in separate bachelor bands, while the females and young, who are marked out by their blue faces, live elsewhere. The monkeys have become isolated in small pockets of mangrove habitat and are unable to travel between communities.

TAIL
The long muscular tail is used as a counterbalance when the monkey makes its impressive leaps between trees.

WEBBED FEET
Proboscis monkeys are good swimmers, helped by partial webbing of the hind feet.

HAND
The monkey's hand has a long palm, which provides a large gripping surface. The short fingers hook over branches.
NOSE
Males have the longest and most bulbous noses, presumably a signal of dominance. The females have more pointed noses.

Macaques

Forming one of the largest groups of Old World monkeys, the 15 macaque species belong to the Cercopthecinae subfamily, along with the baboons and guenons. The opportunistic macaques are one of the most familiar sets of monkeys, with many species living in close proximity to humans.

Stump-tailed Macaque

Macaca arctoides

This species of macaque is almost naked when born, save for a few white wispy hairs, but the thick, shaggy coat grows rapidly. Adults have red markings around the eyes, giving them a somewhat tired look. Like other macaques, this species stores food in cheek pouches.

FACT FILE	
Length:	65cm (25½in)
Weight:	10kg (22lb)
Distribution:	Southeast Asia
Habitat:	Tropical forests
Diet:	Fruits
Status (IUCN Red List):	Vulnerable

Japanese Macaque

Macaca fuscata

Also known as the snow monkey, this species has the most northern distribution of any monkey in the world. It lives across Japan, including the mountainous northern island of Hokkaido. Winters here bring thick snow; the macaques migrate south to avoid the worst weather and grow a thick winter coat.

FACT FILE	
Length:	95cm (37½in)
Weight:	14kg (30lb 14oz)
Distribution:	Japan
Habitat:	Mountain forests
Diet:	Leaves, bark and fruits
Status (IUCN Red List):	Least concern

Rhesus Macaque

Macaca mulatta

A familiar monkey, with a familiar name, the Rhesus monkey is the main species used in vivisection – live animal experiments. The species lends its name to the human Rhesus blood group system, which was discovered through experiments with the monkey's blood.

FACT FILE	
Length:	64cm (25in)
Weight:	12kg (26lb 8oz)
Distribution:	Asia
Habitat:	Forests and woodlands
Diet:	Leaves and fruits
Status (IUCN Red List):	Least concern

Lion-tailed Macaque

Macaca silenus

This is one of the smallest and most endangered of the macaque genus. It gets its name from the tuft of fur at the tip of its tail, similar to the fly swat of lions. They stuff seeds and fruits into their cheek pouches, which have around the same capacity as their stomach.

FACT FILE	
Length:	61cm (24in)
Weight:	10kg (22lb)
Distribution:	Western Ghats, India
Habitat:	Mountain forest
Diet:	Fruits
Status (IUCN Red List):	Endangered

Barbary Macaque

Macaca sylvanus

Sometimes known as the barbary ape because of their apparent tailless appearance – the tail is there but is little more than a stump – this is the only monkey species to live in Europe. Barbary apes were introduced from North Africa to the Rock of Gibraltar in Spain by the Romans.

FACT FILE	
Length:	63cm (24¾in)
Weight:	12.5kg (27lb 8oz)
Distribution:	North Africa and Gibraltar
Habitat:	Dry forest
Diet:	Roots, flowers, fruits and insects
Status (IUCN Red List):	Endangered

Large Old World Monkeys

The cercopthecines include the biggest and toughest monkey species, mostly confined to Africa. These include the drills and baboons. Once thought to be closely related, the quiet forest-dwelling drills are now considered to be a separate group from the baboons that patrol open habitats in menacing troops.

Olive Baboon

Papio anubis

The most widespread of the baboon species, this species is sometimes called the anubis baboon, after the jackal-headed Egyptian god of the afterlife. Like other baboons, the olive species lives in a mixed-sex troop of about 30 monkeys. When on the move, they form a defensive phalanx with the biggest monkeys in front and to the side.

FACT FILE	
Length:	76cm (30in)
Weight:	25kg (55lb)
Distribution:	Sub-Saharan Africa
Habitat:	Grasslands and forests
Diet:	Fruits, leaves and small animals
Status (IUCN Red List):	Least concern

Yellow Baboon

Papio cynocephalus

As is the case with most baboon species, male yellow baboons are twice the weight of the females, and have large canines that are shown off to rivals with threatening yawns. The yellow baboon's skull is more monkey-like than the other dog-faced species.

FACT FILE	
Length:	1.1m (3ft 7in)
Weight:	20kg (44lb)
Distribution:	Eastern Africa
Habitat:	Grasslands and forests
Diet:	Grass, seeds, insects and meat
Status (IUCN Red List):	Least concern

Hamadryas Baboon

Papio hamadryas

The hamadryas baboons are the Spartans of the monkey world, living in a strict and severe social order that is a response to their arid habitat. The baboons roost on cliffs in troops hundreds strong. Troops contain several clans, ruled by combat-ready males sharing a blood line. Each male has a harem of half a dozen females.

FACT FILE	
Length:	76cm (30in)
Weight:	41kg (90lb 8oz)
Distribution:	Horn of Africa and Arabia
Habitat:	Desert hills
Diet:	Plants and small animals
Status (IUCN Red List):	Least concern

Gelada

Theropithecus gelada

Once known as the gelada baboon, this species is now styled simply as the gelada. It lives up in the Ethiopian highlands and is the world's only grass-eating monkey, the last surviving species of its genus. All geladas have red patches on their chests, while the males also grow a mane and a cape of long hairs to impress the females.

FACT FILE	
Length:	72cm (28¼in)
Weight:	20kg (44lb)
Distribution:	Ethiopian highlands
Habitat:	Highland grasslands
Diet:	Grass
Status (IUCN Red List):	Least concern

Drill

Mandrillus leucophaeus

This species is a large forest resident that stays hidden in the deepest and most untouched reaches of the Congo Basin. The adult males are too heavy to climb into the trees, although the females and young forage off the ground. The female's red hindquarters turn blue when she is receptive to mating.

FACT FILE	
Length:	76cm (30in)
Weight:	25kg (55lb)
Distribution:	Central Africa
Habitat:	Forest
Diet:	Fruits and leaves
Status (IUCN Red List):	Endangered

Mandrill

Mandrillus sphinx

The mandrill is the largest monkey species in the world. It lives in the forest of the western Congo. There is a big difference between sexes, with males developing vivid colours on their faces. This war paint is a sign of the monkey's virility, reducing the need for males to test each other's strength in costly and dangerous fights.

FACT FILE	
Length:	76cm (30in)
Weight:	54.5kg (120lb)
Distribution:	Central Africa
Habitat:	Lowland forest
Diet:	Fruits, nuts and roots
Status (IUCN Red List):	Vulnerable

Mandrills live in large groups in the deep forest. They forage on the ground and in the low branches of trees. Many of the males are too heavy to climb very high. When the dominant male signals with a loud double grunt, it is time to move on. At night-time, the troop climbs into the branches to sleep.

COLOURED FACE
Both sexes of mandrill have distinctive ridges on their snouts, but only the male shows his off with bright colouring. These colours become even more vibrant when the monkey is excited.

BUTTOCK PADS
When the male is ready for a fight, blood rushes into his buttocks, turning them lilac.

CANINES
Even with the mouth closed, the males' long canine tusks can be seen between lips set in a permanent snarl.

HANDS
Big mandrills stay on the ground; they walk on the flats of their hands, not on their knuckles.

FEET
The big toe is position like an opposable thumb to help with climbing.

Mangabeys and Allies

The mangabeys are smaller relatives of the baboons. They all live in forest habitats. There are also other members of the cercopithicine group that are harder to pin down. The vervet and talapoin monkeys are possible relatives of the guenons, but share some similarities with other Old World groups.

Grey-cheeked Mangabey

Lophocebus albigena

This species is thought to be a relative of the drill, rather than the main baboon line. It is sometimes known simply as the black mangabey. Males are about 20 per cent larger than the females. It has a long tail, which is the most flexible of any Old World species, although still not truly prehensile.

FACT FILE	
Length:	50cm (19½in)
Weight:	27kg (59lb 8oz)
Distribution:	Central Africa
Habitat:	Rainforest
Diet:	Fruits and nuts
Status (IUCN Red List):	Near threatened

Tana River Mangabey

Cercocebus galeritus

As a member of the Cercocebus genus, this medium-sized species is though to be a descendant of primitive baboons. Like other mangabeys, it lives in mixed-sex groups, and is thought to have a promiscuous mating system, in which all adult group members mate with several others.

FACT FILE	
Length:	55cm (21½in)
Weight:	10kg (22lb)
Distribution:	Kenya
Habitat:	Dry river forest
Diet:	Seeds and leaves
Status (IUCN Red List):	Endangered

Collared Mangabey

Cercocebus torquatus

Also known as the red-capped mangabey, this species makes a lot of noise. They live in mixed-sex groups and make frequent calls to advertise the presence of the group. These calls can be heard more than 1km (half a mile) away through the forest. The monkey bats its white eyelids to woo potential mates.

FACT FILE	
Length:	90cm (35in)
Weight:	14kg (30lb 14oz)
Distribution:	West Africa
Habitat:	Rainforest
Diet:	Fruits
Status (IUCN Red List):	Vulnerable

Talapoin

Miopithecus talapoin

This widespread little monkey lives in swampy forests in the western part of Central Africa, from Cameroon to Angola. Talapoin troops can number 100 individuals. A team of dominant males leads the troop, calling halt each night and selecting feeding grounds. The females and young sleep in the centre, surrounded by the males.

FACT FILE	
Length:	32cm (12½in)
Weight:	1.4kg (3lb)
Distribution:	Central Africa
Habitat:	Forests
Diet:	Insects, plants and eggs
Status (IUCN Red List):	Least concern

Vervet

Chlorocebus pygerythrus

This adaptable species is one of the most widespread of any African primate. Its range runs from Senegal to Somalia and down to South Africa, avoiding the Congo region. Vervets frequently come to the ground and forage in open spaces. They use several alarm calls to warn against different threats.

FACT FILE	
Length:	68cm (26in)
Weight:	9kg (19lb 12oz)
Distribution:	Sun-Saharan Africa
Habitat:	Savannah and woodland
Diet:	Fruits, crustaceans and eggs
Status (IUCN Red List):	Least concern

Guenons

There are 18 species of guenons, forming the largest genus in the Cercopithecine subfamily. The medium-sized monkeys are all African and are characterized by their bright colouring and wise-looking whiskered faces. They also have a non-prehensile tail that is generally longer than the head–body length.

Blue Monkey

Cercopithecus mitis

This species is also named the diademed monkey because it has an arc of white fur on its forehead that looks like a crown (or diadem). Blue monkeys live in harems with one male and up to a dozen females. The male guards his harem jealously, and the females will join in fights with any encroaching neighbours.

FACT FILE	
Length:	65cm (25½in)
Weight:	6kg (13lb 3oz)
Distribution:	Central and southern Africa
Habitat:	Forest
Diet:	Fruits and leaves
Status (IUCN Red List):	Least concern

De Brazza's Monkey

Cercopithecus neglectus

De Brazza's monkeys live in gallery (riverside) forest and tropical swamps and other jungles that are frequently flooded. They never stray more than a few hundred metres from water. They are good swimmers and give loud booming calls to broadcast their territorial rights.

FACT FILE	
Length:	63cm (24¾in)
Weight:	7kg (15lb 8oz)
Distribution:	Eastern and Central Africa
Habitat:	Swampy forest
Diet:	Fruits, insects and worms
Status (IUCN Red List):	Least concern

Red-eared Guenon

Cercopithecus erythrotis

This colourful little guenon lives in the swampy, humid forests between the Niger and Cross rivers in Nigeria. These forests are home to a wide range of monkey species, and the red-eared guenon is seldom alone. The monkeys specialize in the secondary forest layer, where young trees and bushes are filling gaps in the forest.

FACT FILE	
Length:	60cm (23½in)
Weight:	4kg (8lb 13oz)
Distribution:	Nigeria
Habitat:	Tropical forest
Diet:	Fruits
Status (IUCN Red List):	Vulnerable

Greater Spot-nosed Guenon

Cercopithecus nictitans

One of the larger guenon species, the greater spot-nosed guenon lives in harem-based groups, with a single adult male, several females and their offspring. The groups often mingle with other monkeys, especially the crowned guenon. The two species do not compete for food and benefit from each other's protection.

FACT FILE	
Length:	70cm (28in)
Weight:	6kg (13lb 3oz)
Distribution:	Central Africa
Habitat:	Mountain forest
Diet:	Fruit, seeds and leaves
Status (IUCN Red List):	Least concern

Crowned Guenon

Cercopithecus pogonias

When seen from the front while sitting, this monkey looks a speckled brown-grey, except for the blue and white face. However, its rump is a golden yellow, and when the monkey moves around bright flashes of the same colour appear on the inside legs and belly. Males have testicles coloured to match their faces.

FACT FILE	
Length:	68cm (26in)
Weight:	4.5kg (10lb)
Distribution:	Central Africa
Habitat:	Dense forest
Diet:	Fruits
Status (IUCN Red List):	Least concern

Apes

There are 18 species of ape, tailless primates that include the human. Humans are the only animal to live on all seven continents – there has been a permanent population in Antarctica for more than 50 years, although it is not a self-sustaining one. Other apes are restricted to Southeast Asia and Central Africa.

Crested Gibbon

Hylobates concolor

Once found across much of China, this gibbon (or lesser ape) is now restricted to the extreme south of its natural range. It has been hunted for meat and has suffered through wars and deforestation. Male gibbons are black, while the females are a golden colour.

FACT FILE	
Length:	65cm (25½in)
Weight:	9kg (19lb 12oz)
Distribution:	Southwest China and Indochina
Habitat:	Tropical forest
Diet:	Fruit, shoots and leaves
Status (IUCN Red List):	Critically endangered

Lar Gibbon

Hylobates lar

Lar gibbons live in the highest trees in the jungle, swinging acrobatically with their immensely long arms – the span of which is considerably longer than their standing height. The gibbons never sleep in the same nest twice, moving on each night to prevent pythons and other predators from learning their positions.

FACT FILE	
Length:	65cm (25½in)
Weight:	8kg (17lb 10oz)
Distribution:	Southern China to Sumatra
Habitat:	Lowland forest
Diet:	Fruits
Status (IUCN Red List):	Endangered

Siamang

Hylobates syndactylus

The largest of the so-called lesser apes, the siamang's arm span is 1.5m (5ft). That allows them to make swings of 3m (9ft 9in). Siamangs are not good neighbours; they make loud calls using a resonating throat sac to warn others to stay out of a breeding pair's territory. Mates often swing together singing a duet of booms and barks.

FACT FILE	
Length:	90cm (35in)
Weight:	13kg (28lb 10oz)
Distribution:	Malay Peninsula and Sumatra
Habitat:	Rainforest
Diet:	Leaves, fruits and buds
Status (IUCN Red List):	Endangered

Western Lowland Gorilla

Gorilla gorilla

This is the largest primate species. There is some debate over the exact speciation of gorillas, but they are generally divided into two: the western and eastern species. The famous mountain gorillas are a subspecies of the latter. Gorillas are leaf-eaters, and spend a great deal of time sitting around digesting.

FACT FILE	
Length:	1.75m (5ft 9in)
Weight:	140kg (308lb)
Distribution:	West-central Africa
Habitat:	Lowland tropical forests
Diet:	Leaves and shoots
Status (IUCN Red List):	Critically endangered

Chimpanzee

Pan troglodytes

Along with the bonobo, or pygmy chimpanzee, this ape is our closest relative. There is less than 2 per cent difference between our genes, and we are ten times more closely related than mice and rats are. Chimpanzees live in complex social groups made up of nuclear families, friendships, alliances and feuds.

FACT FILE	
Length:	1.7m (5ft 6in)
Weight:	70kg (154lb)
Distribution:	Gambia to Uganda
Habitat:	Tropical forest
Diet:	Plants, insects and meat
Status (IUCN Red List):	Endangered

Chimps not only use stones and sticks as tools and weapons, but will modify sticks to make them work better – a characteristic once thought to be solely human. Their diet is largely plant-based, although they do hunt in teams for monkeys and small deer. This kind of violent co-operation is also used in wars between troops.

Arms
The chimp's arms extend to below the knee, unlike a human's arms, because chimps spend a lot more time climbing in trees.

Face
Chimps communicate with facial expressions. There is no white in a chimp's eye, which facilitates the great nuance in human expressions, so chimps are more demonstrative, using their flexible lips and large teeth to show different moods. A chimp 'smiles' when it is scared or angry.

Opposable toe
As well as having grasping hands, the chimp's big toe forms a thumb-like gripper that holds thin branches while climbing.

Knuckles
Chimps can walk on two feet but generally walk on all fours, resting on the knuckles rather than the flat of the hand.

BIRDS

All birds have wings, and almost all of them can fly. A body built for flying must be light, and birds have hollow bones and versatile muscle systems to cut down on weight.

There are about 9000 species of bird. They are thought to be the last surviving descendents of the dinosaurs, the only ones to have survived the mass extinction 65 million years ago. It is thought that many dinosaurs had feathers, a unique feature of today's birds. Feathers are extensions of a reptile scale and were probably used first for insulation and camouflage, later becoming shaped to power flight.

Left: The leading edge of a bird's wing is made the same bones found in the forelegs of mammals and reptiles. Layers of feathers form the main flight surface.

Flightless Birds

Some of the largest – and strangest – birds are grouped together as the ratites. The ratites are flightless birds. Many are too large to get off the ground and have evolved to be fast runners to escape danger. The smallest ratites are kiwis, which are almost unique among birds in that they can walk almost straight after hatching.

Little Spotted Kiwi

Apteryx owenii

One of three kiwi species that live in New Zealand, this is a nocturnal, burrowing forest-dweller with poor eyesight but – rare for a bird – a good sense of smell. It is a squat, pear-shaped bird with no tail, vestigial wings hidden among its feathers and a long bill with nostrils at the tip.

FACT FILE	
Length:	45cm (17¾in)
Weight:	2kg (4lb 6oz)
Distribution:	North Island, New Zealand
Habitat:	Forest and bushland
Diet:	Grubs, insects and fruits
Status (IUCN Red List):	Near threatened

Cassowary

Casuarius casuarius

The flightless cassowary has a distinctive bony casque on its head, a bright blue head and neck, and red neck wattles. It slices through dense jungle by lowering its head and pointing its casque forward. Its three toes are armed with sharp claws that it uses as weapons in fights. The glossy black feathers are rather like coarse hairs.

FACT FILE	
Length:	1.8m (6ft)
Weight:	60kg (132lb 3oz)
Distribution:	NE Australia, South New Guinea
Habitat:	Rainforest
Diet:	Fallen fruits and seeds
Status (IUCN Red List):	Vulnerable

Emu

Dromaius novaehollandiae

A fast runner that cannot fly, the emu is the obvious Australian counterpart to the ostrich, and is a close second in size and weight. It lives in nomadic groups that travel long distances for food. The females are slightly larger than the males and have more strongly blue-coloured bare skin on the head and neck.

FACT FILE	
Length:	2m (6ft 6in)
Weight:	50kg (110lb)
Distribution:	Most of mainland Australia
Habitat:	Open plains, dry tropical forest
Diet:	Seeds, fruits, leaves and insects
Status (IUCN Red List):	Least concern

Lesser Rhea

Pterocnemia pennata

This is the smaller species of what is sometimes called the American ostrich. There is one major difference: each foot has three toes, unlike the two toes of the ostrich. The rhea cannot fly, but raises its wings to gain some lift when running fast.

FACT FILE	
Length:	1.3m (4ft 3in)
Weight:	25kg (55lb)
Distribution:	S. South America, east of Andes
Habitat:	Open plains
Diet:	Plant roots, leaves and seeds
Status (IUCN Red List):	Near threatened

Ostrich

Struthio camelus

The ostrich is the tallest living bird, and also lays the biggest eggs. It is the fastest running avian, reaching speeds of 90km/h (55mph). Like all ratites, it cannot fly. It has no keel extension on the breastbone to anchor large flight muscles.

FACT FILE	
Length:	2.5m (8ft 3in) tall
Weight:	130kg (286lb)
Distribution:	Africa south of Sahara
Habitat:	Arid savannah and woodland
Diet:	Plant material and insects
Status (IUCN Red List):	Least concern

Southern Rockhopper Penguin

Eudyptes chrysocome

Most penguins move about on land with an ungainly waddle or slide on their bellies. This is because their short legs are positioned far back on their torpedo-shaped bodies. However, the rockhopper has a third mode: as its name suggests, it hops or jumps with both feet together, like a person doing a sack race.

FACT FILE	
Length:	61cm (24in) tall
Weight:	3kg (6lb 10oz)
Distribution:	Antarctic islands, Cape Horn, Australia, New Zealand
Habitat:	Rocky coasts and beaches
Diet:	Small crustaceans and squid
Status (IUCN Red List):	Vulnerable

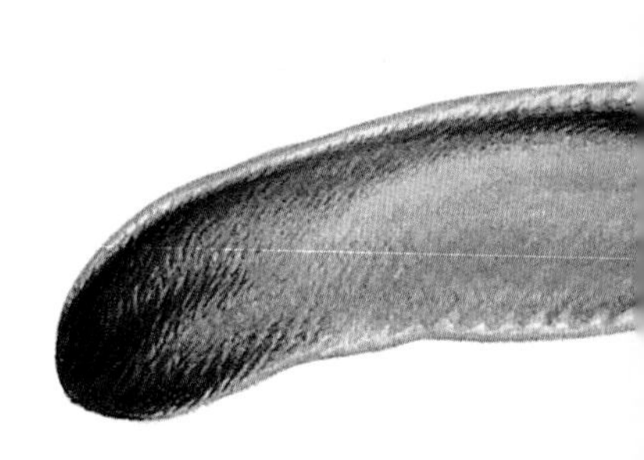

The rockhopper is the most common of the crested penguins; in some places it lives in huge colonies of as many as two and half million birds. They have a strict hierarchy dominated by the biggest breeding males and enforced by cries and displays. A rarer northern rockhopper species lives around Tristan da Cunha and other islands in the South Atlantic.

FEATHERS
The lower part of the feather is covered in a thick down, while the outer sections form a stiff waterproof layer.

FEET
Penguins are warm-blooded, and their hot feet could melt ice, causing them to freeze to the ground in the polar conditions. The solution is to keep the naked feet cold, using a heat exchanger made from blood vessels. Cold blood returning from the feet chills the warm blood arriving from the body.

HEAD PLUMES
Both sexes have a crest of yellow and black feathers flaring above the eyes. The northern species has longer plumes than the southern variety.

BILL
The horny beak is short and stout for grabbing slippery squid and shrimps.

WING
The penguin cannot fly through the air. Its wing forms a flipper that is swung up and down in a flying motion to propel the bird through water.

Grebes

Evolutionary biologists consider grebes to be one of the most ancient groups of birds. They live on the world's lakes and marshes in a way that primitive birds would have survived 70 million years ago. Grebes are diving birds. They have thick waterproof feathers and feet positioned far back on the body to aid with swimming.

Giant Grebe

Podilymbus gigas

The giant grebe became extinct in 1989, when the last two birds disappeared from Lake Atitlán in Guatemala. The bulky species lived only on this high snow-fed volcanic lake. It had no need to fly, and had only very small wings. An earthquake in 1973 fractured the lake bed, causing the water level to drop – spelling the end for this already very rare species.

FACT FILE	
Length:	50cm (19½in)
Weight:	1.2kg (2lb 8oz)
Distribution:	Lake Atitlán, Guatemala
Habitat:	Cold water
Diet:	Water animals
Status (IUCN Red List):	Extinct

Western Grebe

Aechmophorus occidentalis

The largest species of grebe in North America, the western grebe is most common in Canada and the prairie lakes of the western United States. It migrates out of the colder parts of this region in winter and can turn up as far south as Mexico.

FACT FILE	
Length:	74cm (29in)
Weight:	1.4kg (3lb)
Distribution:	Western North America
Habitat:	Lakes
Diet:	Fish, insects and shellfish
Status (IUCN Red List):	Least concern

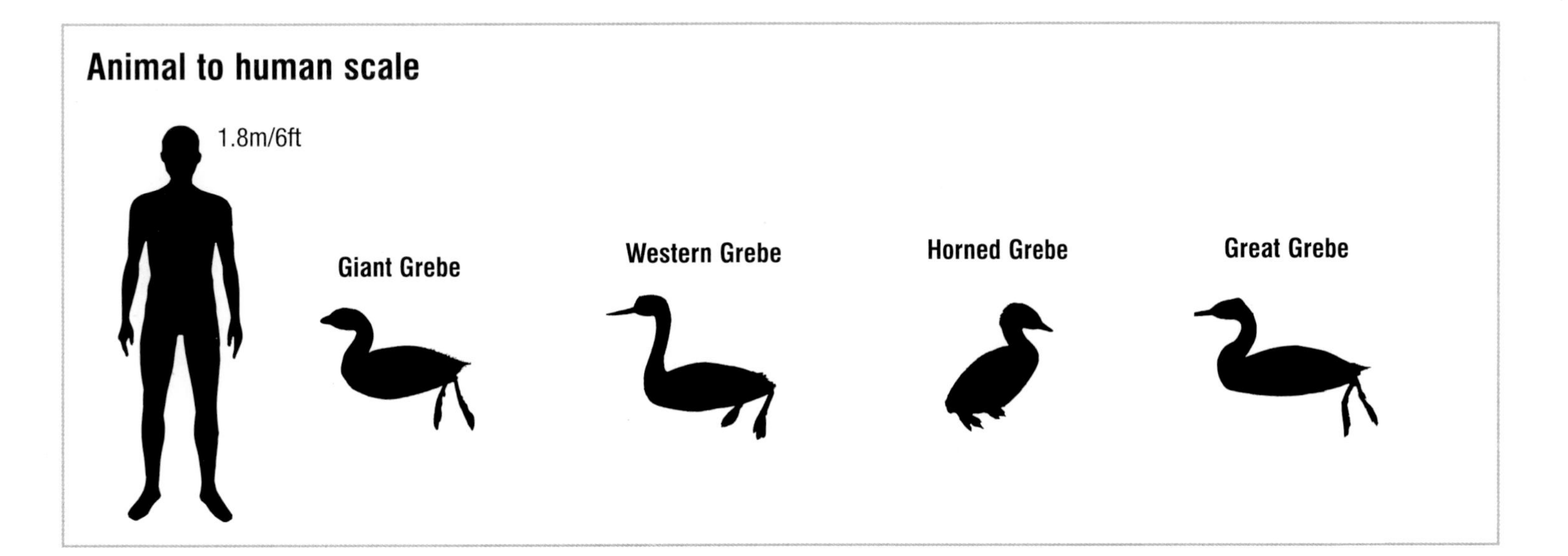

Horned Grebe

Podiceps auritus

The horned grebe's summer plumage is very colourful. It has a rich red-brown on the neck and underparts, and a black head with golden tufts – 'horns' – stretching back from each eye. It performs an elaborate courtship 'dance' in the water before mating, with both male and female rising up, breast-to-breast, in the water.

FACT FILE	
Length:	31–36cm (12¼–14in)
Weight:	570g (20oz)
Distribution:	Europe, Asia and North America
Habitat:	Clean lakes and ponds
Diet:	Fish, insects and crustaceans
Status (IUCN Red List):	Least concern

Great Grebe

Podiceps major

This South American species is the largest grebe on earth. It spends the winter around large bays and sluggish estuaries, but breeds in summer in the thickets around lakes further inland. Despite its large size, the great grebe prefers to hunt for fish smaller than 11cm (4¼in) long.

FACT FILE	
Length:	80cm (32in)
Weight:	1.6kg (3lb 8oz)
Distribution:	Southern South America
Habitat:	Slow-flowing water
Diet:	Fish
Status (IUCN Red List):	Least concern

Fish-Eating Birds

There are several families of birds that are adapted to snatching fish and other animals from water. The albatrosses and petrels are ocean specialists, spending weeks at sea, flying for days on end. The cormorants and darters live in all kinds of water habitats. Similar fish-eaters include the pelicans, gannets and tropicbirds.

Royal Albatross

Diomedea epomophora

This species is divided into northern and southern subspecies. The northern group breeds on the Auckland and Campbell islands to the south of New Zealand. The southern species breeds only on the remote Chatham Islands, which are, perhaps oddly, further to the north. After breeding, the albatrosses circumnavigate the Southern Ocean.

FACT FILE	
Length:	1.2m (4ft)
Wingspan:	3.2m (10ft 6in)
Distribution:	Southern Hemisphere
Habitat:	Oceans
Diet:	Squid and fish
Status (IUCN Red List):	Vulnerable

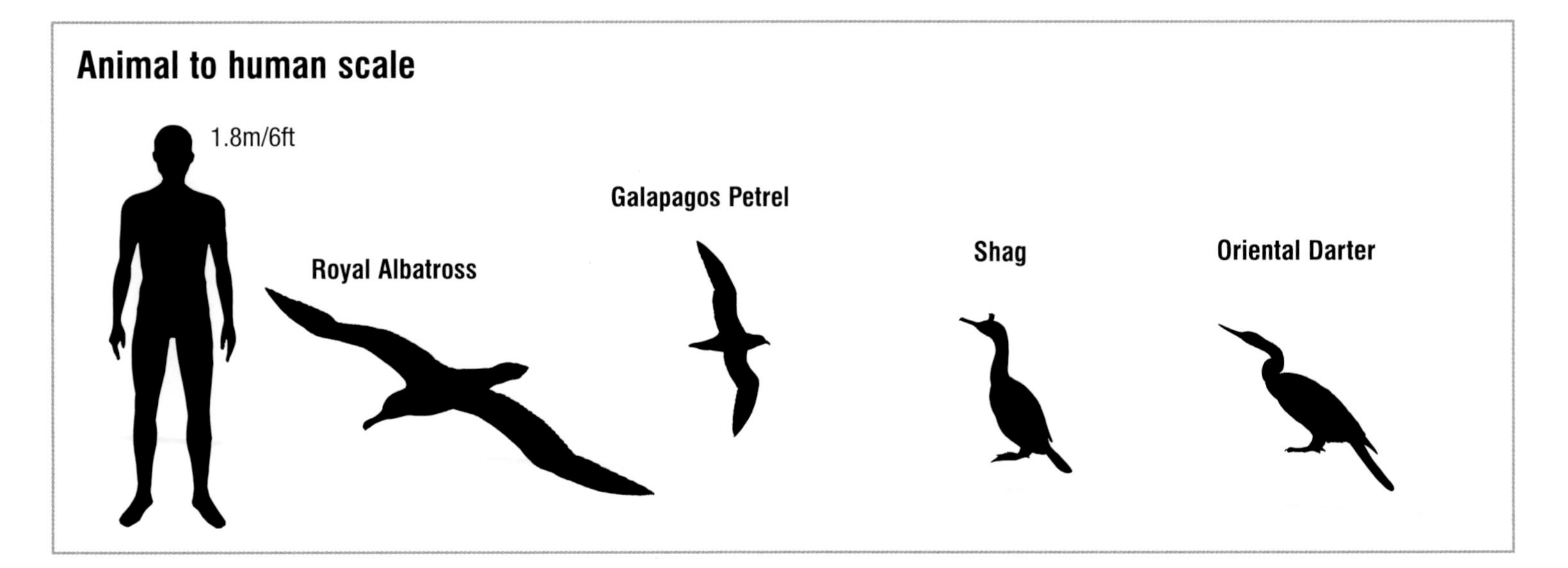

Galapagos Petrel

Pterodroma phaeopygia

This species of petrel nests only on the Galapagos Islands, straddling the equator far out in the Pacific Ocean. They build their nests in the volcanic island's many nooks and crevices, such as craters and sinkholes. The chicks are easy pickings for the cats and rats introduced to the islands, and about 5000 petrels remain.

FACT FILE	
Length:	44cm (17in)
Wingspan:	90cm (35in)
Distribution:	Galapagos Islands, Ecuador
Habitat:	Rocky areas
Diet:	Squid, fish and shellfish
Status (IUCN Red List):	Critically endangered

Shag

Phalacrocorax aristotelis

The shag's greenish plumage is at its most iridescent during the spring mating season. Shags are monogamous. The same pair will often reuse last year's nesting site. The shags make deep dives into sea to catch food and frequently chase prey through the water.

FACT FILE	
Length:	80cm (32in)
Wingspan:	1.05m (3ft 5in)
Distribution:	Europe and North Africa
Habitat:	Rocky coasts
Diet:	Fish, marine worms and shellfish
Status (IUCN Red List):	Least concern

Oriental Darter

Anhinga melanogaster

Darters are close relatives of the cormorants, including the shag. This species is sometimes called the snakebird, not because of its diet but because of its long, flexible neck. The darter hunts in water and often swims along with just its head and neck above the surface.

FACT FILE	
Length:	95cm (37½in)
Wingspan:	1.1m (3ft 7in)
Distribution:	South and southeast Asia
Habitat:	Rivers
Diet:	Fish
Status (IUCN Red List):	Near threatened

Mallard

Anas platyrhynchos

Mallards are the most widespread species of duck. It is a member of the genus Anas, the dabbling ducks, which generally paddle at the surface, duck-diving to feed on submerged plants and gulp water. The mallard has a long neck for reaching the riverbed. When not feeding, the duck folds its neck back between its wings.

FACT FILE	
Length:	65cm (25½in)
Weight:	1.5kg (3lb 5oz)
Distribution:	Northern Hemisphere
Habitat:	Freshwater
Diet:	Water plants
Status (IUCN Red List):	Least concern

Mallards migrate from the coldest northern latitudes in winter, but many flocks stay in one area all year around. Male mallards – the drakes – are one of the most recognizable birds in the world. They have a vibrant, shimmering plumage to attract females – the ducks. Females have a less obvious brown plumage, but are responsible for the iconic quacking call.

BILL
The duck has a hook-like 'nail' at the tip of the bill. This feature is used to crop grass or spear small prey. The duck also sieves food from the water through tooth-like membranes known as lamellae that line the bill.

Iridescence
The drake's shimmering plumage is caused by light reflecting off different layers within the feathers. The reflected light beams interfere to produce the shimmering effect in the same way that light on oil creates a rainbow effect.

Speculum
Both ducks and drakes have a flash of blue feathers on the wing, known as the speculum.

Feet
A duck's feet are highly webbed into a wide paddle.

Ducks

There are more than 100 species of ducks living worldwide. The largest group are the dabbling ducks. Other duck types include the shelducks, steamers and whistling ducks. The eider – a sea duck – is reputed to be the world's strongest flier, capable of cruising at 50km/h (31mph) for days on end during migrations.

Muscovy Duck

Cairina moschata

These ducks are larger than average. The males have a crest on the head that is raised during courtship displays in the spring. The most dominant males maintain a territory and mate with all the females that live within it. Other males may live in it, too, but they will rarely get the chance to mate.

FACT FILE	
Length:	76cm (30in)
Weight:	4.3kg (9lb 8oz)
Distribution:	Central and South America
Habitat:	Forests near water
Diet:	Plants, fish and reptiles
Status (IUCN Red List):	Least concern

White-headed Duck

Oxyura leucocephala

Both male and female white-headed ducks have a distinctive blue bill, although the male one (shown here) is more swollen at the base than the female's. This rare bird lives in alkaline waters, which has a lower freezing point than normal freshwater, so the ducks can feed later into the winter before migrating south.

FACT FILE	
Length:	48cm (19in)
Weight:	1kg (2lb 4oz)
Distribution:	Europe and Asia
Habitat:	Alkaline lakes and marshes
Diet:	Plants and invertebrates`
Status (IUCN Red List):	Endangered

Common Eider

Somateria mollissima

Spending summer on the wind-buffeted Arctic coasts, the female eider has evolved particularly thick and soft down on her breast, which she uses to line the nest and cover the eggs when she is away feeding. For centuries, people have collected this down to make quilts – commonly known as eiderdowns.

FACT FILE	
Length:	70cm (28in)
Weight:	1.8kg (3lb 14oz)
Distribution:	Northern Hemisphere
Habitat:	Mainly coasts and islands
Diet:	Small crustaceans and molluscs
Status (IUCN Red List):	Least concern

Crested Shelduck

Tadorna cristata

No one is sure if any crested shelducks survive in the wild. The males have a highly distinctive plumage, while the otherwise drab females also sport a striking white eye ring. The last confirmed sighting was in 1964, although a Chinese logger claimed to have unwittingly caught and eaten two in the 1980s.

FACT FILE	
Length:	70cm (28in)
Weight:	1.5kg (3lb 5oz)
Distribution:	Eastern Russia, China and Korea
Habitat:	Deep wetlands
Diet:	Water plants and invertebrates
Status (IUCN Red List):	Critically endangered

Comb-billed Duck

Sarkidiornis melanotos

Named after the large disc-shaped growth that protrudes from the male's beak, the comb-billed duck nests close to water. In some areas they are monogamous, while in Africa they have adopted a harem-based society. The male's 'comb' grows to its maximum size during the breeding season.

FACT FILE	
Length:	76cm (30in)
Weight:	2.6kg (5lb 11oz)
Distribution:	Worldwide except Australia
Habitat:	Swamps, rivers and lakes
Diet:	Seeds and invertebrates
Status (IUCN Red List):	Least concern

Large Waterfowl

The waterfowl make up the bird order Anseriformes. Most of its members are the ducks, but this groups also includes swans and geese. The three together form the Anatidae family. There are some more unusual waterfowl, such as the magpie goose and the screamers, which belong to separate families.

Southern Screamer

Chauna torquata

The screamers are unusual waterfowl; for one, they can swim but forage mainly on land. They are named after their loud mating calls, which travel for thousands of metres. Screamers mate for life, and pairs build a platform of reeds and straw in a protected spot near water.

FACT FILE	
Length:	95cm (37½in)
Weight:	4.5kg (10lb)
Distribution:	Southern South America
Habitat:	Near water
Diet:	Leaves, stems and seeds
Status (IUCN Red List):	Least concern

Whooper Swan

Cygnus cygnus

Pronounced 'hooper', the whooper swan spends summer in northern latitudes, before migrating to more temperate areas for the winter. They are not restricted to wetland habitats and often feed on farmland. They look similar to mute swans but have a giveaway honking call.

FACT FILE	
Length:	1.6m (5ft 2in)
Weight:	11kg (24lb 4oz)
Distribution:	Europe and Asia
Habitat:	Wetlands, mudflats and fields
Diet:	Water plants and grass
Status (IUCN Red List):	Least concern

Bean Goose

Anser fabalis

This widespread goose is named after the bird's habit of raiding the winter stubble of bean fields after migrating from the far north. Some ornithologists prefer to divide the species in two, reflecting a split in the goose's breeding grounds: one group breeds in the boggy taiga, while the other heads further north to the barren tundra.

FACT FILE	
Length:	90cm (35in)
Weight:	4kg (8lb 13oz)
Distribution:	Asia and Europe
Habitat:	Bogs and tundra
Diet:	Seeds and water plants
Status (IUCN Red List):	Least concern

Canada Goose

Branta canadensis

The Canada goose has spread far beyond its original habitat of the North American prairies and subarctic tundra to woods, parks and farmland, and (with human help) as far as the British Isles and New Zealand. These distinctively marked geese are generally very tame.

FACT FILE	
Length:	1.1m (3ft 7in)
Weight:	8kg (17lb 10oz)
Distribution:	N. America, Siberia, Europe, NZ
Habitat:	Tundra, grassland and farmland
Diet:	Grasses
Status (IUCN Red List):	Least concern

Cape Barren Goose

Cereopsis novaehollandiae

No one is really sure if this species of goose is more of a swan or even a giant duck. It lives in a patchy population long the south coast of Australia, mostly around the mouth of the Murray and on either side of the Tasman Sea.

FACT FILE	
Length:	1m (3ft 3in)
Weight:	6.8kg (15lb)
Distribution:	Southern Australia and Tasmania
Habitat:	Coast and wetlands
Diet:	Plants
Status (IUCN Red List):	Least concern

American Flamingo

Phoenicopterus ruber

Flamingos are unmistakable, if rather gawky, birds, with disproportionately long legs and neck, a small head, and distinctive rosy-pink plumage. The American flamingo is the largest species. It is also the most widespread. It is, like all flamingos, highly social, feeding and breeding in large flocks.

FACT FILE	
Length:	1.45m (4ft 9in)
Weight:	2.8kg (6lb 3oz)
Distribution:	South America
Habitat:	Shallow salt and soda lakes
Diet:	Invertebrates
Status (IUCN Red List):	Least concern

A flamingo formally feeds standing up – although it can swim – in shallow water. It reaches down to place its bill upside down in the water and sieves microscopic crustaceans from the water. Flamingos live in coastal lagoons and desert lakes, where the water is very salty – too salty for most animals to live.

Pink colour
A flamingo's feathers start out as white, but are turned pink by the pigments in its food.

Bill
The edges of the bill are lined with tooth-like lamellae that trap food as mouthfuls of water are squirted out by the tongue.

Ankle
What looks like the bird's knee is actually its ankle. This high joint makes it easier for the flamingo to sit on its nests, which are mounds of mud, raising eggs and chicks above the burning waters.

Skin
The saline waters of a flamingo's habitat contain corrosive chemicals. The bird's skin resists this process, which would blister the skin of other animals.

Herons

The herons are long-billed wading birds. They stalk fish and other large prey (generally aquatic), and kill with a rapid stab of the pointed beak. They waterproof their plumage with special feathers that crumble as they are rubbed on the others. The powder is then combed through with the flattened claw on the third toe.

Cocoi Heron

Ardea cocoi

This is the largest heron species in South America. It is a common sight in wetlands across the continent, save the lakes of the Andes. It hunts for large fish by standing in the shallows and waiting for a likely prey to pass. It has quite diverse tastes and even picks at carrion.

FACT FILE	
Length:	1.3m (4ft 3in)
Weight:	2kg (4lb 6oz)
Distribution:	South America
Habitat:	Wetlands, rivers and lagoons
Diet:	Fish, frogs, insects and carrion
Status (IUCN Red List):	Least concern

Whistling Heron

Syrigma sibilatrix

This medium-sized heron is named after its loud call. It spends more time on dry land than other herons. It lives in the grasslands of South America, such as the Llanos of Colombia. It hunts in the slow and deliberate way typical of herons, but the whistling heron also runs through the grass after flying insects.

FACT FILE	
Length:	64cm (25in)
Weight:	540g (19oz)
Distribution:	South America
Habitat:	Flooded grasslands
Diet:	Fish, frogs and flying insects
Status (IUCN Red List):	Least concern

Squaacco Heron

Ardeola ralloides

This little heron is named after its squawking call. It has become a frequent visitor to paddy fields as natural wetlands are drained or polluted. It is a migrant species and heads south from the colder parts of its range in winter. The species is quite rare in Europe, but is common elsewhere.

FACT FILE	
Length:	48cm (19in)
Weight:	370g (13oz)
Distribution:	Europe, Africa and western Asia
Habitat:	Lakes, swamps and wetlands
Diet:	Fish, amphibians, invertebrates
Status (IUCN Red List):	Least concern

Green-back Heron

Butorides striatus

Spending much of its time creeping around in the bushes, this small heron is hard to spot. The best way of finding it is to listen for its booming calls. The green-back uses its large bill to good effect and it is one of very few tool-using birds. It lures fish within striking distance by dangling an enticing insect or perhaps a feather.

FACT FILE	
Length:	48cm (19in)
Weight:	250g (8¾oz)
Distribution:	Western North America, Caribbean
Habitat:	Wetlands and salt marshes
Diet:	Frogs, reptiles and crustaceans
Status (IUCN Red List):	Least concern

Boat-billed Heron

Cochlearius cochlearius

The boat-billed heron feeds at night – aided in dim light by its big eyes – and its bill is highly sensitive. At the slightest touch of small aquatic prey the bill opens, drawing in water and prey. The bird also has a drooping crest of black feathers on its head.

FACT FILE	
Length:	51cm (20in)
Weight:	700g (25oz)
Distribution:	Central and South America
Habitat:	Swamps
Diet:	Small fish and shrimps
Status (IUCN Red List):	Least concern

Bitterns and Relatives

Bitterns are related to the herons, sharing the Ardeidae family with them. They are mostly diurnal hunters that stalk fish, frogs and insects through shallow water. The Ardeidae also includes the egrets and tiger herons. The tiger herons produce booming calls similar to the bitterns.

Von Schrenck's Bittern

Ixobrychus eurhythmus

This small bittern spends the summer breeding in northern China and Siberia and then flies south over southeast Asia to winter at wetlands in Laos, Indonesia and the Philippines. It spends the day among thick vegetation, but comes out into the open more in twilight.

FACT FILE	
Length:	38cm (15in)
Weight:	300g (10½oz)
Distribution:	Eastern Asia
Habitat:	Reedbeds
Diet:	Insects, fish and frogs
Status (IUCN Red List):	Least concern

White-crested Tiger Heron

Tigriornis leucolophus

A tiger heron is a halfway house between the herons and bitterns. Like a bittern, a tiger heron has cryptic plumage – its colouring supposedly resembles a tiger's – that helps it stay hidden among swamp plants. However, unlike bitterns, this species hunts mainly at night.

FACT FILE	
Length:	80cm (32in)
Weight:	700g (25oz)
Distribution:	Central and west Africa
Habitat:	Swamps and forests near rivers
Diet:	Fish and other aquatic creatures
Status (IUCN Red List):	Least concern

South American Bittern

Botaurus pinnatus

This species is very similar to its northern neighbour, *Botaurus lentiginosus*, or the North American bittern. The main difference is that this southern species has little need to migrate. The South American bittern is largely nocturnal, and gives a croaking call when flushed out.

FACT FILE	
Length:	76cm (30in)
Weight:	800g (28¼oz)
Distribution:	From Mexico to Argentina
Habitat:	Reedbeds
Diet:	Eels, frogs and reptiles
Status (IUCN Red List):	Least concern

Australian Bittern

Botaurus poiciloptilus

The Australian bittern lives mainly in southeastern Australia and Tasmania, although there are small populations elsewhere in the region. It is active both day and night and gives a loud booming call during the spring breeding season. Its population is seen to fluctuate widely as conditions change year on year.

FACT FILE	
Length:	70cm (28in)
Weight:	750g (26½oz)
Distribution:	S. Australia, South Island of NZ
Habitat:	Freshwater and brackish wetlands
Diet:	Eels, fish, frogs and crayfish
Status (IUCN Red List):	Endangered

Chinese Egret

Egretta eulophotes

The egrets are a small subgroup of herons, known largely for their pure white plumage and the crest on the back of the head. This species is on the large size. It has become vulnerable to extinction due to habitat loss and hunters after the crest plumes. The species is now heavily protected.

FACT FILE	
Length:	68cm (26in)
Weight:	400g (14oz)
Distribution:	Eastern Asia
Habitat:	Tidal mudflats, paddies and ponds
Diet:	Crabs and other shellfish
Status (IUCN Red List):	Vulnerable

Storks and Relatives

Most storks belong to the Ciconiidae family, which contains about three dozen species. The storks are tall birds, with long bills. Most are wading birds, but some species feed in pastures. The long bill is used to probe the bottom of shallow waters, finding prey by touch rather than by sight.

Wood Stork

Mycteria americana

Breeding pairs of wood storks mate for life. They may winter apart but both arrive back at the same nesting site as last year in spring to do it all again. A stork's wings are 50 per cent wider than the bird is high, and that makes them excellent soarers. Before embarking on long flights, wood storks spiral upward on thermals to a great height.

FACT FILE	
Length:	1m (3ft 3in)
Weight:	2.5kg (5lb 8oz)
Distribution:	North America to Argentina
Habitat:	Swamps and tidal flats
Diet:	Fish, frogs and shellfish
Status (IUCN Red List):	Least concern

White Stork

Ciconia ciconia

This is the baby-delivering species of folklore, spring visitors to Middle Europe that set up homes of broad nests on chimneys and telecoms masts. In autumn the storks head south again, crossing the Mediterranean at the narrowest points so as not to lose the lift from thermals rising off dry ground.

FACT FILE	
Length:	1.1m (3ft 7in)
Weight:	8kg (17lb 10oz)
Distribution:	Europe, N. Africa and Middle East
Habitat:	Wetlands, savannah and fields
Diet:	Insects, arachnids, frogs and fish
Status (IUCN Red List):	Least concern

Marabou Stork

Leptoptilos crumeniferus

One of the world's largest flying birds, the marabou has a massive wedge-shaped bill and a bare neck with a large hanging wattle, which it inflates with air during mating displays. It is a scavenger and competes with vultures for the first pick of the flesh of rotting animal carcasses.

FACT FILE	
Length:	1.5m (5ft)
Weight:	9kg (19lb 12oz)
Distribution:	Africa south of Sahara
Habitat:	Open grasslands and marshes
Diet:	Animal carcasses
Status (IUCN Red List):	Least concern

Sacred Ibis

Threskiornis aethiopicus

The long sweeping bill and black head of the ibis make regular appearances in the artwork of ancient Egypt, where this bird was first given sacred status. The species nests on rocky outcrops and has therefore adapted well to urbanization – they now make their homes among brick and concrete.

FACT FILE	
Length:	76cm (30in)
Weight:	1.5kg (3lb 5oz)
Distribution:	Sub-Saharan Africa and Mid East
Habitat:	Close to water
Diet:	Insects, arachnids and shellfish
Status (IUCN Red List):	Least concern

Roseate Spoonbill

Platalea ajaja

The most notable feature of the spoonbills is their rounded bill. This shape develops only as a young bird grows. Spoonbills sweep their bills from side to side in muddy water and grab any prey items that make a break for it.

FACT FILE	
Length:	80cm (32in)
Weight:	10kg (22lb)
Distribution:	Subtropical Americas
Habitat:	Wetlands
Diet:	Crustaceans and small fish
Status (IUCN Red List):	Least concern

Osprey

Pandion haliaetus

The osprey is a hunting bird. It eats fish and is never found very far from water – but that is about its only restriction. Few birds are more widely spread around the world. It is most common in the Northern Hemisphere. In the Southern Hemisphere, it breeds only in Australia; elsewhere it is a seasonal migrant.

FACT FILE	
Length:	58cm (23in)
Weight:	1.4kg (3lb)
Distribution:	Worldwide
Habitat:	Near water
Diet:	Fish
Status (IUCN Red List):	Least concern

The osprey circles up to 60m (200ft) above the water to spot its prey, then swoops and plunges feet-first to grab the fish – often submerging in the process. It may struggle to take off again, but can lift almost its own weight in fish. It carries its meal to a convenient perch to feed.

BILL
The upper bill has a sharp hook for ripping fish apart.

PLUMAGE
An osprey's coat of feathers is thicker than those of many other raptors. Oils make them waterproof – waterlogged wings will not fly.

NARROW WINGS
Wider wings would help the osprey soar above the water while hunting, but it has evolved narrow ones that do not pick up so much water during dives, keeping the weight down as the osprey powers back into the air.

FEET
The osprey's feet are well adapted for fishing. The soles are spiked and the outer toe can be rotated to face backwards to create a pincer.

Kites and Relatives

Most birds of prey, or raptors, belong to the family Accipitridae. The 200-plus species include the kites, medium-sized hunters that live worldwide. There are around 30 species of kite, many of which have a characteristic forked tail. Kites are generally land hunters and live in small colonies.

Brahminy Kite

Haliastur indus

This coastal bird of prey is as much scavenger as it is hunter. It picks over food waste from boats and rubbish tips, but also hunts along the shore for crabs and other small animals. Breeding pairs build a wide nest in the fork of tree, often using traditional nesting sites that have been exploited by kites for generations.

FACT FILE	
Length:	51cm (20in)
Weight:	550g (19½oz)
Distribution:	East Asia to northern Australia
Habitat:	Tropical coastlines
Diet:	Crabs, frogs and small reptiles
Status (IUCN Red List):	Least concern

Snail Kite

Rostrhamus sociabilis

The snail kite has an extremely specialized diet. It eats almost nothing but apple snails, which live in marshes. It flies low over the water, swooping to catch snails with its talons. Many wetlands have been drained in the last century and kite numbers have dropped accordingly.

FACT FILE	
Length:	40cm (16in)
Weight:	450g (16oz)
Distribution:	Florida, Central and South America
Habitat:	Freshwater marshes
Diet:	Freshwater apple snails
Status (IUCN Red List):	Least concern

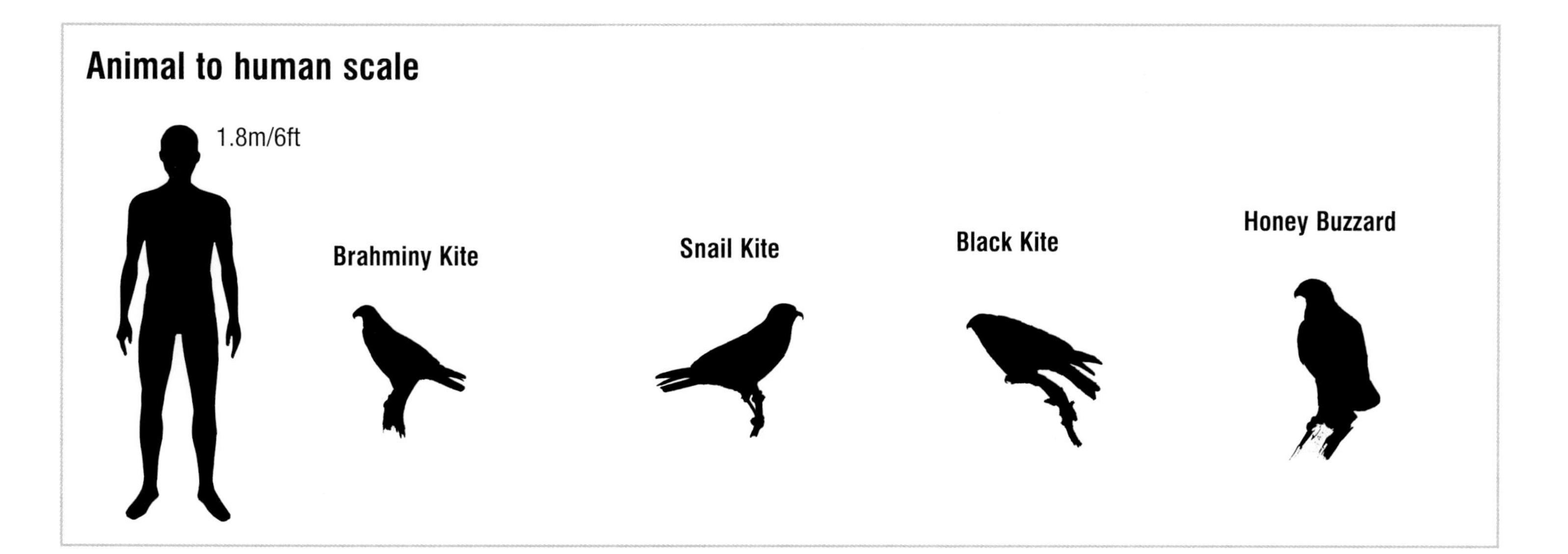

Black Kite

Milvus migrans

Perhaps the most widespread species of raptor, the black kite is equally at home in the African savannah as the pine forest of Siberia. The females are a little larger than the males, but it is tricky to tell the sexes apart. Both display the kites' trademark forked tail.

FACT FILE	
Length:	60cm (23½in)
Weight:	950g (33½oz)
Distribution:	Africa, Australia, Asia and Europe
Habitat:	Everywhere but desert and tundra
Diet:	Carrion, reptiles and insects
Status (IUCN Red List):	Least concern

Honey Buzzard

Pernis apivorus

Despite its name, the honey buzzard is related to the kites, not the true buzzards. It has a specialized diet of larvae harvested from the nests of social insects. It follows honeybees and similar insects to their nest and rips it apart with scaly feet, impervious to stings. The face is also protected by scaly feathers.

FACT FILE	
Length:	60cm (23½in)
Weight:	1kg (2lb 4oz)
Distribution:	Europe and Africa
Habitat:	Forests
Diet:	Insect larvae
Status (IUCN Red List):	Least concern

Fish Eagles

The eagles are the largest members of the Accipitridae, and the mightiest raptor hunters. While other types of raptor, such as the vultures, can grow to a bigger size, they are not steely-eyed hunters like eagles. Many of the largest eagles hunt over water, and are known as the fish, or sea, eagles.

White-tailed Eagle

Haliaeetus albicilla

The white-tailed species is the largest eagle living in Europe. It is a close relative of the bald eagle of North America. Most white-tailed eagles live in the far north, where they can nest on remote cliffs overlooking the sea, river valleys, and even the Arctic tundra. In winter, the birds migrate further south but stay in isolated wilderness areas.

FACT FILE	
Length:	90cm (35in)
Weight:	6.9kg (15lb 3oz)
Distribution:	Northern Europe and Asia
Habitat:	Cliffs near water
Diet:	Fish, mammals and birds
Status (IUCN Red List):	Least concern

Bald Eagle

Haliaeetus leucocephalus

The United States' national bird's main food is dead or dying fish picked up from the shoreline. They often harass other birds – especially ospreys – to force them to drop their catch. The 'bald' name refers to the whiteness of the eagle's head feathers, not the lack of them.

FACT FILE	
Length:	86cm (34in)
Weight:	3kg (6lb 10oz)
Distribution:	North America
Habitat:	Wooded country near open water
Diet:	Fish, small birds, small mammals
Status (IUCN Red List):	Least concern

Grey-headed Fish Eagle

Ichthyophaga ichthyaetus

The grey-headed fish eagle lives up to its scientific name, which means 'fish-eating fish eagle'. The eagle perches on a branch overlooking a body of water and watches the surface, ever-ready to swoop down and snatch prey. It also keeps an eye on the banks and is not averse to mixing its fish diet with reptiles and other small animals.

FACT FILE	
Length:	76cm (30in)
Weight:	3.5kg (7lb 11oz)
Distribution:	South and Southeast Asia
Habitat:	Lowland forest around rivers
Diet:	Fish and reptiles
Status (IUCN Red List):	Near threatened

African Fish Eagle

Haliaeetus vocifer

This widespread species has a lot of free time. Although only about 12 per cent of its hunting forays end in something to eat, the eagle manages to fill its stomach with just ten minutes of active hunting per day. The rest of the time is spent watching – and waiting.

FACT FILE	
Length:	76cm (30in)
Weight:	3.6kg (8lb)
Distribution:	Sub-Saharan Africa
Habitat:	Lakes, river and mangroves
Diet:	Fish
Status (IUCN Red List):	Least concern

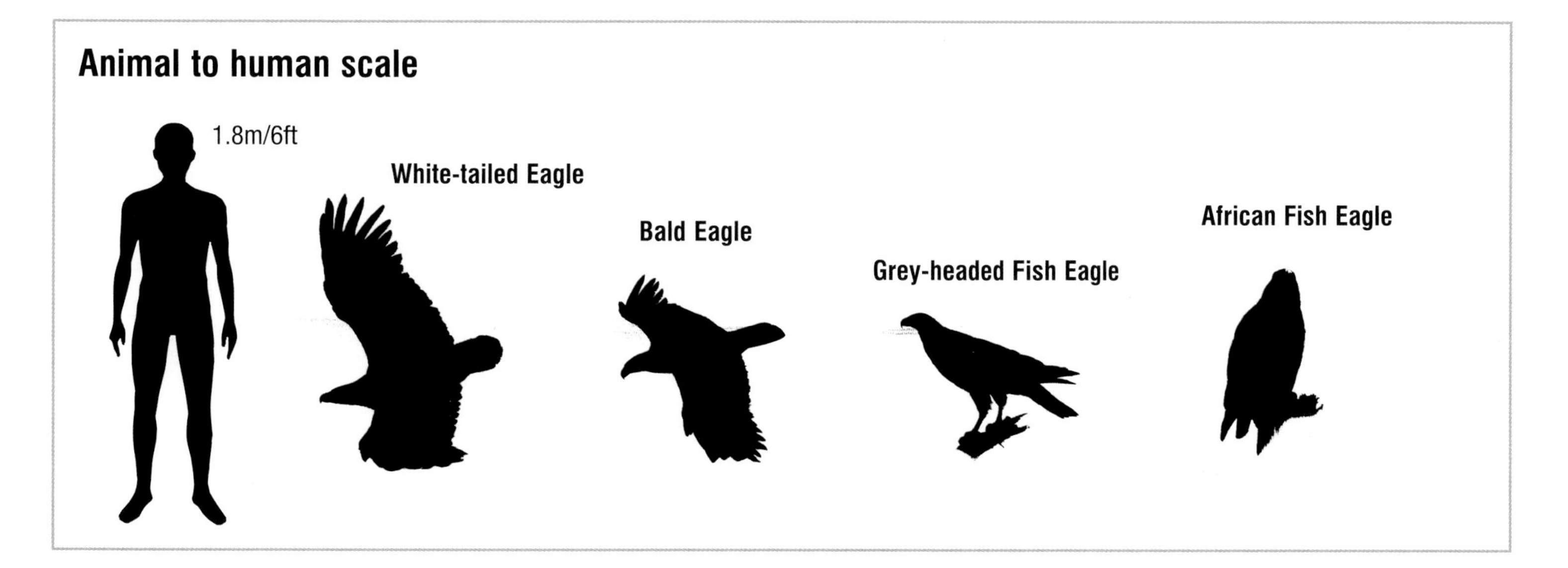

Other Eagles

The largest group of eagles are the 30 species of boot eagle. This name refers to the hunters' thickly feathered legs. A further group is the snake eagles, named after their main prey. The largest eagles belong to the unromantically named buteonid group, which includes the monkey-killing Philippine eagle.

Golden Eagle

Aquila chrysaetos

Perhaps the most familiar of the boot eagles, the golden eagle forms a strong pair bond and mates with the same partner for life. The breeding pair builds its eyrie on top of a precipitous ledge, which they return to year after year and will pass on to their young. As a result, many of these eagle's nests are immense tangles of sticks.

FACT FILE	
Length:	84cm (33in)
Weight:	4.5kg (10lb)
Distribution:	Northern Hemisphere
Habitat:	Mountains and highland forest
Diet:	Hares, rodents and fox cubs
Status (IUCN Red List):	Least concern

Harpy Eagle

Harpia harpyja

The world's biggest eagle, the harpy is the dominant predator of the forest canopy, where it flies almost silently just below the tops of the trees. It is highly manoeuvrable despite its 2.1m (6ft 10in) wingspan, and often chases monkeys through the trees, snatching its prey with its powerful talons. The claws grow 18cm (7in) long.

FACT FILE	
Length:	1m (3ft 3in)
Weight:	9kg (19lb 12oz)
Distribution:	Central and South America
Habitat:	Mainly lowland rainforest
Diet:	Monkeys, sloths and opossums
Status (IUCN Red List):	Least concern

Short-toed eagle

Circaetus gallicus

The short-toed eagle is a snake-eating species. It tackles snakes that are twice as long as it is, generally aiming for slender, non-venomous tree snakes. The snakes are gripped in the raptorial feet and killed with a bite ripping through the vital organs. The eagle then swallows its elongated prey whole.

FACT FILE	
Length:	67cm (26in)
Weight:	2.3kg (5lb 2oz)
Distribution:	Europe, N Africa to Central Asia
Habitat:	Forest and woodland
Diet:	Snakes
Status (IUCN Red List):	Least concern

Crested Serpent Eagle

Spilornis cheela

A snake eagle's toes are short and strong, with a rough under-surface, ideal for grasping their writhing prey. The crested snake eagle is a skilled flyer, but rarely hunts in the air. It watches from a perch for suitable prey, before swooping down to seize its victim on the ground.

FACT FILE	
Length:	70cm (28in)
Weight:	1.8kg (3lb 14oz)
Distribution:	South and east Asia
Habitat:	Mainly forests and woodland
Diet:	Snakes and small mammals
Status (IUCN Red List):	Least concern

Bataleur

Terathopius ecaudatus

The name of this bird means 'tight-rope walker' in French and refers to the way the eagle tilts its wings from side to side as if balancing on a high wire. It can perform many spectacular aerial manoeuvres – even somersaults as it swoops on prey and courts mates.

FACT FILE	
Length:	70cm (28in)
Weight:	1.8kg (3lb 14oz)
Distribution:	Most of Africa south of Sahara
Habitat:	Grassland, scrub, open woodland
Diet:	Carrion, reptiles and amphibians
Status (IUCN Red List):	Near threatened

Secretary Bird

Sagittarius serpentarius

No one is quite sure where this unusual raptor got its common name. It may be that the sparse crown of feathers reminds some of the quill pens tucked behind a scribe's ear. Another possibility is that it is the result of a transliteration of the Arabic word for 'hunting bird', which sounds similar to *secretaire*, the French for secretary.

FACT FILE	
Length:	1.2m (4ft)
Weight:	3.25kg (7lb 2oz)
Distribution:	Most of Africa south of Sahara
Habitat:	Savannah grasslands
Diet:	Reptiles, mammals and insects
Status (IUCN Red List):	Least concern

A secretary bird looks like an eagle crossed with a crane. It is the only raptor to hunt on the ground. It can fly, but normally stalks across grasslands, watching to see if it flushes out snakes and other prey. It then pounces on them with its feet, or snatches them up in its beak, killing them with a single bite.

COLOUR CHANGE
As the secretary bird ages, its eyes turn from grey to brown and the flash of orange skin on the face turns a darker red.
CREST
The crown of quill-like feathers lies flat on the neck most of the time, but is erected during courtship displays.
WINGS
With a wingspan of 1.35m (4ft 5in), the secretary bird can fly. but is a clumsy lander. It uses its wings to escape predators and to reach its messy treetop nests.
FEET
The name 'raptor' applies to a bird of prey's raptorial, or grasping, feet. Although it is a raptor, the secretary bird's feet are made for walking – and stamping on prey – and so are less flexible than those of other raptors.

Hawks and Harriers

The largest subfamily of the Accipitridae are the hawks, small raptors with rounded wings that add up to 53 species. Another group of small birds of prey are the harriers. These are long-legged birds that have a long, square tail and long wings. Both hawks and harriers tend to prey on other birds.

Gabar Goshawk

Micronisus gabar

The gabar goshawk is a small species living in dry parts of Africa and southern Arabia. It is a hunter of other birds, flushing them out and chasing them down in a relentless and acrobatic pursuit. It can kill prey almost as heavy as itself. Gabar goshawks also add spiders to their nests. It is thought that their webs help with camouflage and keep out insect parasites.

FACT FILE	
Length:	35cm (13¾in)
Weight:	250g (8¾oz)
Distribution:	Sub-Saharan Africa and Yemen
Habitat:	Woodland, savannah and bush
Diet:	Small birds
Status (IUCN Red List):	Least concern

Hen Harrier

Circus cyaneus

The hen harrier – known in North America as the marsh hawk – is one of the most widespread species of hawks. Unusually for a hawk, male and female hen harriers differ in colour as well as size; the male is grey and the female is brown. Both have a distinctive white rump patch. Like other harriers, they hunt by gliding low over the ground.

FACT FILE	
Length:	51cm (20in)
Weight:	525g (18oz)
Distribution:	Northern Hemisphere
Habitat:	Woodland
Diet:	Other birds
Status (IUCN Red List):	Least concern

Ferruginous Hawk

Buteo regalis

Like several species of hawk, the ferruginous hawk is an extremely acrobatic flyer. This is most apparent during courtship, when the male and female soar together with their wings almost in a V-shape. The male then swoops in at his mate and grabs her talons. The pair then spiral around each other in a series of mid-air cartwheels.

FACT FILE	
Length:	68cm (26in)
Weight:	1.5kg (3lb 5oz)
Distribution:	North America
Habitat:	Prairies and farmland
Diet:	Rodents, rabbits and birds
Status (IUCN Red List):	Least concern

Harris's Hawk

Parabuteo unicinctus

Harris's hawks live in small, highly structured groups. At their core is a breeding male and female. Other members tend to be non-breeding males. The groups hunt together to kill larger animals such as jackrabbits. The hawks walk through the bush to flush the prey out into the talons of another group member.

FACT FILE	
Length:	61cm (24in)
Weight:	900g (32oz)
Distribution:	Southwest US to Patagonia
Habitat:	Arid woodlands and cactus scrub
Diet:	Rats and mice
Status (IUCN Red List):	Least concern

Scavenging Raptors

Not all birds of prey are hunters. The vultures let other animals do the killing and arrive just in time to snap up the left-over scraps of meat. Condors also scavenge for carrion, but tend to eat animals that have died of natural causes. Scavenging raptors fall into two families, one from the Old World, the other from the New.

Andean Condor

Vultur gryphus

With a wingspan of 3.2m (10ft 6in), this is one of the largest flying animals in the world. The condor rides the rising thermals coming off the mountains all the way to the ocean. On its way, it lands to scavenge the remains of large rodents, llamas and even whales and seals washed up on the shore.

FACT FILE	
Length:	1.3m (4ft 3in)
Weight:	15kg (33lb)
Distribution:	Andes
Habitat:	Mountains
Diet:	Carrion
Status (IUCN Red List):	Near threatened

American Black Vulture

Coragyps atratus

This species of New World vulture lives across the Americas, anywhere it can get a good view of the ground. It is a frequent visitor to rubbish dumps and many populations are sustained by road kills. However, the vulture eats fresh meat occasionally, killing chicks and ducklings.

FACT FILE	
Length:	69cm (27in)
Weight:	2.35kg (5lb 3oz)
Distribution:	North and South America
Habitat:	Open habitats
Diet:	Carrion and rubbish
Status (IUCN Red List):	Least concern

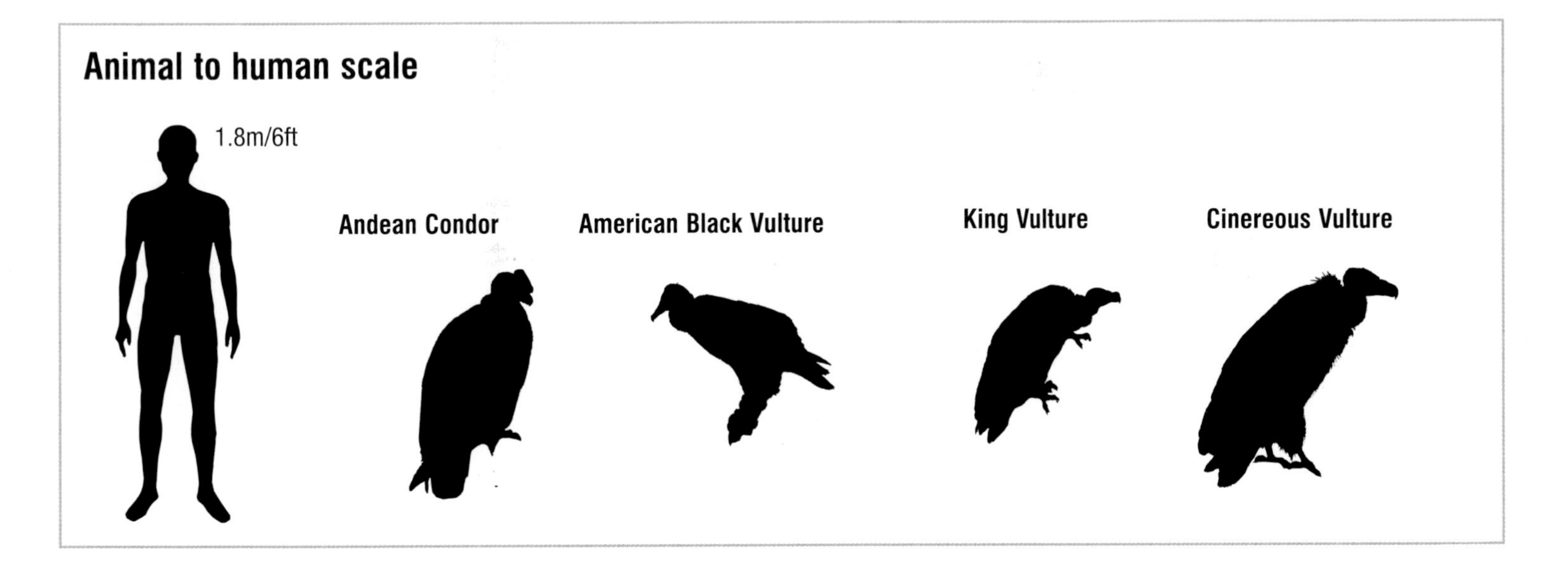

King Vulture

Sarcoramphus papa

The king vulture is the top scavenging bird on the east side of the Andes. It depends a lot on its sense of smell to detect dead meat in the dense jungle below. DNA evidence shows that this species – and other New World vultures – are more closely related to storks than they are to Old World vultures.

FACT FILE	
Length:	80cm (32in)
Weight:	3.75kg (8lb 4oz)
Distribution:	Mexico to northern Argentina
Habitat:	Tropical forests
Diet:	Carrion
Status (IUCN Red List):	Least concern

Cinereous Vulture

Aegypius monachus

Although it does not kill prey, this is the largest bird of prey in the Old World. It soars on vast wings, searching for fresh carcasses with its sharp eyesight. It has a long neck and huge hooked bill, ideal for tearing into the sinews deep inside a dead body.

FACT FILE	
Length:	1.1m (3ft 7in)
Weight:	14kg (30lb 14oz)
Distribution:	S. Europe, N. Africa and Asia
Habitat:	Desert, scrub, grassland, forest
Diet:	Carrion
Status (IUCN Red List):	Near threatened

Lammergeier

Gypaetus barbatus

The translation of the scientific name of this magnificent bird says it all: bearded vulture eagle. Although it has the stature – and lineage – of a vulture, its plumage is distinctly eagle-like. However, the lammergeier is not a hunter. Instead, it soars effortlessly above its arid habitat, looking for the remains of long-dead mammals.

Beard
The bristly moustache and beard feathers obscure much of the robust bill, which is about 8cm (3in) long.

FACT FILE	
Length:	1.1m (3ft 7in)
Weight:	7kg (15lb 8oz)
Distribution:	Western and central Asia
Habitat:	Mountains
Diet:	Bones and carrion
Status (IUCN Red List):	Least concern

This massive vulture has a unique way of feeding. It heaves the bones of dead mammals high into the sky and then drops them on rocky outcrops, smashing them into shards. It takes several years to learn to do this efficiently. Breaking the bones exposes the nutritious marrow inside. The bird then swallows the lumps of bone whole.

Feet
Vultures cannot carry food in their feet – they have little need to. However, the lammergeier's strong toes are used to heave thick bones hundred of metres into the sky.

NECK
Most vultures have only short feathers on the head and neck to minimize mess when probing bloody carcasses. The lammergeier rarely eats flesh and so retains the eagle-style neck plumage.

Falcons

The second largest family of raptors is the falcons. The Falconidae family contains 37 species, including kestrels and caracaras. Falcons have narrower wings than most raptors and are spectacular flyers. The peregrine falcon holds the air-speed record among animals, reaching around 320km/h (200mph) in hunting dives.

Laughing Falcon

Herpetotheres cachinnans

This large falcon hunts snakes slithering on the floor of open forests or through the scrub along the edges of the tree line. They swoop from a perch to tackle prey, landing with a heavy thud that is normally enough to kill the snake. The bird grips the snake's neck so tightly that the head is often ripped off.

FACT FILE	
Length:	44cm (17in)
Weight:	800g (28¼oz)
Distribution:	Central and South America
Habitat:	Forested areas
Diet:	Snakes
Status (IUCN Red List):	Least concern

Yellow-headed Caracara

Milvago chimachima

The caracara is an atypical falcon. Instead of being a swift hunter, this bird is more often seen flapping around ranches, picking the ticks off the hides of cattle. The caracara does prey on small animals but is an avid scavenger and also eats fruits. It rarely spooks flocks of smaller birds, indicating that it is not seen as a threat.

FACT FILE	
Length:	46cm (18in)
Weight:	360g (12¾oz)
Distribution:	Central and South America
Habitat:	Savannah and swamps
Diet:	Reptiles, frogs and carrion
Status (IUCN Red List):	Least concern

Kestrel

Falco tinnunculus

The kestrel is a typical and very widespread member of the falcon family. It is one of the most easy-to-spot birds of prey, hunting as it does during the day, hovering above grasses and watching for a sign that a vole or other small animal is hiding beneath. Male kestrels have a grey head, while the larger females have a brown head.

FACT FILE	
Length:	37cm (14½in)
Weight:	310g (11oz)
Distribution:	Europe, North Africa, Asia
Habitat:	Fields, woodlands and cities
Diet:	Voles and small birds
Status (IUCN Red List):	Least concern

Gyrfalcon

Falco rusticolus

This is the largest falcon species. It often hunts in the air, chasing birds and grabbing them with its talons. Like other falcons, this species was used as a tame hunting bird in the Middle Ages, but only royal falconers were allowed to deploy such magnificent birds.

FACT FILE	
Length:	63cm (24¾in)
Weight:	2.1kg (4lb 10oz)
Distribution:	Arctic
Habitat:	Tundra and mountains
Diet:	Birds, especially Arctic ptarmigan
Status (IUCN Red List):	Least concern

Eurasian Hobby

Falco subbuteo

Like many falcons, the hobby hunts on the wing. Its main prey are flying insects and smaller birds, such as swifts, martins and swallows, which are no match for the hobby's flying skills. The hobby can be spotted shadowing a farm vehicle, waiting for prey to be flushed out into the air.

FACT FILE	
Length:	36cm (14in)
Weight:	340g (12oz)
Distribution:	Africa, Europe and Asia
Habitat:	Areas with a few trees
Diet:	Insects, small birds and bats
Status (IUCN Red List):	Least concern

Domestic Fowl

With a population of more than 24 billion, the chicken is the most popular domestic animal in the world. The chicken is a relative of the wild partridges and pheasants, ground-dwelling gamebirds that may also be eaten. Two more landfowl species raised for food are guinea fowl and turkey, which belong to two smaller families.

Turkey

Meleagris gallopavo

It is believed that the native peoples of Mexico first domesticated the wild turkey; the Spanish brought it to Europe in the sixteenth century. The wild species still lives in scattered woodland areas. It is a big bird that roosts in trees but feeds and nests on the ground. Males defend harems of females by strutting and displaying their fanned tail, while making a 'gobble-gobble' call.

FACT FILE	
Length:	1.25m (4ft 1in)
Weight:	8.2kg (18lb)
Distribution:	Worldwide
Habitat:	Woodland in the wild
Diet:	Seeds, nuts, berries, some insects
Status (IUCN Red List):	N/A

Red Junglefowl

Gallus gallus

This species from the pheasant family is the wild ancestor of the domestic chicken. In the wild, the birds live in large flocks that stalk through a wide range of habitats, pecking food from the ground. The flock has a strict pecking order, and in the spring breeding season the younger cocks are forced out of the flock.

FACT FILE	
Length:	76cm (30in)
Weight:	1.4kg (3lb)
Distribution:	South and Southeast Asia
Habitat:	Scrub, forests and mangroves
Diet:	Seeds and insects
Status (IUCN Red List):	Least concern

Ko Shamo Chicken

Gallus gallus

The shamo is an attractive Japanese chicken. Shamo means 'fighter' in Japanese, and the chicken was bred for this. There are several breeds of shamos, with the ko shamo being a smaller variety. All shamos can be very tame if treated considerately, and even beg for food.

FACT FILE	
Length:	45cm (17¾in)
Weight:	1kg (2lb 4oz)
Distribution:	Worldwide
Habitat:	Domesticated
Diet:	Seeds, insects and fruit
Status (IUCN Red List):	N/A

Dorking Chicken

Gallus gallus

The Dorking breed originated in Italy at least 2000 years ago. This versatile breed is kept for both egg and meat production. Dorkings have a large comb and produce a white-shelled egg. A chicken usually lays an egg a day until it has a clutch of around 12 eggs. It then stops laying for a couple of days before beginning again.

FACT FILE	
Length:	65cm (25½in)
Weight:	3.6kg (8lb)
Distribution:	Worldwide
Habitat:	Domesticated
Diet:	Seeds, insects and fruit
Status (IUCN Red List):	N/A

Helmeted Guineafowl

Numida meleagris

The helmeted guineafowl – so called because of the horny casque on its head – is the ancestor of the domesticated guineafowl. Flocks roost in trees at night, and in the morning come down and move together in single file to water to drink. They run rather than fly away from their enemies.

FACT FILE	
Length:	63cm (24¾in)
Weight:	1.3kg (2lb 12oz)
Distribution:	Originally Africa
Habitat:	Brushland and forest
Diet:	Insects; seeds and leaves
Status (IUCN Red List):	N/A

Wild Landfowl

There are more than 200 wild species of landfowl living worldwide. The largest family is the Phasianidae, which includes the quails, partridges and peacocks. Other families include grouse and guans, while the megapodes are a group of island fowl known for incubating eggs in heaps of rotting plants and even volcanic ash.

Great Curassow

Crax rubra

Both sexes of curassow have curly crests of feathers on their heads. The male's plumage is mainly almost black, while the females take on three colour forms in different regions, ranging from reddish-brown to a striped pattern. The bird forages in leaf litter on the forest floor for fruits and other food.

FACT FILE	
Length:	1m (3ft 3in)
Weight:	4.8kg (10lb 10oz)
Distribution:	Southern Mexico to Ecuador
Habitat:	Tropical rainforest
Diet:	Fruits, berries and seeds
Status (IUCN Red List):	Least concern

Mikado Pheasant

Syrmaticus mikado

This species is the national bird of Taiwan. Local people know it as the 'king of the mist' because it lives in the island's mountainous interior among the rhododendron thickets that clothe the slopes. The large males have a long shimmering tail and striking red cheeks, in contrast to the females' brown plumage.

FACT FILE	
Length:	86cm (34in) including tail
Weight:	1.3kg (2lb 12oz)
Distribution:	Taiwan
Habitat:	Dense undergrowth
Diet:	Seeds, leaves and insects
Status (IUCN Red List):	Near threatened

Crimson Horned Pheasant

Tragopan satyra

It is not unusual for a male pheasant to have colourful plumage, but few match that of this Himalayan species. Also known as the satyr tragopan, this bird is covered in black-edged white spots, or ocelli, scattered over the deep crimson and brownish plumage. The female is a much duller brown.

FACT FILE	
Length:	70cm (28in)
Weight:	2kg (4lb 6oz)
Distribution:	Kashmir to central China
Habitat:	Mountain forest
Diet:	Insects and plants
Status (IUCN Red List):	Near threatened

Congo Peafowl

Afropavo congensis

This beautiful peafowl was unknown to scientists until the 1930s. Before that, the only evidence of this resplendent bird was the feathers used in traditional headdresses. This species is the only African member of the pheasant family; all others are natives of Asia and Europe.

FACT FILE	
Length:	70cm (28in)
Weight:	2kg (4lb 6oz)
Distribution:	Congo River basin
Habitat:	Tropical rainforest
Diet:	Fallen fruits and insects
Status (IUCN Red List):	Vulnerable

Reeve's Pheasant

Syrmaticus reevesii

The males of this species grow some of the longest feathers of any bird. The splendid tail makes up almost two-thirds of the total body length. Females have a shorter tail and their facial patterns are more muted than the males' striking black-and-white masks.

FACT FILE	
Length:	2.1m (6ft 10in) including tail
Weight:	1.5kg (3lb 5oz)
Distribution:	Central China
Habitat:	Forests
Diet:	Fruits, seeds and insects
Status (IUCN Red List):	Vulnerable

Hoatzin

Opisthocomus hoazin

The hoatzin is a very curious species that has provided a puzzle for scientists. It was traditionally classified as a gamebird – local people call the Amazonian species the 'stinky turkey' because its meat is less than tasty. However, recent studies have shown that despite outward looks, the hoatzin is more closely related to cuckoos.

FACT FILE	
Length:	60cm (23½in)
Weight:	790g (28oz)
Distribution:	Amazon and Orinoco River basins
Habitat:	Forest bordering rivers
Diet:	Mainly leaves
Status (IUCN Red List):	Least concern

The hoatzin is a strange bird with a small head and large wings, although it flies poorly. It lives in small flocks in the riverine forests of South America. It has an unusually large crop in the chest, which serves as a fermentation tank, digesting tough leaves. The almost naked chicks can crawl on branches soon after hatching.

Bill
The hoatzin's jaw muscles are very strong and its bill works like a pair of clippers, cutting through tough leaves.

WEAK WINGS
The bulbous breast of the hoatzin is not packed with flight muscles like most birds, but filled with the crop. Its weak wings are used really only to flutter between branches.

CLAWED WINGBONE
In a feature that mirrors those of the most ancient birds, hoatzin chicks have claws on the tips of some wingbones to help them clamber around.

TAIL
The hoatzin climbs through the trees more than it flies, and its wide tail is used as a balance and prop.

Waders and Shorebirds

A huge number of birds from multiple families live along the edge of water, especially the tidal zones. Many of these shorebirds are long-legged waders, while others feed on wet mud and sand, moving with the ebb and flow of the tide. Other birds, like the skuas, launch hunting raids out at sea from a coastal base.

Jerdon's Courser

Rhinoptilus bitorquatus

Although coursers are classified as wading birds due to their close relationship to oystercatchers and sheathbills, they do not forage in water. This rare Indian species wades through the patchy grass and scrub in the Eastern Ghat mountains. The name 'courser' refers to its habit of living on the run, stopping only when it spots food.

FACT FILE	
Length:	27cm (10½in)
Weight:	300g (10½oz)
Distribution:	Eastern Ghats, India
Habitat:	Dry scrub
Diet:	Insects
Status (IUCN Red List):	Critically endangered

Southern Lapwing

Vanellus chilensis

The southern lapwing lives across South America, but avoids the jungles of the Amazon and the soaring peaks of the Andes. It hunts at night, running along the banks or through nearby grasslands, stopping suddenly to watch for any insects or other prey attempting to scramble out of the bird's path.

FACT FILE	
Length:	38cm (15in)
Weight:	420g (15oz)
Distribution:	South America
Habitat:	Lakes and river banks
Diet:	Insects and other invertebrates
Status (IUCN Red List):	Least concern

Lesser Sand Plover

Charadrius mongolus

These little birds makes big migrations each year. In summer, they breed in the north of eastern Siberia, fuelling themselves and their chicks on the insects that flourish in the short summer. As autumn arrives, the birds head south to India, South Africa and even Australia to see out the northern winter on tidal mudflats and beaches.

FACT FILE	
Length:	21cm (8¼in)
Weight:	85g (3oz)
Distribution:	Asia, Africa and Australia
Habitat:	Boggy tundra and tidal flats
Diet:	Insects, worms, snails, shellfish
Status (IUCN Red List):	Least concern

Black-faced Sheathbill

Chionis minor

The name 'sheathbill' refers to the horny covering on the top of the bird's bill, partially protecting the nostrils. This species is a bold scavenger, gobbling everything from seal placenta to faeces if the opportunity arises. The sheathbill can fly and swim well, but is most likely to be seen on the ground.

FACT FILE	
Length:	40cm (16in)
Weight:	525g (18oz)
Distribution:	Indian Ocean sector of Antarctica
Habitat:	Coastlines
Diet:	Seaweed, eggs, fish and carrion
Status (IUCN Red List):	Least concern

Long-tailed Skua

Stercorarius longicaudus

The smaller skuas are also known as jaegers, the German word for 'hunter'. This skua species does sometimes hunt fish and small mammals such as lemmings, but the birds are more likely to be pirates – robbing other seabirds of their catch.

FACT FILE	
Length:	55cm (21½in)
Weight:	310g (11oz)
Distribution:	Arctic and northern oceans
Habitat:	Coasts and islands
Diet:	Fish, small mammals and eggs
Status (IUCN Red List):	Least concern

Sandpipers

There are 81 species of sandpiper, forming the family Scolopacidae. The sandpipers are close cousins of the plovers and avocets. They all have long pointed bills used to probe for food, and most – but not all – live in wetland habitats. Many sandpiper species are migratory and arrive on shorelines in great flocks, almost overnight.

Eurasian Woodcock

Scolopax rusticola

The woodcock spends the summer far from the coast in the dense undergrowth of woodlands, in northern Europe and Siberia. In winter, the birds head south to avoid the long, frozen winter and can be found on mudflats, where they probe the ground for worms and shellfish with their long bills.

FACT FILE	
Length:	38cm (15in)
Weight:	210g (7½oz)
Distribution:	Europe and Asia
Habitat:	Woodlands and mudflats
Diet:	Worms
Status (IUCN Red List):	Least concern

Spotted Redshank

Tringa erythropus

Like many of its relatives, the redshank is a long-distance migrator. It breeds in the bogs of the far north of Scandinavia and Russia, laying its eggs in a scrape in the ground. As these wetlands begin to freeze, the bird's dark summer plumage fades to grey and it heads to wetlands and coastal waters further south.

FACT FILE	
Length:	33cm (13in)
Weight:	180g (6oz)
Distribution:	Europe, Asia and Africa
Habitat:	Wetlands
Diet:	Insects, worms and shellfish
Status (IUCN Red List):	Least concern

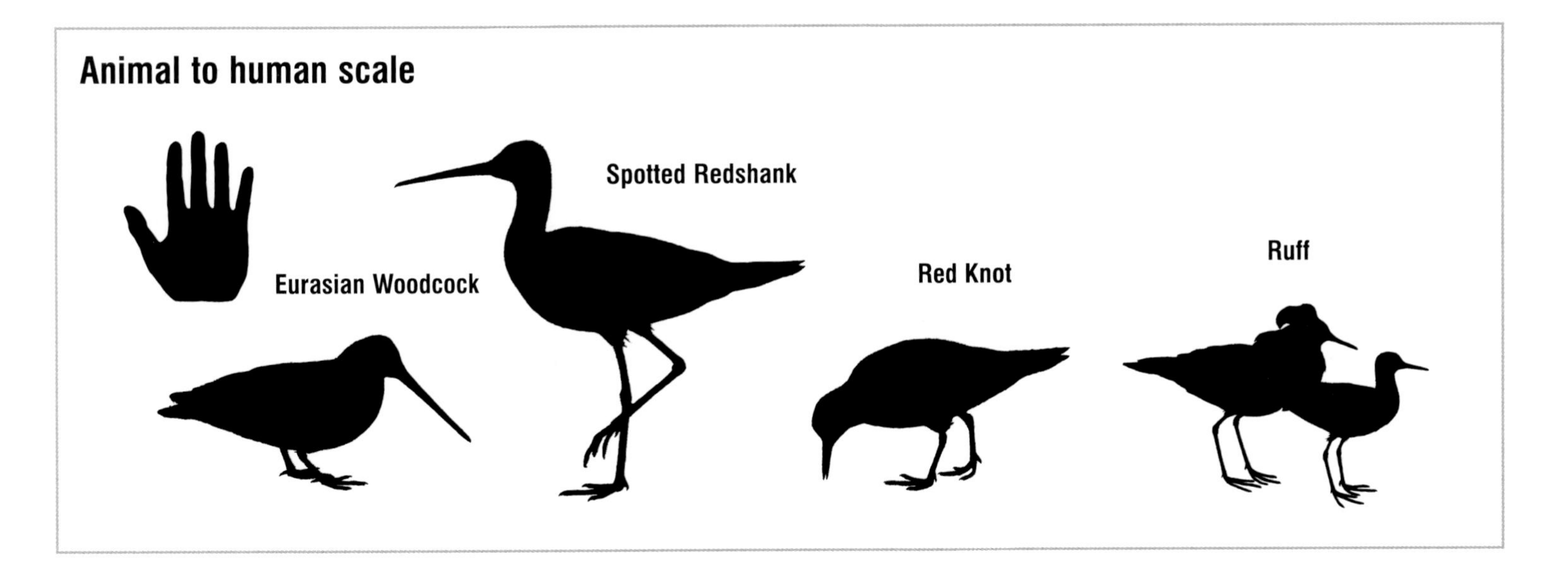

Red Knot

Calidris canutus

The red knot is a cosmopolitan species, with breeding grounds that circle the Arctic ocean. After the short northern summer, the birds make extraordinary migrations covering thousands of kilometres. Some subspecies end up on the northern coast of Australia and the tip of South America.

FACT FILE	
Length:	25cm (10in)
Weight:	220g (7¾oz)
Distribution:	Worldwide
Habitat:	Tundra and mudflats
Diet:	Insects, worms and shellfish
Status (IUCN Red List):	Least concern

Ruff

Philomachus pugnax

In the breeding season, male ruffs develop long tufts and an elaborate feathered collar, hence the name. The male birds gather in a display arena called a lek, where they strut and engage in mock-fights to attract the females – known as reeves. Darker-ruffed males are generally dominant.

FACT FILE	
Length:	32cm (12½in)
Weight:	180g (6oz)
Distribution:	Europe, Asia, Africa and Australia
Habitat:	Wetlands and grassland
Diet:	Insects, worms and seeds
Status (IUCN Red List):	Least concern

Gulls and Relatives

Often described as seabirds, gulls are actually very much tied to land and rarely venture too far out to sea. In fact, many opportunistic species do well in cities, where tall buildings take the place of cliffs, and rubbish spills substitute for food scattered along the shore.

Pacific Gull

Larus pacificus

This large gull is often mistaken for an albatross. It is not a common species and does not form large crowds. Instead, it can be seen floating effortlessly on the sea breezes or wandering the shoreline looking for carrion and dead fish. It is also known to crack captured shellfish by dropping them from a great height onto rocks.

FACT FILE	
Length:	68cm (26in)
Weight:	1kg (2lb 4oz)
Distribution:	Southern Australia
Habitat:	Coasts
Diet:	Fish and shellfish
Status (IUCN Red List):	Least concern

Greater Black-backed Gull

Larus marinus

The largest species of gull has a conspicuous red spot on the bill. Chicks beg for food by tapping the spot on the parent's bill, stimulating the parent to regurgitate food. These gulls are visitors to rubbish tips, sometimes miles from the sea, where they prey on pigeons and rodents.

FACT FILE	
Length:	79cm (31in)
Weight:	2.2kg (4lb 13oz)
Distribution:	North Atlantic
Habitat:	Coasts and coastal waters
Diet:	Fish, pigeons, rats and mice
Status (IUCN Red List):	Least concern

Common Tern

Sterna hirundo

The main difference between a gull and a tern is that the latter has a distinctive forked tail, similar to the unrelated swallow's. Common terns breed in huge colonies, and large flocks migrate southwards in winter. Terns hunt by hovering over water – both fresh and salt – and then plunge-diving to catch their prey.

FACT FILE	
Length:	36cm (14in)
Weight:	110g (4oz)
Distribution:	Breeds in north, winters south of equator
Habitat:	Coasts and inland waters
Diet:	Fish and prawns
Status (IUCN Red List):	Least concern

Inca Tern

Larosterna inca

This unusual tern is restricted to the coasts of Peru and Chile, where the chilled but food-rich waters of the Humboldt Current supports large shoals of small fish. The Inca tern has a unique moustache of white feathers on both sides of its head. It nests in small burrows on rocky cliffs.

FACT FILE	
Length:	40cm (16in)
Weight:	130g (4½oz
Distribution:	Peru and Chile
Habitat:	Cold coastal waters
Diet:	Fish
Status (IUCN Red List):	Near threatened

Black Skimmer

Rynchops niger

Aptly named, this bird has a unique method of feeding by skimming along the water surface with its bill open. The lower mandible is about 2.5cm (1in) longer than the upper; it cuts through the water to scoop up small fish, shrimps and other items.

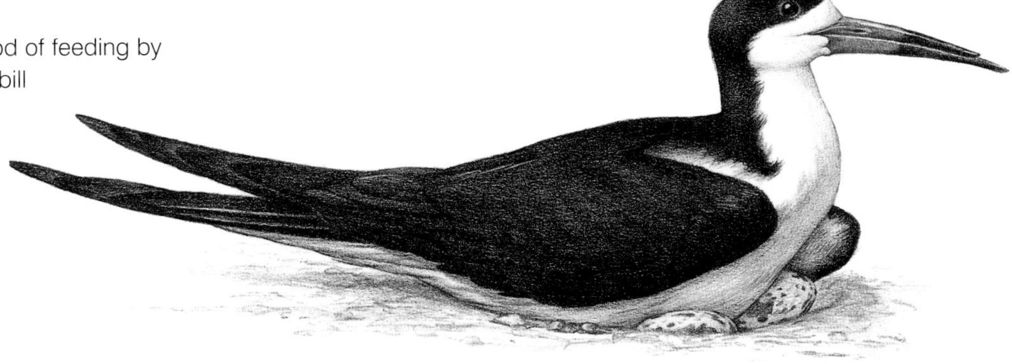

FACT FILE	
Length:	51cm (20in)
Weight:	310g (11oz)
Distribution:	North and South America
Habitat:	Coasts and major rivers and lakes
Diet:	Fish and other marine creatures
Status (IUCN Red List):	Least concern

Atlantic Puffin

Fratercula arctica

With its big, colourful bill, the common puffin is one of the most comical-looking birds. They look similar to the penguins of the Southern Hemisphere, and fill much the same ecological niche. The biggest difference is that puffins are cliff birds and can fly, often swooping fast and low over the water.

PLUMAGE
A thick layer of feathers forms a water- and windproof coat that keeps water away from the skin. If the skin got wet, the puffin would soon get very cold in the strong winds.

FACT FILE	
Length:	38cm (15in)
Weight:	550g (19½oz)
Distribution:	North Atlantic
Habitat:	Breeds on coasts; winters at sea
Diet:	Fish and other marine creatures
Status (IUCN Red List):	Least concern

Like penguins, puffins use their waterproof wings to fly underwater when chasing small fish for food. They carry fish back to their young in their massive bills. The puffins nest on cliffs in large colonies. Breeding pairs work together to dig burrows in the soft earth with their bills.

WINTER PLUMAGE
In the autumn, the puffin sheds the colourful plates on its bill, showing a grey breeding colouring.

WINGS
The short, narrow wings are the right shape for diving into the water. To get back into the air, puffins must beat their wet wings very quickly.

BILL
The bill has a fleshy hinge that helps the mouth to open wide. Puffins hold one fish with their tongue against the upper mandible, leaving the lower one free to grab another.

Pigeons

It is sometimes hard to imagine that something so common as a pigeon can be special. However, they are some of the strongest flyers around, with a third of their body weight taken up by the flight muscles in their pigeon chests. There are 300 species of pigeon worldwide. The largest is almost 1m (3ft 3in) tall.

Rock Pigeon

Columba livia

The billions of feral pigeons in towns and cities worldwide are all ultimately descended from the rock dove. These descendants are so common that truly wild rock doves live only in relatively isolated areas of mountains and cliffs. Pigeons do so well in cities because there are few predators, such as falcons, to keep their numbers down.

FACT FILE	
Length:	33cm (13in)
Weight:	360g (12¾oz)
Distribution:	Worldwide
Habitat:	Rocky cliffs in the wild
Diet:	Plant matter and rubbish
Status (IUCN Red List):	Least concern

Common Wood Pigeon

Columba palumbus

While the rock pigeon dominates the cities, the wood pigeon is another opportunist that has spread widely through suburban neighbourhoods from its original habitat of deciduous and conifer woodland. Wood pigeons are easily distinguished from the city birds by their large size and stout build.

FACT FILE	
Length:	44cm (17in)
Weight:	500g (17½oz)
Distribution:	Northern Hemisphere
Habitat:	Woodland, gardens and farmland
Diet:	Seeds, buds and nuts
Status (IUCN Red List):	Least concern

Nicobar Pigeon

Caloenas nicobarica

Also known as vulterine pigeons, these birds fly in large flocks between the islands of Indonesia, the Andaman Sea, and along the coasts of the Malay Peninsula and Indochina. The birds fly in single file, with each bird following the white tail markings of the bird in front.

FACT FILE	
Length:	40cm (16in)
Weight:	600g (21oz)
Distribution:	Southeast Asia
Habitat:	Forests
Diet:	Seeds, fruits and buds
Status (IUCN Red List):	Near threatened

Domestic Pigeon

Columba livia

The domestic pigeon, a descendant of the rock pigeon, was domesticated at least 5000 years ago. Many pigeon fanciers, as pigeon owners are known, keep their birds for homing and racing. There are more than 300 breeds of 'fancy' pigeons, developed for their ornamental feathers and unusual calls.

FACT FILE	
Length:	33cm (13in)
Weight:	360g (12¾oz)
Distribution:	Worldwide
Habitat:	All regions and climates
Diet:	Grains and seeds
Status (IUCN Red List):	N/A

Tooth-billed Pigeon

Didunculus strigirostris

This species is the national bird of Samoa. This Pacific island is the only place in the world where this unusual pigeon lives. It has no close relatives and its generic name, *Didunculus*, means 'little dodo'. It has been speculated that this species is a link between the pigeons and that now-extinct iconic island species.

FACT FILE	
Length:	33cm (13in)
Weight:	360g (12¾oz)
Distribution:	Samoa
Habitat:	Forests
Diet:	Mahogany fruits
Status (IUCN Red List):	Endangered

Old World Parrots

There are more than 300 species of parrots living across the tropical regions and further afield in the Southern Hemisphere. The Old World as a whole has fewer species than other regions. There are no parrots living in Europe; the world's most northerly species is the slatey-headed parrot of Afghanistan.

Alexandrine Parakeet

Psittacula eupatria

Named after Alexander the Great, who is said to have been one of the first people to export parrots from India to Europe, the male Alexandrine parakeet is a popular pet species; the birds are easy to tame and are good talkers. In the wild, Alexandrine parakeets form noisy flocks at dusk.

FACT FILE	
Length:	61cm (24in)
Weight:	260g (9oz)
Distribution:	South and Southeast Asia
Habitat:	Forest, woodland and fields
Diet:	Seeds, nuts, blossoms and fruit
Status (IUCN Red List):	Least concern

African Grey Parrot

Psittacus erithacus

The African gray is considered to be the best talker of all the parrots. It is a highly intelligent species, probably the brightest of all birds. To engage their lively brains, birds should be provided with puzzle toys and foraging toys, in which they must learn how to extract food from the toy.

FACT FILE	
Length:	40cm (16in)
Weight:	400g (14 oz)
Distribution:	Western and central Africa
Habitat:	Rainforest
Diet:	Seeds, nuts, vegetables and fruit
Status (IUCN Red List):	Near threatened

Fischer's Lovebirds

Agapornis fischeri

This small parrot is named after the nineteenth-century German explorer Gustav Fischer. It is popular with pet owners because of its gorgeous multicoloured plumage. These highly sociable birds should always be kept with a companion in a roomy cage or aviary.

FACT FILE	
Length:	15cm (6in)
Weight:	55g (2oz)
Distribution:	Tanzania
Habitat:	Trees on grassy plains
Diet:	Seeds, vegetables and fruit
Status (IUCN Red List):	Near threatened

Plum-headed Parakeet

Psittacula cyanocephala

These are highly sociable birds and will tolerate being in a mixed aviary unless they are breeding, when they can become more aggressive. This species has a variety of melodic calls, a shrill note when in flight, and a potentially loud scream.

FACT FILE	
Length:	33cm (13in)
Weight:	85g (3oz)
Distribution:	South Asia
Habitat:	Forest and woodland
Diet:	Seeds, blossoms, buds and fruit
Status (IUCN Red List):	Least concern

Rose-ringed Parakeet

Psittacula krameri

Also known as the ringnecked parakeet, this was one of the first pet parrot species. The Indian subspecies of the rose-ringed parakeet has established large feral populations of escaped and introduced birds in many European cities, Japan, Florida, and Israel. There is a particularly large population in southeast England.

FACT FILE	
Length:	40cm (16in)
Weight:	140g (5oz)
Distribution:	African subspecies: Guinea to Sudan; Indian subspecies: India, Pakistan and Nepal
Habitat:	Forests to fields
Diet:	Seeds, nuts, fruit, vegetables, buds
Status (IUCN Red List):	Least concern

American Parrots

In 1904, the Carolina parakeet became extinct, leaving no other parrot species in the mainland of North America. Today's American parrots barely reach the southern border of the United States, although the jungles of Central and South America are home to the macaws, some of the largest parrot species of all.

Scarlet Macaw

Ara macao

The scarlet macaw has been known to live for 75 years, which makes keeping a scarlet macaw as a pet a big commitment. The birds require extremely large cages and frequent interaction with their owners. In the wild, their hooked bills rip into unripe fruits, and flocks make frequent visits to salt licks to top up on essential minerals.

FACT FILE	
Length:	84cm (33in)
Weight:	1.2kg (2lb 8oz)
Distribution:	Central and South America
Habitat:	Rainforest, woodland, savannah
Diet:	Nuts and fruit
Status (IUCN Red List):	Least concern

Military Macaw

Ara militaris

Named after the often vibrant dress uniforms of Latin American armies, this medium-sized macaw is now rare in the wild but is bred in captivity for the pet trade. These birds enjoy human interaction and can develop a large vocabulary. They can live for 60 years in the wild.

FACT FILE	
Length:	74cm (29in)
Weight:	900g (32oz)
Distribution:	Mexico to Argentina
Habitat:	Forest and woodland
Diet:	Seeds, nuts and fruit
Status (IUCN Red List):	Vulnerable

Blue-and-yellow Macaw

Ara ararauna

This bird is one of the longest parrots. All macaws have relatively bare, light-coloured facial patches. The powerful beak and harsh, loud voice of such a large macaw makes this species unsuitable for most first-time owners. Its white face turns pink when excited. The black beak is used for crushing nuts and hanging from trees in the wild.

FACT FILE	
Length:	86cm (34in)
Weight:	1.3kg (2lb 12oz)
Distribution:	South America
Habitat:	Bush and scrub close to water
Diet:	Seeds, nuts, flowers and fruit
Status (IUCN Red List):	Least concern

Thick-billed Parrot

Rhynchopsitta pachyrhyncha

In its natural habitat, the thick-billed parrot feeds almost exclusively on pine seeds, using its big beak to prise them from cones. The species has been endangered by logging of its habitat, and birds are frequently taken from the wild for the pet trade. This is the only species that is seen wild – just occasionally in the United States.

FACT FILE	
Length:	38cm (15in)
Weight:	300g (10½oz)
Distribution:	Sierra Madre Occidental, Mexico
Habitat:	Mountain conifer forests
Diet:	Pine seeds and acorns
Status (IUCN Red List):	Endangered

Blue-fronted Amazon

Amazona aestiva

The amazon parrots are among the best mimics of the human voice, and are commonly kept as caged birds. It lives in more open forest than many South American parrots, feeding and nesting in the treetops and often forming large groups. They may raid fields for grain.

FACT FILE	
Length:	37cm (14½in)
Weight:	450g (16oz)
Distribution:	Brazil, Bolivia and Argentina
Habitat:	Forests
Diet:	Fruits, seeds, nuts, buds, flowers
Status (IUCN Red List):	Least concern

Kakapo

Strigops habroptilus

The kakapo is unique in several ways. It is the heaviest, if not the longest, of all parrots, with males weighing up to 3.4kg (7lb 8oz). It is also the only flightless parrot, living mainly on the ground, but clambering into trees and bushes for food, then sometimes gliding down.

FACT FILE	
Length:	64cm (25in)
Weight:	3.4kg (7lb 8oz)
Distribution:	Few New Zealand islands
Habitat:	Wooded slopes
Diet:	Fruit, berries, nuts and seeds
Status (IUCN Red List):	Critically endangered

The kakapo is one of the few nocturnal parrots, and also one of the rarest. Predators such as rats and dogs – introduced first by Maori settlers and then by Europeans – gradually killed the defenceless kakapos. Transferring survivors to small predator-free islands has saved the species for now, but only around 60 birds survive.

WINGS
The kakapo is too heavy to fly off the ground, but its wings are used to slow its descent as it jumps from bushes to the ground, perhaps mirroring the behaviour of bird's non-flying dinosaur ancestors.

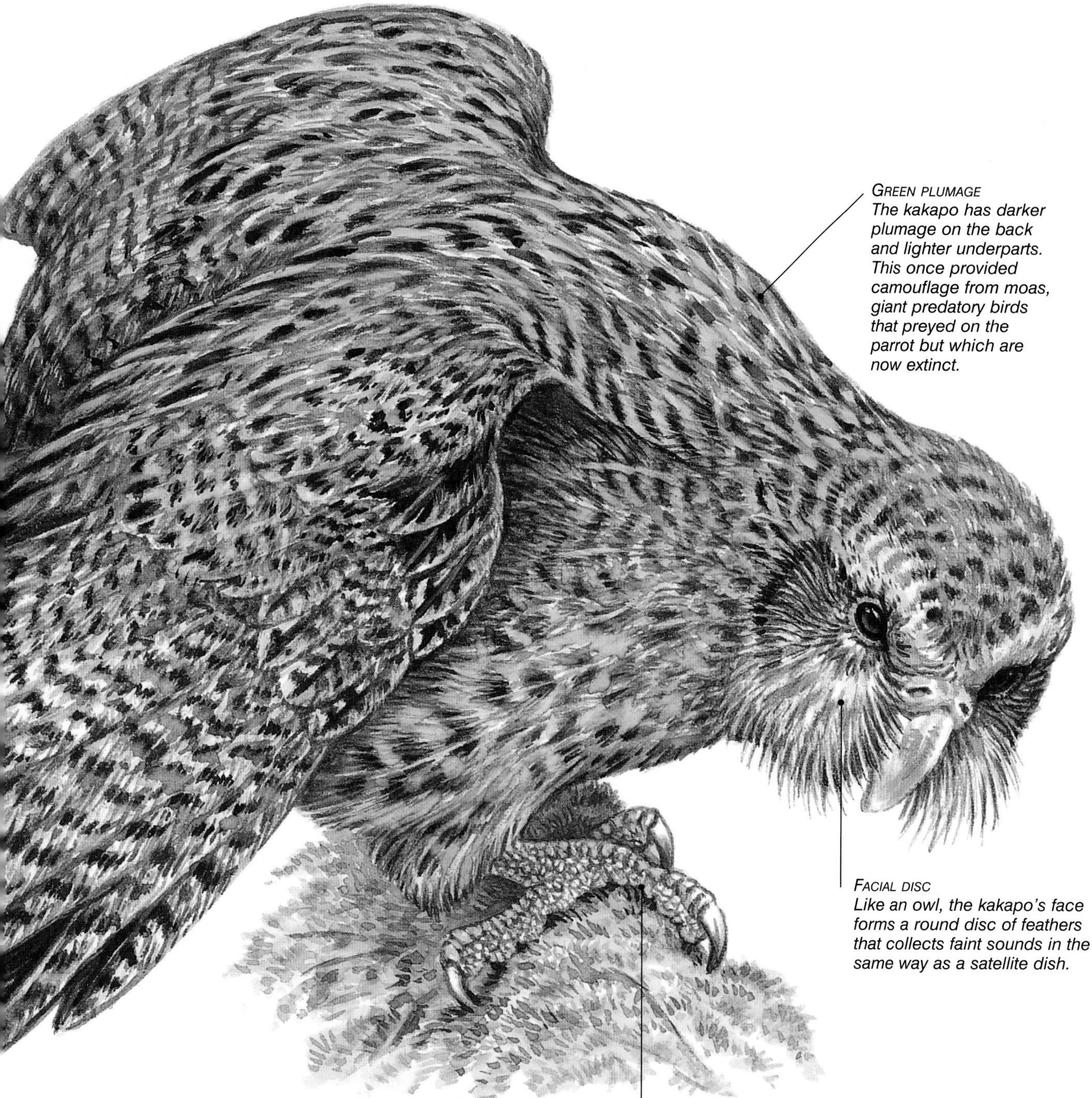

GREEN PLUMAGE
The kakapo has darker plumage on the back and lighter underparts. This once provided camouflage from moas, giant predatory birds that preyed on the parrot but which are now extinct.

FACIAL DISC
Like an owl, the kakapo's face forms a round disc of feathers that collects faint sounds in the same way as a satellite dish.

FEET
Like all parrots, the kakapo has two toes facing forwards and two facing back. This provides a solid platform and helps the bird to grip branches as it climbs.

Parrots of Australia and New Zealand

Australasia is home to many unusual species of parrot, including the lories, which lick nectar with feathery tongues, and the budgerigar, the only domestic species of parrot. (Its name means 'good food' in an Aboriginal language.) In New Zealand, parrots have evolved to live in the most unusual ways.

Salmon-crested Cockatoo

Cacatua moluccensis

Also known as the Moluccan cockatoo, this species has a particularly loud call. Like other large cockatoos, it can engage in destructive behaviour when kept in captivity. Despite being a popular pet, the species is endangered, so trade in birds trapped in the wild is illegal.

FACT FILE	
Length:	50cm (19½in)
Weight:	925g (33oz)
Distribution:	Indonesia
Habitat:	Scrub and woodland
Diet:	Fresh fruits
Status (IUCN Red List):	Vulnerable

Galah

Cacatua roseicapilla

This pretty cockatoo is native to Australia, where it is one of the most common birds. Also known as the rose-breasted cockatoo, the galah lives in huge flocks. This social behaviour makes these birds very rewarding, and very chatty, pets. However, as with all parrots, they are long-lived and tend to suffer if they outlive their owners.

FACT FILE	
Length:	35cm (13¾in)
Weight:	400g (14oz)
Distribution:	Australia
Habitat:	Open habitats to urban areas
Diet:	Seeds, nuts, berries and fruits
Status (IUCN Red List):	Least concern

Cockatiel

Nymphicus hollandicus

The smallest birds in the cockatoo family, cockatiels are the second most popular caged bird, after the budgerigar. Males and females usually have grey plumage with orange patches on the ear areas. Cockatiels are better at mimicking whistles and ringtones than speech. They can even copy the sound of flushing toilets.

FACT FILE	
Length:	33cm (13in)
Weight:	110g (4oz)
Distribution:	Inland Australia
Habitat:	Bush and scrub close to water
Diet:	Seeds, nuts, berries and fruits
Status (IUCN Red List):	Least concern

Kea

Nestor notabilis

Named after its loud 'keea' call, the kea is a parrot that lives like a raven, scavenging in rocky mountainous habitats. It amuses tourists with its thieving habits but is less popular with sheep farmers. Keas are known to occasionally kill sheep, although they tend only to scavenge on the carcasses of fallen stock.

FACT FILE	
Length:	48cm (19in)
Weight:	1kg (2lb 4oz)
Distribution:	South Island, New Zealand
Habitat:	Mountains
Diet:	Carrion, insects and grubs
Status (IUCN Red List):	Vulnerable

Pesquet's Parrot

Psittrichas fulgidus

This endangered parrot is native to New Guinea. It has bare black facial skin and a fairly long bill, giving the bird a vulture-like profile – and providing it with its alternative name, the vulturine parrot. The bare face is an adaptation to avoid feather matting from the sticky figs that are this bird's sole food.

FACT FILE	
Length:	46cm (18in)
Weight:	800g (28¼oz)
Distribution:	New Guinea
Habitat:	Forest
Diet:	Figs
Status (IUCN Red List):	Vulnerable

Eclectus Parrot

Eclectus roratus

Males and females of this species look completely different, exhibiting the most extreme sexual dimorphism of all the parrots. The females are bright red and purple with a black beak; the males are largely green, with a blue or red tail and wing feathers, and sport an orange upper mandible and a black lower one.

FACT FILE	
Length:	35cm (13¾in)
Weight:	600g (21oz)
Distribution:	S.E. Asia to N.E. Australia and Solomon Islands
Habitat:	Rainforest canopy
Diet:	Seeds, nuts, leaves and fruit
Status (IUCN Red List):	Least concern

When they were first observed, it was thought that the eclectus cocks were a different species from the hens. Cocks tend to make better pets, because the hens can be aggressive. Neither sex will become a proficient talker. Ten Eclectus subspecies have been observed across Indonesia and the Pacific islands.

Budgerigar

Melopsittacus undulatus

While many eclectus parrots and others like it are kept as pets, no other parrot has been so thoroughly domesticated as the budgerigar. Millions of these bird live in cages around the world, and there are several ornamental breeds with bright plumage. In the wilds of its native Australia, the bird is sometimes seen in flocks numbering in the millions. The flocks travel long distances to find food and water. The name is possibly derived from the Aboriginal term for 'tasty', and the birds are a traditional food for some native peoples.

Eclectus Parrot

Cuckoos and Relatives

The cuckoo is one of the most iconic birds. It is named after its flutey double call, and has long been associated with the coming of spring. Behind the romance, many cuckoos are brood parasites, leaving their eggs in the nests of other birds for their chicks to be raised by another species.

Chestnut-winged Cuckoo

Clamator coromandus

In the case of the red-winged crested cuckoo, the female chooses babblers and laughing thrushes to dupe into raising her chick. Unlike the common cuckoo and other species, the young of this species do not evict the foster parents' true offspring from the nest, but are raised as part of the brood.

FACT FILE	
Length:	45cm (17¾in)
Weight:	290g (10oz)
Distribution:	India, China, Southeast Asia
Habitat:	Woodland, open forest, scrubland
Diet:	Mainly insects
Status (IUCN Red List):	Least concern

Channel-billed Cuckoo

Scythrops novaehollandiae

This unusual species is the largest type of cuckoo, and the largest brood parasite in the world. It lays a single egg in the nests of crows, butcherbirds and Australian magpies. The cuckoo chick dominates the food supply from its foster parents and the host's chicks usually starve.

FACT FILE	
Length:	68cm (26in)
Weight:	925g (33oz)
Distribution:	Australia, New Guinea, Indonesia
Habitat:	Forests and mangroves
Diet:	Fruits, figs, insects and seeds
Status (IUCN Red List):	Least concern

Yellow-billed Cuckoo

Coccyzus americanus

This American cuckoo is not a parasite but forms strong pair bonds. Both parents work to build the nest; they also share the incubation and feed the chicks for a week or two after they hatch. The species is migratory, and heads into South America during the northern winter.

FACT FILE	
Length:	30cm (12in)
Weight:	55g (2oz)
Distribution:	Eastern N. America and S. America
Habitat:	Woodlands and shrubs
Diet:	Insects
Status (IUCN Red List):	Least concern

Greater Roadrunner

Geococcyx californianus

Roadrunners are not strong flyers and prefer to run and walk. The male even chases a female on foot during courtship. The desert birds will eat almost anything they can get their bills on. They leap into the air to snatch insects and march through scrubland, dashing forwards when they spot prey.

FACT FILE	
Length:	61cm (24in)
Weight:	290g (10oz)
Distribution:	Southwest United States
Habitat:	Deserts
Diet:	Reptiles, invertebrates and birds
Status (IUCN Red List):	Least concern

Great Blue Turaco

Corythaeola cristata

This colourful species is the largest of the Cuculiformes, the cuckoo-like birds. It belongs to a separate African family and is related to the go-away birds (so named because their calls supposedly sound like 'go away'). The turacos appear to form a link between the passerines and other land birds.

FACT FILE	
Length:	76cm (30in)
Weight:	1.2kg (2lb 8oz)
Distribution:	Central Africa
Habitat:	Forest
Diet:	Fruits
Status (IUCN Red List):	Least concern

Owls

These night-time hunters fly on silent wings. Most birds create a swishing sound as they fly, as the wings cut through the air. However, an owl's wings are fitted with a stealth system. Velvety feathers on the leading edge split the air rushing over the wings into tiny streams. Each stream creates a sound, but they are too faint to hear.

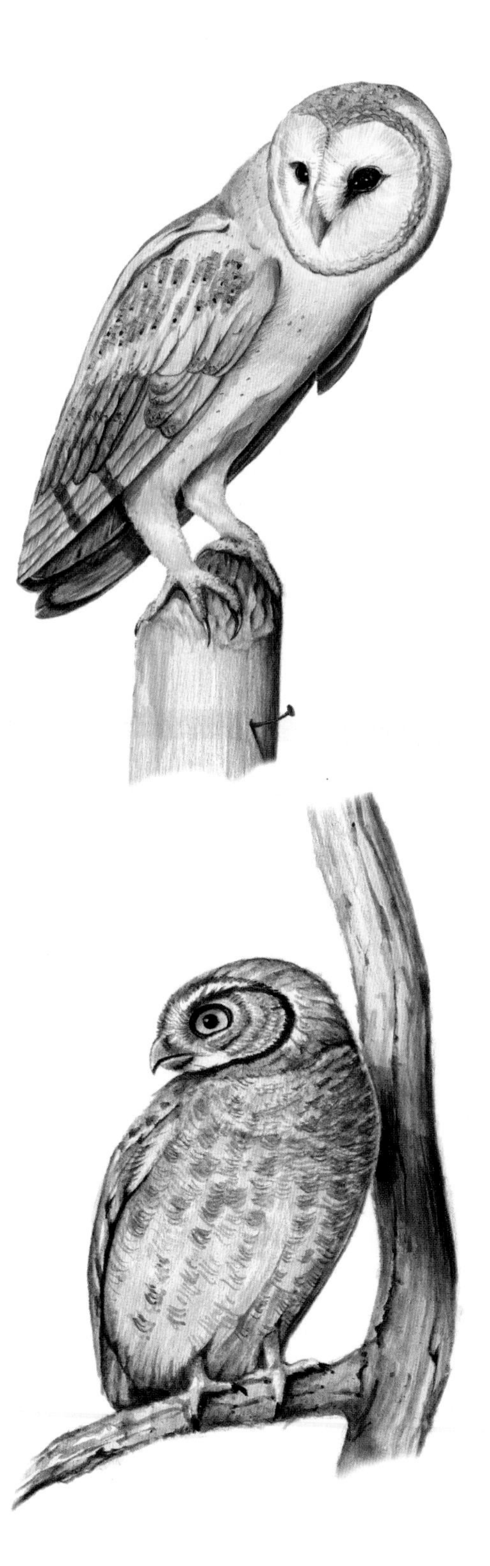

Barn Owl

Tyto alba

Barn owls have a heart-shaped facial disc. They have probably lived near human settlements for thousands of years, and their eerie shrieking call and ghostly appearance when flying overhead at night have no doubt given rise to many legends of haunted ruins.

FACT FILE	
Length:	36cm (14in)
Weight:	500g (17½oz)
Distribution:	Worldwide except extreme north
Habitat:	Open country with trees
Diet:	Small mammals and small birds
Status (IUCN Red List):	Least concern

Elf Owl

Micrathene whitneyi

This is the world's smallest owl species. It hunts at night, mainly for insects captured in the air or on the ground, and also preys on small mammals and snakes. Elf owls are good climbers and often clamber through low vegetation in search of food, beating the leaves to dislodge prey items.

FACT FILE	
Length:	14cm (5½in)
Weight:	55g (2oz)
Distribution:	Southwest USA and Mexico
Habitat:	Desert and dry woodlands
Diet:	Insects
Status (IUCN Red List):	Least concern

Long-eared Owl

Asio otus

Those long 'ears' are, in fact, plumes of feathers meant to make the owl looks longer than they really are. When perched, both sexes – although females are larger – press down the feathers and stretch the neck to maximize the effect. The purpose is to make the medium-sized owl look like a tree stump.

FACT FILE	
Length:	40cm (16in)
Weight:	340g (12oz)
Distribution:	Northern Hemisphere
Habitat:	Thick vegetation
Diet:	Voles and mice
Status (IUCN Red List):	Least concern

Little Owl

Athene noctua

This widespread species is the most diurnal of the owls and often hunts during the day, although it is also active at night. It sits and waits for prey, swooping down from a perch to grab larger animals with its feet, while smaller ones are snatched in the mouth.

FACT FILE	
Length:	23cm (9in)
Weight:	85g (3oz)
Distribution:	Europe, Asia and East Africa
Habitat:	Open country
Diet:	Small mammals, birds and reptiles
Status (IUCN Red List):	Least concern

Nightbirds

While the owls dominate the nocturnal bird world, hunting for large prey, other nightbirds, such as nightjars, nighthawks and frogmouths, prey on smaller animals – mostly insects. The nightjars are found worldwide and number more than 72 species, while the frogmouths, or false owls, live in southern Asia and Australia.

Spotted-eared Nightjar

Eurostopodus argus

There is still debate over whether this largely Australian species belongs to the main nightjar family or has a separate lineage, known as the eared nightjars (thanks to some feathered ear tufts). Whatever the precise relationship, the bird uses typical nightbird defence tactics, sitting motionless pretending to be a broken branch during the day.

FACT FILE	
Length:	25cm (10in)
Weight:	110g (4oz)
Distribution:	Australia and Indonesia
Habitat:	Dry forests
Diet:	Insects
Status (IUCN Red List):	Least concern

Tawny Frogmouth

Podargus strigoides

Named frogmouth for its huge, gaping mouth, this species spends its day motionless on a branch, so well camouflaged that it looks like a dead tree stump. At dusk it watches the ground for prey and then flies down on its weak, rounded wings to pounce on it.

FACT FILE	
Length:	45cm (17¾in)
Weight:	250g (8¾oz)
Distribution:	Australia
Habitat:	Anywhere there are trees
Diet:	Ground-living insects
Status (IUCN Red List):	Least concern

Oilbird

Steatornis caripensis

Oilbirds nest in deep caves and emerge at night to feed on palm fruits. They have large eyes, although these are useless in the gloom of a cave, and they find their way by echolocation, like bats. They make a clicking noise and locate obstacles by the echo.

FACT FILE	
Length:	45cm (17¾in)
Weight:	250g (8¾oz)
Distribution:	Northern South America
Habitat:	Mountainous and coastal areas
Diet:	Oily tree fruits, especially palms
Status (IUCN Red List):	Least concern

Pauraque

Nyctidromus albicollis

This American nightjar lives as far north as Texas and extends all the way to southern Brazil. The pauraque is more terrestrial than other nightjars. It has long legs and bare toes to help it walk over rough ground. It spends the day on the ground and often runs for cover rather than flying away.

FACT FILE	
Length:	28cm (11in)
Weight:	190g (6¾oz)
Distribution:	North and South America
Habitat:	Open woodland and grasses
Diet:	Insects
Status (IUCN Red List):	Least concern

Swifts

As their name suggests, the swifts are fast-flying birds that make up the family Apodidae. There are 71 species, and the family name means 'without legs', referring to the birds' very short legs. The nests of certain cave-living Asian swifts are collected for bird's nest soup. Such nests are made from the birds' dried saliva.

American Black Swift

Nephoecetes niger

This is the largest swift species in North America. It has a patchy distribution and is mostly found in British Colombia and western Mexico. The swift is an aerial combatant and takes insects, such as flying ants, on the wing. The black swift frequently makes its nests behind waterfalls.

FACT FILE	
Length:	25cm (10in)
Weight:	50g (1¾oz)
Distribution:	Western North America
Habitat:	Mountain forests
Diet:	Flying insects
Status (IUCN Red List):	Least concern

Sabine's Spinetail

Rhaphidura sabini

The spinetail swifts have spiny feather tips extending beyond the end of their tails, helping them to be extremely fast flyers. They can exceed 100km/h (62mph) when swooping during courtship displays. The species is named after nineteenth-century naturalist Joseph Sabine.

FACT FILE	
Length:	13cm (5in)
Weight:	23g (¾oz)
Distribution:	Central Africa
Habitat:	Forest
Diet:	Insects
Status (IUCN Red List):	Least concern

Grey-rumped Treeswift

Hemiprocne longipennis

Belonging to the crested swift family (Hemiprocnidae), this species perches on a tree branch, ready to swoop down to catch any passing insects. It builds tiny nests, about 3cm (just over an inch) across, made from fragments of papery bark and feathers, glued together (and fixed to a thin branch) with the birds' saliva.

FACT FILE	
Length:	23cm (9in)
Weight:	85g (3oz)
Distribution:	Malaysia and Indonesia
Habitat:	Lowland forest edges
Diet:	Small flying insects
Status (IUCN Red List):	Least concern

Alpine Swift

Tachymarptis melba

Swifts are the one of the most aerial of birds. They have been tracked travelling more than 1600km (1000 miles) in three days, flying at more than 160km/h (100mph). They feed, drink, bathe, sleep and even mate in the air. Like other swifts, the Alpine swift catches small insects in its gaping mouth as it flies.

FACT FILE	
Length:	20cm (8in)
Weight:	100g (3½oz)
Distribution:	Southern Europe, Asia and Africa
Habitat:	Craggy uplands, cliffs, buildings
Diet:	Small flying insects
Status (IUCN Red List):	Least concern

Hummingbirds

The 315 species of the Trochilidae family are generally known as hummingbirds, thanks to the noise their delta-shaped wings make as they flap at incredible speed – up to 78 beats per second. Hummingbirds are the masters of high-speed flight and can hover in front of flowers as they lick nectar from blooms.

White-tipped Sicklebill

Eutoxeres aquila

The white-tipped sicklebill has evolved its strongly curved bill to feed on the nectar of heliconias and certain orchids that cannot be reached by other hummingbirds. As a consequence, they cannot feed from other flowers. The curved bill makes it awkward to feed while hovering, so the birds perch rather clumsily on their short legs.

FACT FILE	
Length:	13cm (5in)
Weight:	10g (⅓oz)
Distribution:	C. and S. America west of Andes
Habitat:	Lowland humid forest
Diet:	Nectar and insects
Status (IUCN Red List):	Least concern

Ecuadorian Hillstar

Oreotrochilus chimborazo

This is the highest living species of hummingbird, although several other hillstar species live above 4000m (13,120ft). It feeds in the grasslands, scrub and stunted woodlands that grow on the high slopes. It reduces its body temperature by night, becoming torpid (inactive) in order to conserve energy. It may in roost caves.

FACT FILE	
Length:	13cm (5in)
Weight:	10g (⅓oz)
Distribution:	Ecuador to N. Chile and Argentina
Habitat:	Rocky slopes
Diet:	Nectar, insects and small spiders
Status (IUCN Red List):	Least concern

Sword-billed Hummingbird

Ensifera ensifera

All hummingbirds have long bills, but none are longer than that of the sword-billed species. This bird has the longest bill of any bird in relation to its size. The sword-bill feeds from long, trumpet-shaped passionflowers. The sweet nectar fuels their energetic flight, while tiny insects in the flowers are the birds' main source of protein.

FACT FILE	
Length:	25cm (10in) including bill
Weight:	10g (½oz)
Distribution:	Andes, from Venezuela to Bolivia
Habitat:	Bushy slopes and forest edges
Diet:	Nectar and insects
Status (IUCN Red List):	Least concern

Giant Hummingbird

Patagona gigas

For a hummingbird, this species is a bit of a monster, with some adults reaching the length of a starling – when including the long bill. As its name suggests, this is the largest of all hummingbirds. It lives in dry scrub and woodlands on the mid-mountain slopes of the Andes.

FACT FILE	
Length:	21cm (8¼in)
Weight:	23g (¾oz)
Distribution:	Colombia to northern Argentina
Habitat:	Dry woodland
Diet:	Nectar and insects
Status (IUCN Red List):	Least concern

Ruby-throated Hummingbird

Archilochus colubris

The most widespread species of hummingbird, this is the species most often seen buzzing around gardens in the United States, although it is also found as far south as Panama. The birds reach New England in summer, but migrate to the sultry south when the weather turns bad.

FACT FILE	
Length:	9cm (3½in)
Weight:	8g (¼oz)
Distribution:	Eastern USA and Central America
Habitat:	Forests and gardens
Diet:	Nectar and insects
Status (IUCN Red List):	Least concern

Kingfishers and Relatives

The kingfishers form the Alcedinidae family, containing 86 species. They are closely linked to insect-eating bee-eaters and todies, while the woodpeckers, hornbills and rollers are also related. One feature the kingfishers share with all of these groups is a large, pointed bill, generally used for catching prey.

Green Kingfisher

Chloroceryle americana

The green kingfisher lives in wooded areas beside rivers and other bodies of freshwater. It prefers to perch on a leafless branch extending above the water, where it can get a good look at passing fish below. Once the bird selects a target, it gives a couple of flaps to set it on a diagonal dive into the water. It rarely enters the water, but scoops up fish and other animals from just below the surface.

FACT FILE	
Length:	19cm (7½in)
Weight:	35g (1¼oz)
Distribution:	S.W. USA, Mexico and C. America
Habitat:	Freshwater
Diet:	Fish
Status (IUCN Red List):	Least concern

Common Kingfisher

Alcedo atthis

Despite a sharp decline in this widespread species due to pollution in waterways reducing the amount of food available, the common kingfisher can still be found from Japan to England and south of the Sahara. It hunts by watching for prey on a waterside perch and then plunge-diving to grab the fish in its 4cm (1½in) bill.

FACT FILE	
Length:	19cm (7½in)
Weight:	28g (1oz)
Distribution:	Europe, Asia and Africa
Habitat:	Freshwater
Diet:	Fish and other aquatic animals
Status (IUCN Red List):	Least concern

White-tailed Trogon

Trogon viridis

Trogons are thought to be related to kingfishers, hornbills and woodpeckers, although only distantly. These colourful forest-living birds are found across the tropics. This American species has serrations on its bill that help in plucking fruits from trees. They do this in flight, then perch on a branch to eat. They catch insects in a similar manner.

FACT FILE	
Length:	24cm (9½in)
Weight:	70g (2½oz)
Distribution:	Central and South America
Habitat:	Rainforest and open woodland
Diet:	Fruit, insects
Status (IUCN Red List):	Least concern

Great Hornbill

Buceros bicornis

This huge bird is unmistakable. The large, fruit-crushing bill is crowned by a horny casque. The birds nest in hollow trees, and pairs use mud and droppings to almost close the entrance, sealing the female inside. The male feeds his partner through a narrow slit, until the eggs hatch and she regrows her moulted feathers.

FACT FILE	
Length:	1.5m (5ft)
Weight:	3kg (6lb 10oz)
Distribution:	Southern Asia
Habitat:	Lowland forests
Diet:	Mainly fruits
Status (IUCN Red List):	Near threatened

Hoopoe

Upupa epops

The hoopoe is unmistakable with its prominent crest and triple-hoot call. It probes with its long bill for small creatures to eat. It can walk and run well, and flies up into trees to roost. It has unpleasant nesting habits, polluting its hole with droppings and food; the female also has a strong musty smell.

FACT FILE	
Length:	28cm (11in)
Weight:	85g (3oz)
Distribution:	Europe, Asia and Africa
Habitat:	Forest edges
Diet:	Worms, insects and small lizards
Status (IUCN Red List):	Least concern

Laughing Kookaburra

Dacelo novaeguineae

The largest of all kingfishers, the kookaburra makes a loud, cackling call in a characteristic posture on its perch, with its head and tail raised. The purpose of the call is to claim and advertise the bird's territory. One bird will often be joined by other nearby birds, generating a whole chorus of manic 'laughter'.

FACT FILE	
Length:	45cm (17¾in)
Weight:	450g (16oz)
Distribution:	Australia
Habitat:	Woodland and open forest
Diet:	Insects, reptiles and rodents
Status (IUCN Red List):	Least concern

Young kookaburras stay in their parents' territory for several years as helpers. They protect the territory, collect food for nestlings and even take turns incubating the eggs. The birds' diet includes rodents and snakes. They seize snakes, even venomous ones, behind the head, and kill them by dropping or battering them.

Giant Kingfisher

Megaceryle maxima

The kookaburra is run a close second for the title of largest kingfisher by the aptly named giant kingfisher, which lives just about everywhere in Africa south of the Sahara, save for the arid dunes of the Namib in the far south-west. The bird grows to about 42cm (16.5in) long. Instead of a laugh, it communicates with a loud 'wak wak wak' call.

Laughing Kookaburra

Toucans and Woodpeckers

The woodpeckers and toucans belong to the Piciformes order, which also contains honeyguides and jacamars. The main family in the order is the Picidae, which is made up of around 200 species of woodpecker. The toucans – all American birds – have a lifestyle similar to hornbills, their Old World cousins.

Toco Toucan

Ramphastos toco

A toucan's giant bill has a honeycomb structure, which makes it strong but also very light. The bird makes only short flights and generally hops nimbly along branches, picking fruits with the tip of its bill and then tossing them back to swallow them. The toco toucan has the biggest bill of any toucan, 20cm (8in) in length.

FACT FILE	
Length:	64cm (25in)
Weight:	750g (26½oz)
Distribution:	Eastern South America
Habitat:	Lowland forest
Diet:	Mainly fruits
Status (IUCN Red List):	Least concern

Great Spotted Woodpecker

Dendrocopos major

This is the most common European woodpecker. Ironically, its spots are partly hidden when the wings are folded, creating white bars. Like other woodpeckers, this species has a cushion at the base of the bill to protect against injury as the bird chisels into bark and wood to get at the insect grubs underneath.

FACT FILE	
Length:	23cm (9in)
Weight:	55g (2oz)
Distribution:	Much of Europe and Asia
Habitat:	Forests and woodland
Diet:	Wood-boring insects and seeds
Status (IUCN Red List):	Least concern

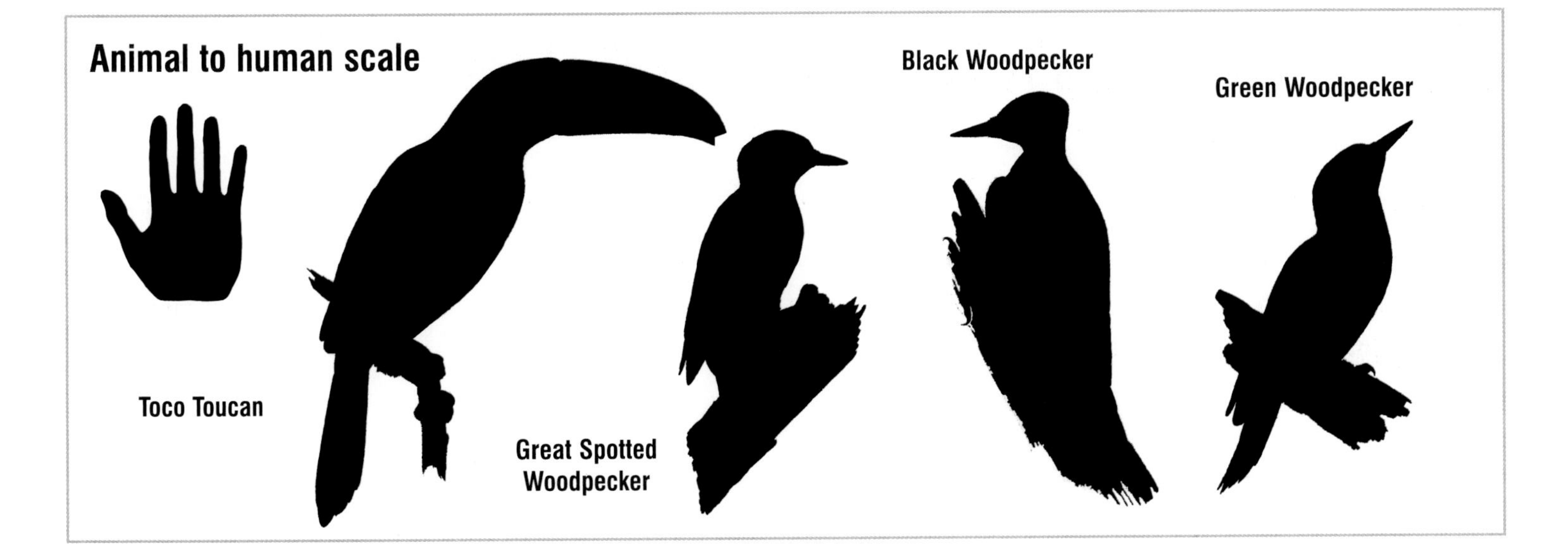

Black Woodpecker

Dryocopus martius

The biggest woodpecker in Europe is sometimes mistaken for a crow. The giveaway is the red crown. This colouring is a dominance signal; rival males wave their heads with the bill pointing upwards. Such tournaments last for an hour before one bird gives up.

FACT FILE	
Length:	47cm (18½in)
Weight:	100g (3½oz)
Distribution:	Europe, Asia north of Himalayas
Habitat:	Forest
Diet:	Tree-living insects, especially ants
Status (IUCN Red List):	Least concern

Green Woodpecker

Picus viridis

This European species does not drill wood like its cousins. Instead, it forages mainly on the ground, using its long tongue to lick up ants and other insects. The tongue is coiled up in the skull when not used, and secretes a sticky saliva to snare prey.

FACT FILE	
Length:	36cm (14in)
Weight:	70g (2½oz)
Distribution:	Europe
Habitat:	Deciduous woodlands
Diet:	Ants
Status (IUCN Red List):	Least concern

Songbirds

More than half of all birds, about 5000 species, belong to the passerine order. The passerines are little birds and have feet built for perching – they can even sleep standing up. Four-fifths of passerines, including tits, robins and finches, belong to the suborder Passeri, the songbirds, and share the ability to make melodic calls.

Greater Short-toed Lark

Calandrella brachydactyla

This is a small species of lark, slightly dumpier and with a stouter beak than its bigger cousins the skylark and woodlark. Like all larks, it has a small crest on the head, although this is less showy than in other species. Short-toed larks feed in short grasses and fields. They migrate into Africa and southern Asia in winter.

FACT FILE	
Length:	15cm (6in)
Weight:	13g (½oz)
Distribution:	Southern Europe, Asia, N. Africa
Habitat:	Grasslands and fields
Diet:	Insects and seeds
Status (IUCN Red List):	Least concern

Common Yellowthroat

Geothlypis trichas

A member of the New World warblers, the common yellowthroat is a noisy bird, frequently producing sharp chirps to drive out intruding birds and making a 'witchity' call to attract mates. It searches thick shrubs for its insect food and sometimes pecks seeds off the ground.

FACT FILE	
Length:	14cm (5½in)
Weight:	13g (½oz)
Distribution:	Alaska to northern S. America
Habitat:	Bushes and fields
Diet:	Insects and seeds
Status (IUCN Red List):	Least concern

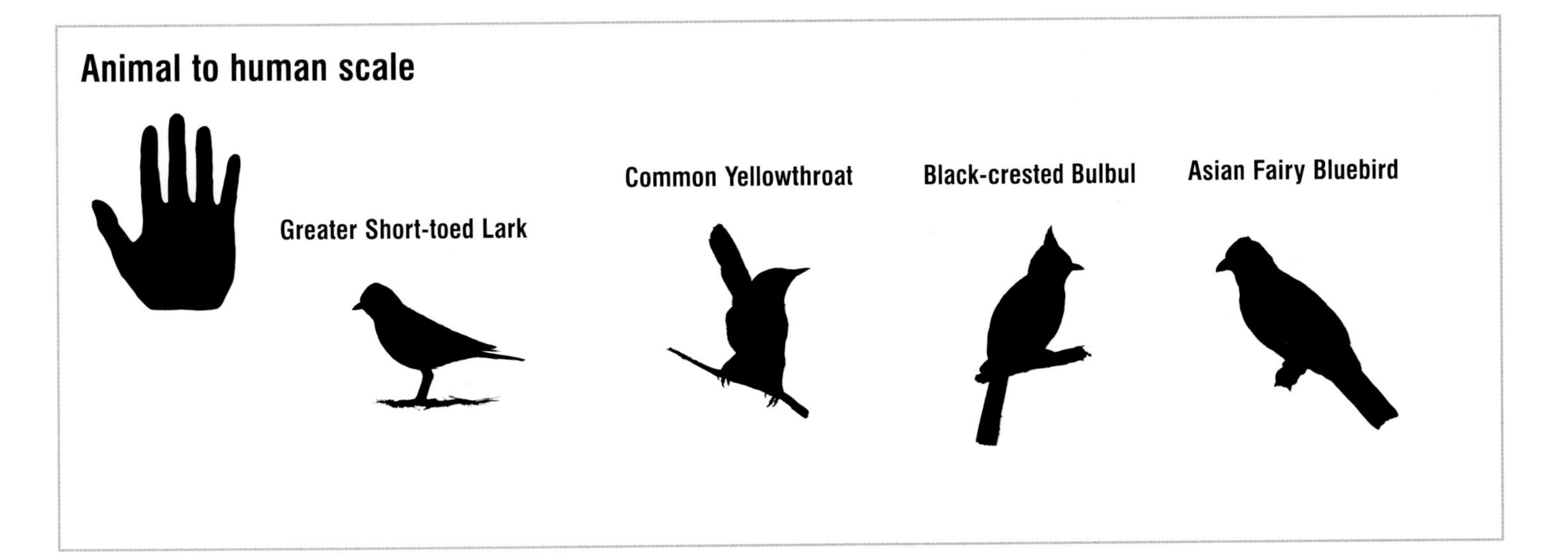

Black-crested Bulbul

Pycnonotus melanicterus

The bulbuls are medium-sized passerines living across the Old World region. Like this species, many bulbuls have colourful plumage and a crest on the head. The group is also characterized by a short neck. The black-crested bulbul lives in bushy areas, feeding on fruits and insects.

FACT FILE	
Length:	19cm (7½in)
Weight:	23g (¾oz)
Distribution:	South Asia and Indonesia
Habitat:	Forest and scrub
Diet:	Insects and fruit
Status (IUCN Red List):	Least concern

Asian Fairy Bluebird

Irena puella

This beautiful bird is a member of the leafbird family. It lives high in trees, where the male's black underparts make it difficult to spot. The female is less colourful than the male, with green and brown plumage. Fairy bluebirds have a melodious, fluent song, and males make striking aerial displays at breeding times.

FACT FILE	
Length:	26cm (10¼in)
Weight:	78g (2¾oz)
Distribution:	India to Java and Philippines
Habitat:	Upland forest
Diet:	Fruit (especially wild figs), nectar
Status (IUCN Red List):	Least concern

Swallows and Martins

There is no real distinction between a swallow and a martin; both belong to the Hirundinidae, with representatives found worldwide. Often the names are interchangeable, with the sand martins of Europe known as bank swallows in the United States. All these birds have a distinctive forked tail.

Barn Swallow

Hirundo rustica

Named after its habit of nesting in outbuildings in summer, this bird heralds the arrival of summer in many parts of the world. Each year, swallows fly thousands of kilometres in large flocks between Northern Hemisphere breeding sites and their Southern Hemisphere winter refuges.

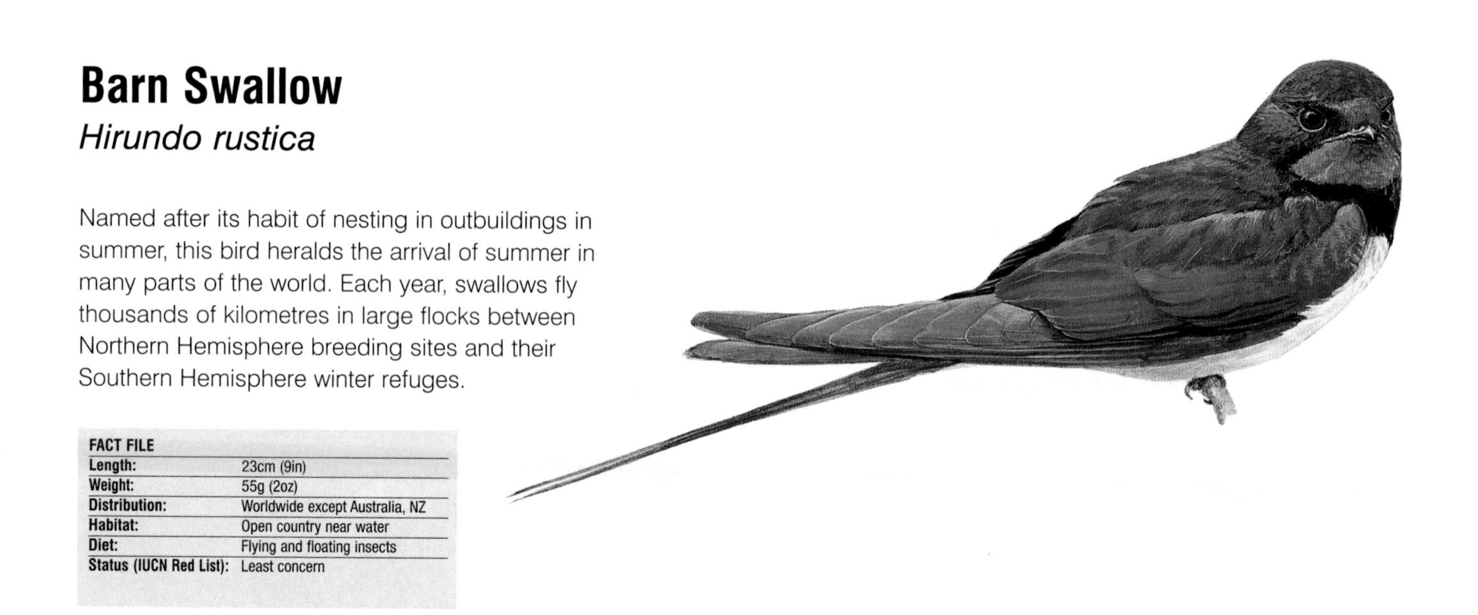

FACT FILE	
Length:	23cm (9in)
Weight:	55g (2oz)
Distribution:	Worldwide except Australia, NZ
Habitat:	Open country near water
Diet:	Flying and floating insects
Status (IUCN Red List):	Least concern

White-eyed River Martin

Pseudochelidon sirintarae

This is one of the rarest birds in the world. It is known only from one location in Thailand, where it is thought to spend the winter. Its breeding grounds are unknown, and there have been no confirmed sightings of the bird since 1980. This is one of just two species of river martin; the other lives in Central Africa.

FACT FILE	
Length:	18cm (7in)
Weight:	40g (1½oz)
Distribution:	Central Thailand
Habitat:	Forest
Diet:	Insects
Status (IUCN Red List):	Critically endangered

White-winged Swallow

Tachycineta albiventer

This is a small swallow species from the tropical region of South America. The white-winged swallow is often found near water, feeding on the insects that buzz around the banks. The swallow is often found in flocks and builds the small cup-shaped nests from mud and feathers typical of swallows the world over.

FACT FILE	
Length:	13cm (5in)
Weight:	23g (⅘oz)
Distribution:	South America
Habitat:	Forests near water
Diet:	Insects
Status (IUCN Red List):	Least concern

Nepal House Martin

Delichon nipalensis

This Asian house martin breeds on the sides of steep cliffs, so it is no great departure for it to glue its cup-shaped nests of mud and grass to walls and other manmade structures. The house martin often feeds in large flocks, swooping in and out of swarms of gnats and other flying insects.

FACT FILE	
Length:	13cm (5in)
Weight:	23g (⅘oz)
Distribution:	Himalayas to northern Vietnam
Habitat:	River valleys
Diet:	Insects
Status (IUCN Red List):	Least concern

Tits

Most birds named 'tit' belong to the Paridae family, and all but two of these family members belong to the same genus, *Parus*. That makes the tits a very closely related group of birds, which look similar and live in similar ways. A typical tit has short legs and a sturdy but short bill. Many have a dark cap or crest on the head.

Crested Tit

Parus cristatus

The crested tit lives in the conifer forests of Europe and a few deciduous woodlands in Central Europe. It gleans pine needles for insects and may also eat conifer seeds and the odd berry. The female digs a nest hole in a rotten stump and is fed by her mate as she broods the eggs.

FACT FILE	
Length:	12cm (4¾in)
Weight:	23g (¾oz)
Distribution:	Europe
Habitat:	Conifer forests
Diet:	Insects
Status (IUCN Red List):	Least concern

Great Tit

Parus major

The great tit is one of the largest, boldest and most widespread tit species, occurring from Morocco to Japan, Norway to Indonesia. Not surprisingly for such a widespread species, its blue, yellow and green plumage varies considerably over its range.

FACT FILE	
Length:	14cm (5½in)
Weight:	23g (¾oz)
Distribution:	Europe, N.W. Africa, South Asia
Habitat:	Forest, fields, hedges and gardens
Diet:	Insects, snails, seeds and fruits
Status (IUCN Red List):	Least concern

Animal to human scale

Crested Tit

Great Tit

Yellow-cheeked Tit

Crested Shriketit

Yellow-cheeked Tit

Parus spilonotus

This noisy little tit lives in the mixed forests of southern Asia and is a frequent visitor to gardens in the region. It is a noisy bird that feeds on berries, buds and insects in the middle to lower levels of the forest.

FACT FILE	
Length:	12cm (4¾in)
Weight:	23g (¾oz)
Distribution:	South and Southeast Asia
Habitat:	Tropical forests
Diet:	Buds, berries and insects
Status (IUCN Red List):	Least concern

Crested Shriketit

Falcunculus frontatus

This species belongs to the Pachycephalidae family, an unconnected group of Australian birds more closely related to thrushes than true tits. The family is known as the thickheads – a translation of the scientific term. The shriketit uses its parrot-like beak to strip bark from trees to reveal the insects beneath.

FACT FILE	
Length:	17cm (6¾in)
Weight:	70g (2½oz)
Distribution:	Australia
Habitat:	Eucalyptus forest
Diet:	Insects
Status (IUCN Red List):	Least concern

Pied Flycatcher

Ficedula hypoleuca

A representative of the Old World flycatchers (subfamily Muscicapinae), the pied flycatcher is a relative of the thrushes and warblers. The bird perches – often on a branch – watching for a passing insect; then it dashes out to snatch its prey in mid-air. The flycatcher always returns to its perch before starting to feed.

FACT FILE	
Length:	13cm (5in)
Weight:	13g (½oz)
Distribution:	Europe, West Asia and Africa
Habitat:	Woodland, orchards and gardens
Diet:	Mainly flying insects
Status (IUCN Red List):	Least concern

The flycatcher spends winter in Africa and western Asia before heading north to breed in northern Europe. It builds small cup-shaped nests in the fork of a tree, and is always ready to set up home in a nestbox.

BILL
Like all flycatchers, this species has a short, stubby beak. There are stiff hairs around the bill, which protect the eyes and nostrils from attacks by insect prey.

FEMALE
The female pied flycatcher is smaller than the male and has a dull brown plumage. She also lacks the white spots above the eyes.

TAIL
The long, broad tail lets the bird turn sharply in flight as it pursues evasive insects.

FOOT
Flycatchers have small, weak feet. They are not used in hunting and the toe positions – three forward and two back – is typical of a passerine, or perching bird.

Flycatchers

As the name suggests, a flycatcher is a bird that snatches insects from mid-air. There are two distinct groups: the Old World flycatchers belong to the thrush family, and are found from Scandinavia to New Zealand; the New World flycatchers, or tyrant flycatchers, are a completely separate family.

Bluethroat

Luscinia svecica

This secretive bird lives in dense bushes and thickets, where it gleans the stems and leaves for insects and spiders. It also collects worms and shrimps from water, both fresh and salt. The males have a blue throat, while the females have white colouring with a necklace of dark spots.

FACT FILE	
Length:	15cm (6in)
Weight:	28g (1oz)
Distribution:	Europe, Asia and North America
Habitat:	Dense vegetation
Diet:	Insects and spiders
Status (IUCN Red List):	Least concern

Pied Bushchat

Saxicola caprata

This flycatcher is often seen perching on top of a thorny shrub, scanning the surroundings for prey. They catch most of their food on the ground. The male has black plumage, with black eyes and legs, while the female is a drab brown. The 'pied' name comes from the flash of white on the male's wings.

FACT FILE	
Length:	15cm (6in)
Weight:	28g (1oz)
Distribution:	Asia
Habitat:	Thorn scrubs and grasslands
Diet:	Insects
Status (IUCN Red List):	Least concern

Brown-throated Wattle-eye

Platysteira cyanea

Some authorities place this species and other wattle-eyes in a separate family known as the Platysteiridae, although others regard them as Old World flycatchers. The species is named after the bright red fleshy wattle above the male's eyes. The birds are insect hunters.

FACT FILE	
Length:	14cm (5½in)
Weight:	23g (¾oz)
Distribution:	Central Africa
Habitat:	Forests and woodlands
Diet:	Insects
Status (IUCN Red List):	Least concern

Indian Verditer Flycatcher

Eumyias thalassina

This brightly coloured species is most abundant in the Himalayas. It is named after its pale blue-green plumage, which is said to resemble the verdigris corrosion of copper. The males have a dark string behind the bill. The females lack this feature and their plumage is a paler blue.

FACT FILE	
Length:	17cm (6¾cm)
Weight:	28g (1oz)
Distribution:	India
Habitat:	Mountains
Diet:	Insects
Status (IUCN Red List):	Least concern

Thrushes and Relatives

The thrush family, Muscicapidae, is the largest group of passerines (perching birds). As well as thrushes, the family includes warblers, babblers and some flycatchers. As the name of this last group hints, the thrushes are generally insect-hunting birds. The iconic robin and the blackbird are two of the 1390 species in the family.

Barred Warbler

Sylvia nisoria

This widespread species is the largest warbler in the world. It breeds in Europe and Asia, and the world's population gathers to spend the winter in east Africa, mainly in Kenya. Like many insectivorous passerines, the the warbler is a gleaner, picking insects from leaves and twigs in the bushy understory or higher in the trees.

FACT FILE	
Length:	15cm (6in)
Weight:	28g (1oz)
Distribution:	Europe to Asia and East Africa
Habitat:	Forest
Diet:	Insects
Status (IUCN Red List):	Least concern

Dartford Warbler

Sylvia undata

Named after an English town on the Thames estuary, this species is found in similar coastal and marshy heath habitats across western Europe and northwest Africa. The Dartford population has been extinct for about a century and the UK-wide population fell to just 20 birds in the 1960s but has since recovered.

FACT FILE	
Length:	13cm (5in)
Weight:	23g (¾oz)
Distribution:	Western Europe, Northwest Africa
Habitat:	Heathlands
Diet:	Insects and berries
Status (IUCN Red List):	Near threatened

Eastern Bluebird
Sialia sialis

Not only does this bluebird have a colourful combination of bright blue, orange-red and white plumage, but it is also – like many members of the thrush family – a fine singer. The female has similar but slightly duller colouring. Its relatives, the western bluebird and the mountain bluebird (*S. currucoides*), also live in North America.

FACT FILE	
Length:	19cm (7½in)
Weight:	28g (1oz)
Distribution:	Southern Canada to Nicaragua
Habitat:	Open woodland and parks
Diet:	Insects, fruits and berries
Status (IUCN Red List):	Least concern

Rufous-tailed Rock-thrush
Monticola saxatilis

This large thrush breeds in southern Europe and east all the way to Northern China. In winter, the population migrates to south of the Sahara. It is more omnivorous than other thrushes, preying on insects and reptiles and supplementing this diet with fruits.

FACT FILE	
Length:	20cm (8in)
Weight:	35g (1¼oz)
Distribution:	Southern Europe, Africa and Asia
Habitat:	Dry hilly areas
Diet:	Insects, fruits and reptiles
Status (IUCN Red List):	Least concern

American Robin
Turdus migratorius

The American robin is a much bigger bird than the Eurasian species. American robins were originally woodland birds but adapted well to human expansion. They are among the most common and best-loved American garden birds. They have a sweet song, a sure sign of spring in many areas.

FACT FILE	
Length:	25cm (10in)
Weight:	78g (2¾oz)
Distribution:	North America
Habitat:	Woodland and forest edges
Diet:	Berries, insects and snails
Status (IUCN Red List):	Least concern

Great Grey Shrike

Lanius excubitor

Shrikes are the most predatory of the passerines, the songbird counterparts to owls or even hawks. The great grey shrike hunts mainly for insects, but also takes small warm-blooded animals. It keeps watch for prey from a high perch, then swoops to catch it in mid-air or on the ground; it sometimes hovers like a hawk when hunting.

FACT FILE	
Length:	25cm (10in)
Weight:	70g (2½oz)
Distribution:	N. America, Europe, Asia, N. Africa
Habitat:	Woodland, marsh, tundra, desert
Diet:	Insects and small vertebrates
Status (IUCN Red List):	Least concern

The shrike generally returns to its perch to eat with its strong, hooked bill, but may impale it on a thorn or barbed wire to eat later. Such a 'larder' of impaled prey is a good sign that a grey shrike is around. Northern populations migrate southwards in winter.

Scarlet minivet

Pericrocotus Flammeus

The shrikes have a sister group known as the cuckooshrikes (family Campephagidae). The scarlet minivet is an Asian member of the group and is an aerial hunter like it shrike cousins. The bird flushes insects from a bush by buffeting the foliage with hard wing beats. Only the male scarlet minivet actually has any scarlet markings – more orange in the western areas of its range. The female is grey and yellow.

Great Grey Shrike

Buntings and Cardinals

The bunting family, Emberizidae, is made up of more than 550 species; they are also known as tanagers, grosbeaks and honeycreepers. They are one of the most widespread group of birds, found even in the High Arctic. However, the family does not cross the so-called Wallace Line between Indonesia and New Guinea.

Yellowhammer

Emberiza citrinella

In the winter, yellowhammers gather in large flocks and roost together in shrubs and marshy areas. In the spring, these flocks disperse and individual yellowhammers can be seen singing from high perches. The birds are seed-eaters and plunder cereal crops, perching in the tall stems.

FACT FILE	
Length:	17cm (6¾in)
Weight:	28g (1oz)
Distribution:	Europe
Habitat:	Farmland and bushy areas
Diet:	Seeds
Status (IUCN Red List):	Least concern

Scarlet Tanager

Piranga olivacea

This bright species spends summers in the northwestern region of the United States and southern Canada, and migrates to South America during the northern winter. They are insect hunters and forage everywhere from the ground and in low bushes to the tops of trees.

FACT FILE	
Length:	17cm (6¾in)
Weight:	35g (1¼oz)
Distribution:	North and South America
Habitat:	Deciduous forests
Diet:	Insects
Status (IUCN Red List):	Least concern

White-bridled Finch

Melanodera melanodera

Although known as a finch, this species is a member of the bunting family and not the Fringillidae group of true finches. The similarity lies in this species' adaptations for feeding; it uses its heavy bill to get at a wide variety of plant seeds. There is a subspecies of this finch living on the Falkland Islands.

FACT FILE	
Length:	15cm (6in)
Weight:	28g (1oz)
Distribution:	Chile and Argentina
Habitat:	Flat, open areas
Diet:	Seeds
Status (IUCN Red List):	Least concern

Cardinal

Cardinalis cardinalis

The male cardinal is an unmistakable red, but the female is a much duller brown. The species is named after the vibrant robes of a Catholic cardinal. Cardinals mostly live and search for their food in thickets and undergrowth, but they are common visitors to back yards in most of eastern and southern North America.

FACT FILE	
Length:	23cm (9in)
Weight:	40g (1½oz)
Distribution:	North and Central America
Habitat:	Thickets, parks and gardens
Diet:	Mainly seeds and berries
Status (IUCN Red List):	Least concern

Indigo Bunting

Passerina cyanea

This bunting is a member of the cardinal subfamily. It is a seed-eater for much of the year, collecting food in and around low bushes. In the spring breeding season, it turns to insects, which become more abundant around this time and provide an energy boost during this busy period.

FACT FILE	
Length:	13cm (5in)
Weight:	23g (⅘oz)
Distribution:	North and Central Africa
Habitat:	Forest edges
Diet:	Insects, seeds and berries
Status (IUCN Red List):	Least concern

Honeyeaters

Members of the honeyeater family, Meliphagidae, have a bristle-tipped tongue, like a paintbrush, which they use to extract flower nectar and fruit pulp. They have a major presence in Australia and New Zealand, although some species are found in southern Africa, too.

Tui

Prosthemadera novaeseelandiae

Nicknamed the parson bird because the tufts of white feathers at its throat look like a clergyman's bands, the tui is one of New Zealand's most renowned songbirds. It sings from a perch high in a tree. In the breeding season, males and females chase each other around the nest, and sing duets.

FACT FILE	
Length:	30cm (12in)
Weight:	85g (3oz)
Distribution:	New Zealand
Habitat:	Forests, woodland and gardens
Diet:	Nectar, fruits and insects
Status (IUCN Red List):	Least concern

Yellow Wattlebird

Anthochaera paradoxa

This is the largest species of honeyeater in the world. It is named after the vibrant wattles that dangle from each cheek. These become brighter during the breeding season. The wattlebird sips nectar from eucalyptus and banksia flowers and drinks the honeydew secreted by sap-sucking insects.

FACT FILE	
Length:	45cm (17¾in)
Weight:	200g (7oz)
Distribution:	Australia
Habitat:	Forests
Diet:	Nectar, fruit, seeds and honeydew
Status (IUCN Red List):	Least concern

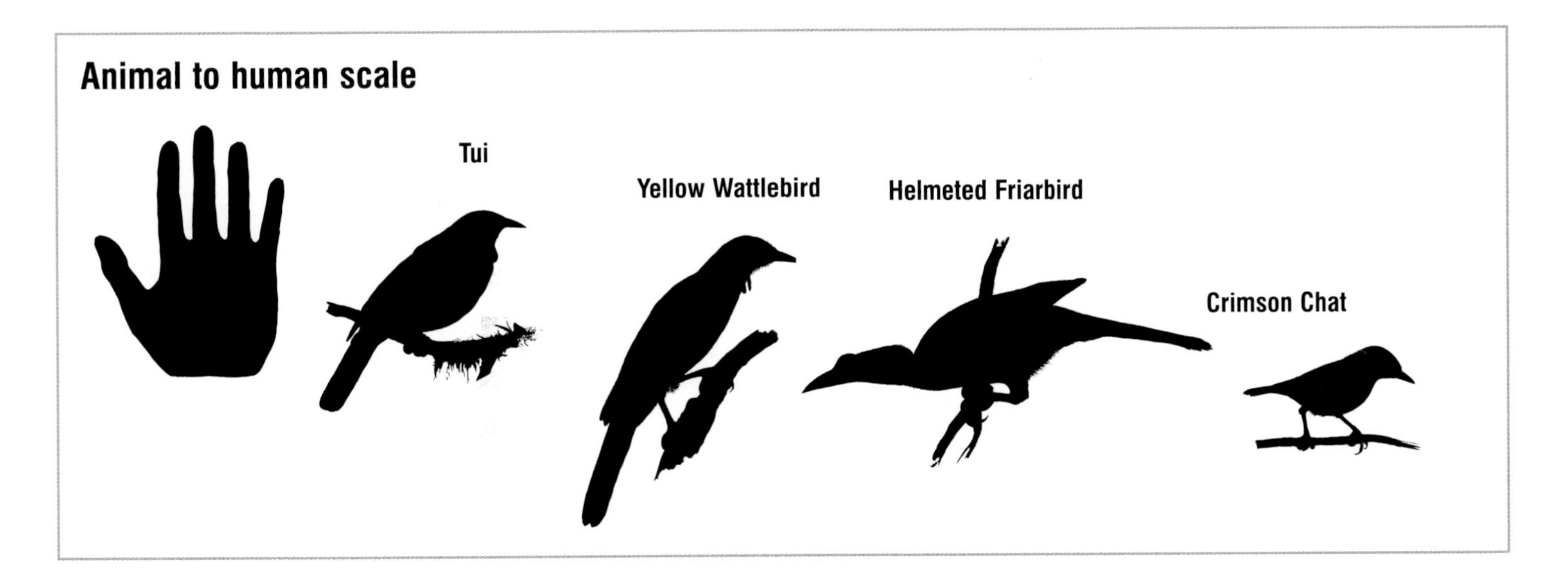

Helmeted Friarbird

Philemon buceroides

Friarbirds are known for their drably coloured plumage; they have dark bare skin on the head, which has earned this bird the alternative name leatherhead. It is also identified by its heavy, curved bill, which has an upright knob on the upper mandible (responsible for it being called 'knobby-nose').

FACT FILE	
Length:	36cm (14in)
Weight:	110g (4oz)
Distribution:	Australia and Indonesia
Habitat:	Tropical dry forests
Diet:	Fruits, nectar, pollen and insects
Status (IUCN Red List):	Least concern

Crimson Chat

Epthianura tricolor

The long, slightly hooked beak of a crimson chat holds a feathery tongue that is used to sip nectar and haul out seeds from flowers. The birds also patrol the ground around shrubs, pecking up insects and other invertebrates. The chats may breed twice in one year; once in spring and again in autumn.

FACT FILE	
Length:	13cm (5in)
Weight:	13g (½oz)
Distribution:	Australia
Habitat:	Dry woodlands
Diet:	Insects, spiders and nectar
Status (IUCN Red List):	Least concern

American Blackbirds

The Icteridae family goes by many names. As well as the American blackbirds, they are also known as cowbirds and New World orioles. The family is a diverse one: cowbirds are brood parasites, like the cuckoos of the Old World, while oropendolas weave some of the most complex nests in the animal kingdom.

Scarlet-rumped Cacique

Cacicus uropygialis

This tropical species flaps through the forest in small flocks, foraging for food on the leaves of trees. They are often seen alongside a range of species, including flycatchers and grosbeaks. The birds build bag-like nests in trees that are often also home to wasp's nests. These stinging neighbours are thought to keep monkeys away.

FACT FILE	
Length:	23cm (9in)
Weight:	55g (2oz)
Distribution:	Honduras to Ecuador
Habitat:	Lowland forest
Diet:	Insects, spiders and fruits
Status (IUCN Red List):	Least concern

Baltimore Oriole

Icterus galbula

Despite their common name, these birds spend only the summer in the eastern United States. In winter they head to Central America. They avoid farmland, but are equally at home nesting in a city park as they would be in a forest wilderness. They rarely gather in large numbers.

FACT FILE	
Length:	20cm (8in)
Weight:	35g (1¼oz)
Distribution:	North America
Habitat:	Forests
Diet:	Insects
Status (IUCN Red List):	Least concern

Crested Oropendola

Psarocolius decumanus

The plumage of this large bird is kept well oiled by scented oil produced by the preen gland. As a result, these birds have a distinctive smell, a rare feature for a bird. The nests of these species are woven baskets more than 1m (3ft 3in) long, which hang out of reach of predators from high branches.

FACT FILE	
Length:	46cm (18in)
Weight:	300g (10½oz)
Distribution:	South America
Habitat:	Forest edges
Diet:	Insects and fruit
Status (IUCN Red List):	Least concern

Bobolink

Dolichonyx oryzivorus

If this unusual name were not enough, this species is also known as the butter bird or skunk black bird – in reference to its fluffy hindquarters resembling the tail of skunk. The species spends the winter months in South America; vast flocks migrate 10,000km (6210 miles) to the north, one of the longest migrations of any passerine.

FACT FILE	
Length:	20cm (8in)
Weight:	35g (1¼oz)
Distribution:	North and South America
Habitat:	Grasslands
Diet:	Seeds and insects
Status (IUCN Red List):	Least concern

Eastern Meadowlark

Sturnella magna

This species of icterid does not generally migrate but toughs out the bad weather in all but the most northern parts of its distribution. It spends a lot of time foraging on the ground, probing the soil for burrowing grubs and other insect larvae. In summer, it adds seeds to the menu.

FACT FILE	
Length:	26cm (10¼in)
Weight:	120g (4¼oz)
Distribution:	USA and Central America
Habitat:	Grasslands and fields
Diet:	Insects and seeds
Status (IUCN Red List):	Least concern

Superb Lyrebird

Menura novaehollandiae

This bird is the world's longest passerine – the raven beats it to the title of heaviest. The superb lyrebird lives more like a ground pheasant than a perching bird. It has long legs and sturdy feet for a passerine, although it retains the same perching adaptations. The lyrebird is not a sweet singer but has a spectacular courtship ritual.

FACT FILE	
Length:	1m (3ft 3in) including tail
Weight:	1.2kg (2lb 8oz)
Distribution:	Southeastern Australia
Habitat:	Rainforest
Diet:	Insects, worms and snails
Status (IUCN Red List):	Least concern

The male's tail feathers form a lyre shape; it is seen only during courtship. This courtship display takes place on a mound of earth, when the male accompanies spectacular dancing with not only his normal calls and song but also the accurately mimicked calls of other birds.

TAIL
The tail is moulted and regrown each year, and reaches 60cm (23½in) in length. Two outer feathers form the lyre shape; 12 lacy feathers and two wire plumes stick up in the middle. At the climax of the courtship ritual, the mail lyrebird's tail arches over his body, quivering and shimmering.

FEMALE
The female is smaller than the male and has a simple tail. After mating, the female builds a nest, incubates the egg and raises the young, while the male may mate with several other females.

FEET
Like other passerines, the lyrebird's feet have three forward-facing toes and a single hind toe – the system used for perching. However, the lyrebirds' feet are flattened for walking on the ground.

True Finches

Characterized by their short, robust beaks, the true finches are songbirds that occupy the Fringillidae family. True finches are found all over the world and total more than 150 species. Their beaks are generally put to work extracting seeds from cones and casings.

European Goldfinch

Carduelis carduelis

This colourful finch's sharply pointed bill is well adapted to prising the deep-seated seeds from thistle and teasel heads. Goldfinches often feed in small flocks, known as 'charms'. The male's courtship display involves showing the bright yellow wing bars.

FACT FILE	
Length:	12cm (4¾in)
Weight:	23g (¾oz)
Distribution:	Europe, Western Asia, North Africa
Habitat:	Farmland, woodland and gardens
Diet:	Seeds; young feed on insects
Status (IUCN Red List):	Least concern

Common Redpoll

Carduelis flammea

The common redpoll is a cosmopolitan finch, found across the Northern Hemisphere. It breeds during the short summer in northern conifer forests and heads to warmer southern woodlands and gardens in winter. To combat cold spells, the bird crams seeds into cheek pouches and then finds a warmer spot to eat them.

FACT FILE	
Length:	14cm (5½in)
Weight:	23g (¾oz)
Distribution:	Asia, Europe and North America
Habitat:	Conifer forest, fields and gardens
Diet:	Seeds
Status (IUCN Red List):	Least concern

Common Crossbill

Loxia curvirostra

As its name suggests, the upper and lower mandibles of this finch cross at the tip. This skewed-looking instrument is used to prise open pine cones to get at the seeds. When feeding, crossbills often shuffle sideways along a branch, parrot-fashion, or even hang upside down to reach a cone.

FACT FILE	
Length:	16.5cm (6½in)
Weight:	40g (1½oz)
Distribution:	Europe, Asia, N. and C. America
Habitat:	Coniferous forests
Diet:	Conifer seeds
Status (IUCN Red List):	Least concern

Hawfinch

Coccothraustes coccothraustes

One of the largest finches, this species is equipped with a massive beak for cracking seeds and cones. They forage on fallen fruits and seeds and are easiest to spot in autumn, when the food supply is at its peak but the increasingly leafless trees are offering less cover.

FACT FILE	
Length:	18cm (7in)
Weight:	50g (1¾oz)
Distribution:	Europe and Asia
Habitat:	Woodland
Diet:	Seeds and buds
Status (IUCN Red List):	Least concern

Brambling

Fringilla montifringilla

Bramblings are often mistaken for chaffinches, especially the females and younger birds, which lack the male's distinctive orange breast. The brambling's white rump is a way to distinguish it from its lookalike, which has a pinker underbelly. Adult bramblings eat seeds, but they catch insects for their nestlings.

FACT FILE	
Length:	15cm (6in)
Weight:	23g (¾oz)
Distribution:	Europe and northern Asia
Habitat:	Open forest
Diet:	Seeds
Status (IUCN Red List):	Least concern

Weavers and Waxbills

The true finches are not alone in using a tough beak to tackle hard foodstuffs. Two other songbird families, the Estrildidae (including the parrotfinches and waxbills, among others) and the Ploceidae (weavers), share this trait. As a result, many members also go by the name 'finch'.

Common Waxbill

Estrilda astrild

The waxbill gets its name because its bright bill and eye stripes resemble the colour of sealing wax. These little birds live across Africa, apart from the desert and forest regions. They forage in large flocks, raiding stands of tall grass for their seeds. In the breeding season, they supplement their diet with protein-rich insects.

FACT FILE	
Length:	13cm (5in)
Weight:	13g (½oz))
Distribution:	Sub-Saharan Africa
Habitat:	Grasslands and swamps
Diet:	Grass, seeds and insects
Status (IUCN Red List):	Least concern

Java Sparrow

Padda oryzivora

This large estrilidid finch was given the name 'sparrow' because it was once a common resident of rural Indonesia, like its drabber namesake is elsewhere. The bird was also a damaging pest of rice crops, and became the target of farmers. Sadly, this persecution has made the Java sparrow a rare species.

FACT FILE	
Length:	17cm (6¾in)
Weight:	40g (1½oz)
Distribution:	Java and Bali
Habitat:	Grasslands and paddy fields
Diet:	Rice seeds
Status (IUCN Red List):	Vulnerable

Zebra Finch

Taeniopygia guttata

This tiny bird is named after the black and white bars on its tail. It is one of the most common birds in Australia and is seen in large flocks. The zebra finch flies long distances in search of food and water; Aboriginals in central Australia found water supplies by following the birds.

FACT FILE	
Length:	10cm (4in)
Weight:	13g (½oz)
Distribution:	Australia, southeastern Indonesia
Habitat:	Grasslands and woodland
Diet:	Grass seeds and insects
Status (IUCN Red List):	Least concern

Eastern Paradise Whydah

Vidua paradisaea

The male paradise whydah grows tail feathers twice as long as the rest of his body during the breeding season. He makes elaborate display flights, the tail feathers held out at a right angle, to court a female. After they mate, she lays eggs in another bird's nest cuckoo-fashion.

FACT FILE	
Length:	Male 38cm (15in), female half this
Weight:	40g (1½oz)
Distribution:	Eastern and southern Africa
Habitat:	Dry scrub and savannah
Diet:	Seeds
Status (IUCN Red List):	Least concern

Gouldian Finch

Erythrura gouldiae

The bold plumage of male Gouldian finches made them popular cage birds, a popularity that threatened the wild population. Wild-caught birds were exported from Australia until 1959. The species has dwindled since to a few thousands, as their woodland habitat has shrunk to a few isolated patches.

FACT FILE	
Length:	12cm (4¾in)
Weight:	13g (½oz)
Distribution:	Northern Australia
Habitat:	Dry woodlands
Diet:	Seeds
Status (IUCN Red List):	Endangered

Red-billed Oxpecker

Buphagus erythrorhynchus

One of two species of oxpecker, both from Africa, this bird has an unusual lifestyle. Much of its time is spent perched on the back of a large mammal, such as an antelope, hippopotamus or buffalo. The host tolerates the bird's presence because it cleans off the lice and ticks feasting on the mammal's blood and skin.

FACT FILE	
Length:	22cm (8½in)
Weight:	50g (1¾oz)
Distribution:	Sub-Saharan Africa
Habitat:	Savannah
Diet:	Insects, ticks and blood
Status (IUCN Red List):	Least concern

Wings
The oxpecker holds its wings half-open to help it balance as it clings to its swaying ride.

Oxpeckers play both sides. While they are clearing away parasites on behalf of their host mammals, they are also benefiting from the blood that their tick and insect prey have already sucked up. The birds can also be seen lapping blood from wounded mammals.

Tail
The stiffened fan of tail feathers provides extra support as the oxpecker edges across its host's back looking for food.

BEAK
The long beak is flattened on the side, making it a useful probe that slides into mammal fur, nipping at skin lice and ticks.

FEET
The oxpecker's four-toed feet provide a stable platform on their frequently moving perch. The claws grip the thick hide.

Birds of Paradise

Legend has it that Europeans first saw these birds in the sixteenth century when they were brought back by sailors returning from Magellan's first voyage around the world. The stuffed specimens had no legs, and it was surmised that the wondrous birds were akin to heavenly angels, staying aloft effortlessly with no need of a perch.

Western Parotia

Parotia sefilata

This species is also known as the six-wired bird of paradise because the males have three wire-like feathers growing from each side of the head, each of them ending in a small black plume. Males compete for females in a shared display area, or lek, displaying their finery in the hope of being chosen as a mate.

FACT FILE	
Length:	25cm (10in)
Weight:	250g (8¾oz)
Distribution:	Western New Guinea
Habitat:	Montane rainforest
Diet:	Fruits, berries and insects
Status (IUCN Red List):	Least concern

Magnificent Riflebird

Ptiloris magnificus

This bird's name comes from its call, a series of two to four explosive whistles, the last of which is deeper and more abrupt than the others. It is one of only a few birds of paradise that extend into northern Australia. Males display from a jealously guarded territory; the older, stronger ones attract several mates.

FACT FILE	
Length:	M: 33cm (13in); f: 28cm (11in)
Weight:	300g (10½oz)
Distribution:	New Guinea; northeast Australia
Habitat:	Canopy of rainforest
Diet:	Fruits, berries and insects
Status (IUCN Red List):	Least concern

Twelve-wired Bird of Paradise

Seleucidis melanoleuca

The males have rich yellow plumes on its flanks, topped off with a red eye ring. Twelve stiff filaments emerge from the plumes, curving around the bird's tail and rump. The male perches on a tree trunk to show off his adornments, with his green fringed breast fully fluffed up.

FACT FILE	
Length:	33cm (13in)
Weight:	300g (10½oz)
Distribution:	New Guinea and Salawati
Habitat:	Tropical forest
Diet:	Fruits and insects
Status (IUCN Red List):	Least concern

Wallace's Standardwing

Semioptera wallacii

The westernmost bird of paradise, this species was named after Alfred Russell Wallace, a nineteenth-century naturalist who made surveys of the region – and formulated the theory of evolution independently of Charles Darwin as he did so. The bird's wings are by no means standard, but named after flag-like adornments.

FACT FILE	
Length:	28cm (11in)
Weight:	260g (9oz)
Distribution:	Moluccan Islands
Habitat:	Tropical forest
Diet:	Fruits and insects
Status (IUCN Red List):	Least concern

Greater Bird of Paradise

Paradisaea apoda

This species was named by the great Swedish naturalist Carolus Linnaeus in the eighteenth century. Although he obviously knew it had feet by this time, he referred to the old angel myth by giving it the species name *apoda*, meaning 'without feet'.

FACT FILE	
Length:	M: 44cm (17in); f: 36cm (14in)
Weight:	340g (12oz)
Distribution:	Southeastern New Guinea
Habitat:	Lowland rainforest
Diet:	Fruits, berries and insects
Status (IUCN Red List):	Least concern

Crows and Relatives

To many people, the crow family, Corvidae, are the crooks of the bird world, from the thuggish ravens to the thieving magpies. However, these comparisons are unfair; the crows are some of the cleverest birds around. They can pick a person out from a crowd years after their first meeting.

Green Magpie

Cissa chinensis

Like its European relative, the green magpie is often seen in pairs or larger groups. They forage on the floor of thick forests and have varied tastes: one meal could be fallen fruit, the next a frog. Also typical of magpies, this species lays eggs on a rough platform nest high in tangled vines or bamboo.

FACT FILE	
Length:	39cm (15½in)
Weight:	120g (4¼oz)
Distribution:	South and Southeast Asia
Habitat:	Forests
Diet:	Insects, eggs, reptiles, frogs, fruit
Status (IUCN Red List):	Least concern

White-necked Raven

Corvus albicollis

An African relative of the larger raven, the white-necked raven swoops and rolls playfully above the escarpments of southern Africa. It scans for large insects scuttling over the ground and dives in for the kill. Like other crows, it is an early arrival at roadkills, picking at the carrion.

FACT FILE	
Length:	56cm (22in)
Weight:	800g (28¼oz)
Distribution:	East and southern Africa
Habitat:	Highland regions
Diet:	Insects, carrion and fruits
Status (IUCN Red List):	Least concern

Red-billed Blue Magpie

Urocissa erythrorhyncha

If it were not for its enormous tail feathers, this species would be similar in size to the European magpie. The tail, however, makes up three-fifths of the total body length of this east Asian bird. It searches for food in and around the stunted trees growing on rugged mountainsides.

FACT FILE	
Length:	63cm (24¾in)
Weight:	160g (5½oz)
Distribution:	Himalayas, China and Vietnam
Habitat:	Hill forest
Diet:	Seeds, fruits, eggs and insects
Status (IUCN Red List):	Least concern

White-throated Magpie-jay

Calocitta formosa

This gregarious bird has a crest of feathers on its head, varying from black to blue and white across its range. The species is thought to hybridize with the very similar, although slightly larger, blue-throated magpie-jay, which lives further to the north.

FACT FILE	
Length:	56cm (22in)
Weight:	210g (7½oz)
Distribution:	Central America
Habitat:	Cactus and woodland
Diet:	Insects, eggs, frogs and lizards
Status (IUCN Red List):	Least concern

Green Jay

Cyanocorax yncas

The green jay lives in two distinct populations: one edges into Texas and extends to Honduras; then there is a large gap before the birds reappear in South America. Families of green jays stick together; a flock can contain the parents and several years' worth of maturing offspring.

FACT FILE	
Length:	29cm (11½in)
Weight:	110g (4oz)
Distribution:	Central and South America
Habitat:	Open woodland
Diet:	Insects, eggs, frogs and lizards
Status (IUCN Red List):	Least concern

Common Raven

Corvus corax

A large bird with a threatening reputation, ravens are just about as big as crows get. The common raven shares the title of largest passerine with the thick-billed raven of Ethiopia, although its calls are more cackle than melody. Ravens make up for lack of singing talent with acrobatic skills seen in displays above hillsides and cliffs.

FACT FILE	
Length:	68cm (26in)
Weight:	1.3kg (2lb 12oz)
Distribution:	Northern Hemisphere
Habitat:	Highland areas, cliffs, woodland
Diet:	Carrion and seeds
Status (IUCN Red List):	Least concern

Thanks to their high intelligence, ravens have made a success of living in all climates, from the ice of the Arctic to an empty desert and perhaps even a castle wall. The birds prefer rocky habitats with plenty of places to perch. After centuries of persecution by farmers, these birds are now most common in remote areas.

TAIL
The feathers form a more wedge-shaped tail than that of the ravens' smaller cousins, such as the carrion crow and the rook.

Plumage
The raven's famously jet-black feathers show off a rainbow of other colours when strong sunlight interferes with their fine comb structure, producing the same shimmering effects of fuel oil layered on water.

Bill
The big bill has sharp cutting edges for slicing flesh, but is also used to hammer prey to death.

Talons
Ravens catch and kill food with their beaks; the taloned feet are used for perching. Pairs of ravens have been known to hold each other's feet as they swoop together in play.

REPTILES

Reptiles range from sea-going turtles to legless lizards that burrow underground. There are some common features: for example, all reptiles have scaly skin and lay hard-shelled, waterproof eggs.

At the last count, there were at least 8000 species of reptile. Most of them are reptiles and snakes, which form a relatively recent group of reptiles called the squamates, that took over once the dinosaurs died out 65 million years ago. By contrast, the turtles and crocodiles were common creatures nearly a quarter of a billion years ago.

Left: The crocodiles and alligators are the sole-surviving members of an ancient group of big reptiles called the archosaurs, which also included the dinosaurs.

Turtles and Terrapins

The species in the order Testudines grow a bony shell around their bodies, with little more than their heads and legs poking out. These reptiles are known as tortoises, turtles and terrapins. There is no strict definition of each type, but turtles tend to be aquatic, while tortoises are land-based. Terrapins are smaller turtles.

Common Snakeneck Turtle

Chelodina longicollis

As its name suggests, this species of turtle has an extremely lengthy neck, which can be as long as its carapace. It is a side-necked turtle, which means that it bends its neck sideways into its shell rather than pulling it directly back. Also known as the 'stinker', this turtle gives off a strong smell from its scent glands when it is threatened.

FACT FILE	
Length:	46cm (18in) including neck
Distribution:	Eastern Australia
Habitat:	Swamps, dams and lakes
Diet:	Minnows, worms and insects
Reproduction:	8–24 eggs
Status (IUCN Red List):	Near threatened

Ringed Sawback

Graptemys oculifera

Perhaps for obvious reasons, this species is also known as the ringed map turtle, as the mottled pattern on the shell reminds some people of land masses on a map. The curved teeth on the back are the inspiration for its main name. The sawback is a powerful swimmer and can swim against the current of its home river.

FACT FILE	
Length:	10cm (4in)
Distribution:	Pearl River, Louisiana, USA
Habitat:	Fast-flowing rivers
Diet:	Insects and plants
Reproduction:	Eggs laid in sandbars
Status (IUCN Red List):	Endangered

Painted Terrapin
Callagur borneoensis

The carapace of this large, river-dwelling terrapin features a bony ridge running from the head to the tail. The painted terrapin's upturned nose is used as a snorkel. It lives in tidal rivers, feeding on the vegetation and fruits on their banks. When nesting, females move to sandy areas a few kilometres from the river to lay eggs.

FACT FILE	
Length:	60cm (23½in)
Distribution:	Indonesia, Malaysia and Thailand
Habitat:	Tidal rivers
Diet:	Leaves, fish and insects
Reproduction:	20 eggs
Status (IUCN Red List):	Critically endangered

Indian Roofed Turtle
Kachuga tecta

This widespread river turtle is named after the domed carapace (upper shell), which has a central orange stripe that looks like the tiles on a roof. The roofed turtle spends the early morning basking on the riverbank. When warm enough, it slides into the water and feeds in the soft sediments on the riverbed.

FACT FILE	
Length:	23cm (9in)
Distribution:	South Asia
Habitat:	Streams and rivers
Diet:	Water plants, snails and crabs
Reproduction:	12 eggs laid in burrow
Status (IUCN Red List):	Least concern

Radiated Tortoise
Geochelone radiata

The radiated tortoise's name comes from the striking yellow lines that radiate from the centre of each plate on its shell. It has yellowish feet, tail and head. Males have longer tails than females. Most pet tortoises belong to this species, and as a result the animal is very rare in the wild.

FACT FILE	
Length:	40cm (16in)
Distribution:	Southern Madagascar
Habitat:	Dry brush and woodland
Diet:	Grasses
Reproduction:	3–12 eggs
Status (IUCN Red List):	Critically endangered

Leatherback Turtle

Dermochelys coriacea

The largest living species of turtle, the leatherback turtle is also bigger than almost all other reptiles. Only the largest crocodile species grow bigger. The leatherback is an ocean-going species. Once they make it to the ocean after hatching, males never touch land again – although the females return to lay their own eggs.

FACT FILE	
Length:	2.7m (8ft 9in)
Distribution:	Worldwide
Habitat:	Open ocean
Diet:	Jellyfish
Reproduction:	Eggs buried on beach
Status (IUCN Red List):	Critically endangered

Leatherbacks – like all sea turtles – are air breathers, although they can stay underwater for more than an hour on one breath. The turtles dive more than 1000m (3280ft) into dark cold water. They have a layer of fat and a heat exchange system in the flippers to retain body heat, and so are found well outside of tropical waters.

EYES
The turtle has large eyes for seeing in gloomy water.

MOUTH
Leatherbacks prey on jellyfish. They slice up food with their horny beak; spikes in the throat burst the jellyfish before they are swallowed.

LEATHER BACK
The turtle's carapace does not have the horny scutes of other turtles. Instead, it is covered in a rubbery skin. Keels along the shell stabilize the turtle in water.

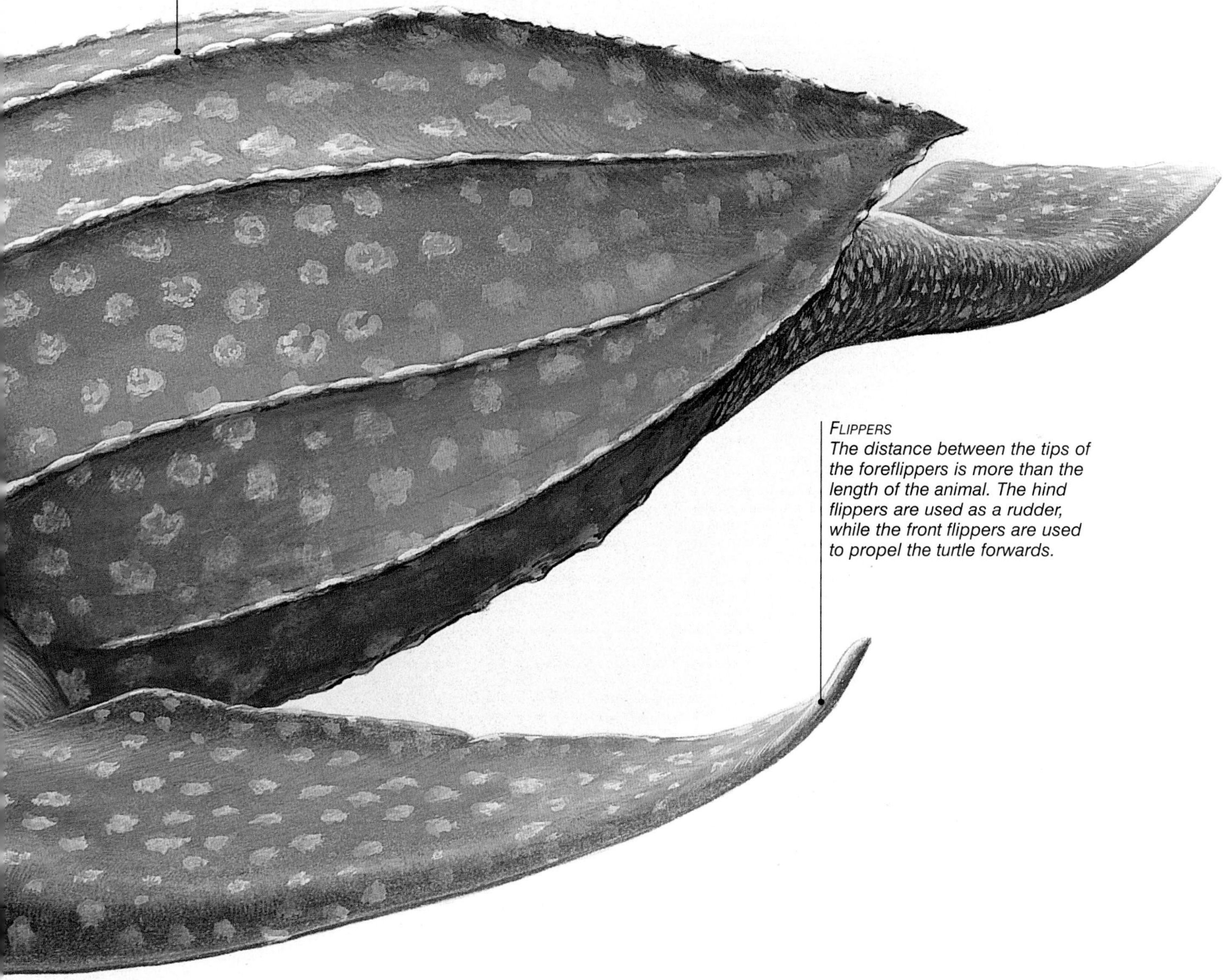

FLIPPERS
The distance between the tips of the foreflippers is more than the length of the animal. The hind flippers are used as a rudder, while the front flippers are used to propel the turtle forwards.

Crocodiles and Alligators

The crocodilians are the largest reptiles of all. The saltwater crocodile of northern Australia and Southeast Asia grows to 8m (26ft 3in) long, perhaps even more. Crocodiles, alligators and caimans are truly ancient hunters and have remained largely unchanged for 240 million years.

Chinese Alligator

Alligator sinensis

FACT FILE	
Length:	1.45m (4ft 9in)
Distribution:	Lower Yangtze Basin
Habitat:	Wetlands, rivers and lakes
Diet:	Fish, snails, clams and birds
Reproduction:	10–40 eggs laid in mound nest
Status (IUCN Red List):	Critically endangered

The Chinese alligator is one of the most endangered species of crocodilian. Its closest relative is the much more common American alligator of the Deep South of the United States. This species lives in a colder habitat than other crocs; it digs itself a burrow in the muddy riverbank to lie dormant during cold periods.

Black Caiman

Melanosuchus niger

FACT FILE	
Length:	6m (19ft 7in)
Distribution:	Amazon Basin
Habitat:	Slow-flowing rivers
Diet:	Fish and rodents
Reproduction:	40 eggs laid in nest mound
Status (IUCN Red List):	Least concern

The black caiman is the largest predator in South America. It is a relative of the alligators. The animal is not particularly black when young, but algae growing on its armoured scutes darken the skin as the animal ages. The female lays eggs in a warm nest of decaying grass and mud.

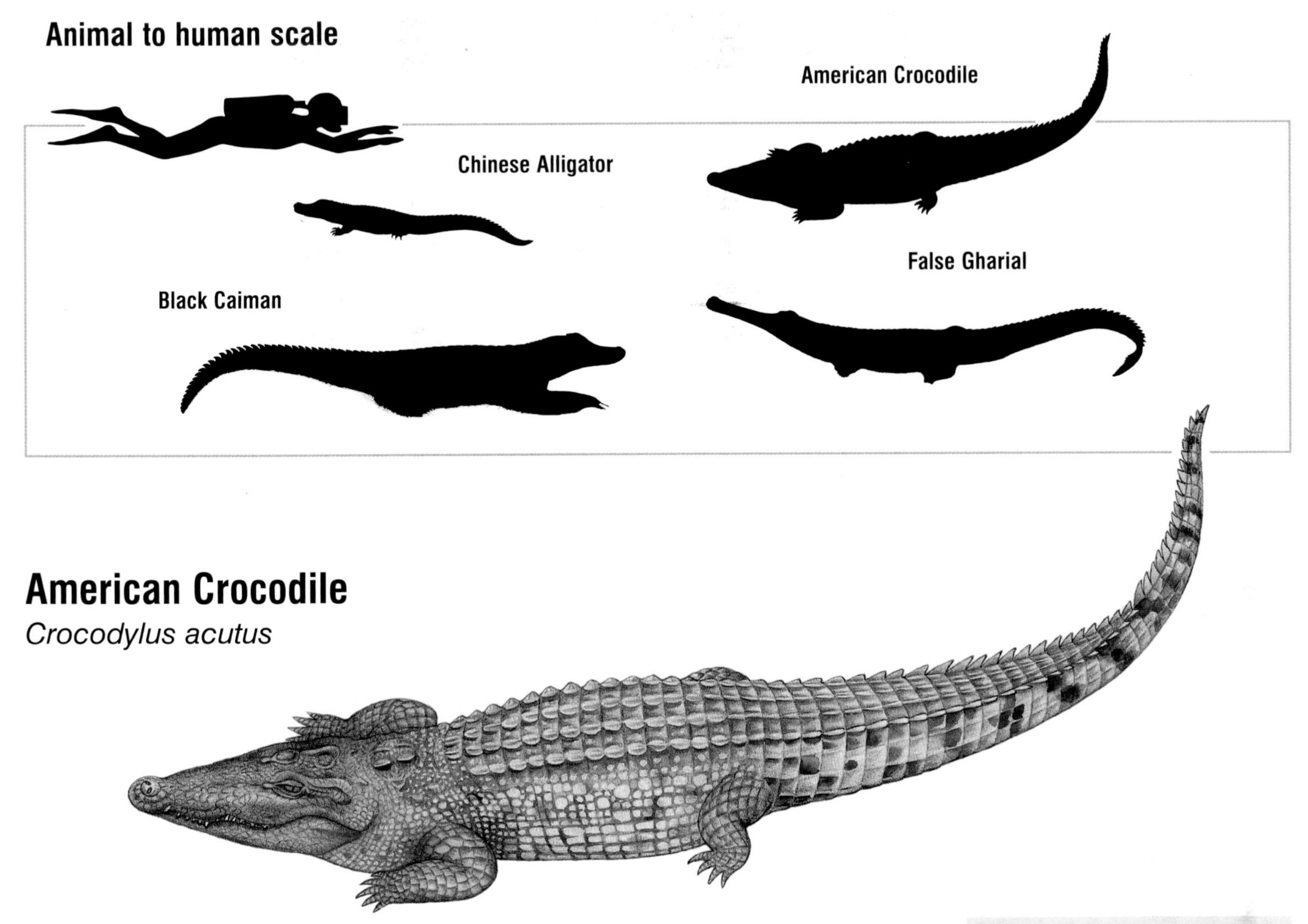

American Crocodile

Crocodylus acutus

The lesser known North American crocodilian is also the largest. This species is more closely related to the crocodiles of the Old World than the alligators and caimans of the Americas. It survives in coastal waters; subspecies live on some Caribbean islands.

FACT FILE	
Length:	7m (23ft)
Distribution:	Caribbean and Central America
Habitat:	Freshwater and coastal waters
Diet:	Fish, frogs and turtles
Reproduction:	30–60 eggs laid in nest
Status (IUCN Red List):	Vulnerable

False Gharial

Tomistoma schlegelii

The gharial is an unusual Indian crocodilian with a long narrow snout that is adapted to snaring fish from river water. The false gharial shares this feature but has evolved it independently, since it is generally thought to be more closely related to the crocodiles.

FACT FILE	
Length:	5m (16ft 6in)
Distribution:	Southeast Asia to Borneo
Habitat:	Freshwater swamps and rivers
Diet:	Fish
Reproduction:	20–30 eggs laid in mound
Status (IUCN Red List):	Endangered

Iguanas and Relatives

More than 1000 species of lizard belong to a group called the Iguania. As one might expect, this suborder includes the iguanas of the Americas; it also contains the agamas and chameleons of Africa and Asia. The members of the Iguania tend to be tree-living species.

Green Iguana

Iguana iguana

This is one of the most widespread species of iguana and the largest lizard in the United States. (The largest iguanas live on Caribbean islands and the Galapagos.) Most iguanas are less than 1m (3ft 3in) long and spend much of their time in trees. Eggs are buried in dry soil and hatch when rains arrive.

FACT FILE	
Length:	1.75m (5ft 9in)
Distribution:	Central and South America
Habitat:	Forests
Diet:	Leaves and fruits
Reproduction:	20 eggs buried in ground
Status (IUCN Red List):	Least concern

Short-horned Lizard

Phrynosoma douglassi

These rotund lizards are often known as horned toads, although they are very much reptiles. They have a startling defence technique: when handled roughly, the lizards squirt blood from their eyes at the attacker. They do this by allowing blood pressure to build up in the head until it bursts out.

FACT FILE	
Length:	15cm (6in)
Distribution:	North America
Habitat:	Dry areas
Diet:	Insects
Reproduction:	Up to 20 babies born in summer
Status (IUCN Red List):	Least concern

Frill-necked Lizard

Chlamydosaurus kingii

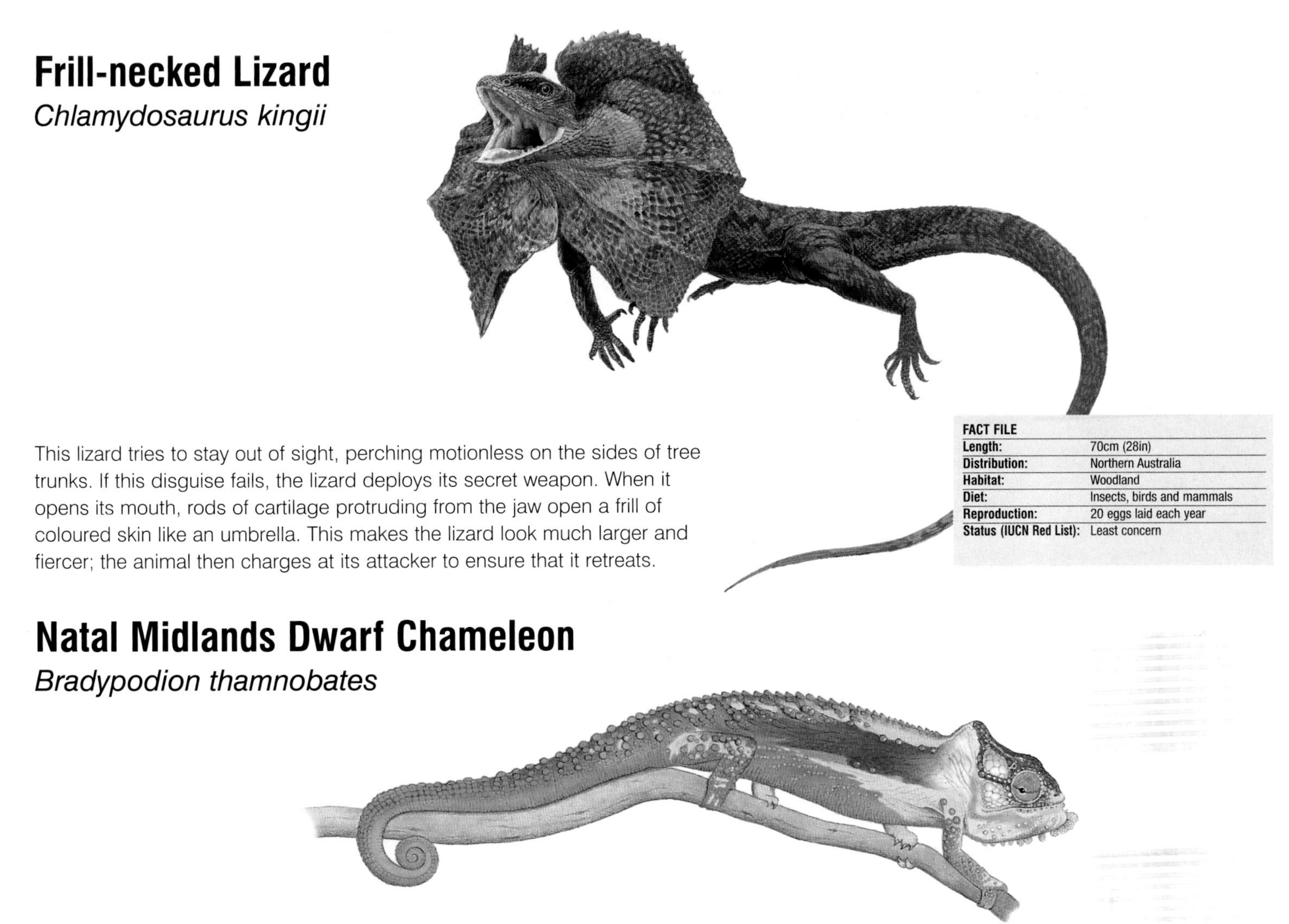

This lizard tries to stay out of sight, perching motionless on the sides of tree trunks. If this disguise fails, the lizard deploys its secret weapon. When it opens its mouth, rods of cartilage protruding from the jaw open a frill of coloured skin like an umbrella. This makes the lizard look much larger and fiercer; the animal then charges at its attacker to ensure that it retreats.

FACT FILE	
Length:	70cm (28in)
Distribution:	Northern Australia
Habitat:	Woodland
Diet:	Insects, birds and mammals
Reproduction:	20 eggs laid each year
Status (IUCN Red List):	Least concern

Natal Midlands Dwarf Chameleon

Bradypodion thamnobates

As its name suggests, this little chameleon has a specific distribution: the midland region of South Africa's KwaZulu-Natal province. Like all chameleons, it can alter its skin colour to display mood and blend into its surroundings. Most of the time it is a brown-green, although males sometimes show off a yellow stripe.

FACT FILE	
Length:	19cm (7½in)
Distribution:	Natal, South Africa
Habitat:	Woodlands
Diet:	Insects
Reproduction:	Eggs buried in ground
Status (IUCN Red List):	Least concern

Eastern Bearded Dragon

Pogona barbata

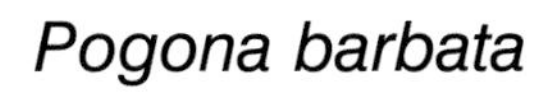

The bearded dragon's 'beard' is actually a movable throat pouch bristling with spines. The beard is usually folded under the chin, but when danger approaches, the lizard gapes open its mouth to show off a startlingly yellow interior and displays its barbed flap in an attempt to spook predators.

FACT FILE	
Length:	61cm (24in)
Distribution:	Eastern Australia
Habitat:	Woodland
Diet:	Insects, lizards and rodents
Reproduction:	Lays eggs
Status (IUCN Red List):	Least concern

Jackson's Chameleon

Chamaeleo jacksonii

This medium-sized chameleon lives in the high, humid woodlands of East Africa. These chameleons spend their entire lives in trees, slowly manoeuvring themselves within striking distance of insect prey. The chameleon catches prey by splatting it with a lightning-fast flick of its immensely long and sticky tongue.

FACT FILE	
Length:	30cm (12in)
Distribution:	Kenya and Tanzania
Habitat:	Highland woodlands
Diet:	Insects
Reproduction:	Up to 30 babies born each year
Status (IUCN Red List):	Least concern

Horns
While females have a single horn, males of this species grow three horns on the front of their faces. They are used largely for display; males with bigger horns are dominant, but when combat is the only option, the chameleons joust with their horns, attempting to unbalance their rival.

Most chameleons lay eggs; the females dig a long trench for them in the ground. It is tough work and many females die of exhaustion after their first breeding season. However, a female Jackson's chamelon retains her eggs in her body. The eggs hatch inside and the babies are born in large numbers. This still takes a toll, and female life expectancy is lower than that of the males.

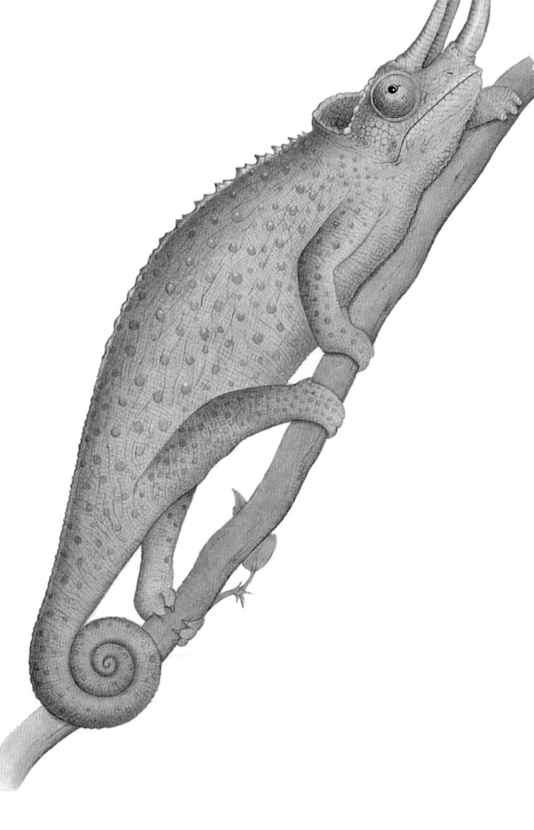

Eyes
Chameleon eyes are located on the sides of their heads. They are housed in swivelling turrets that move independently of each other, so the lizard can look at two things at once.

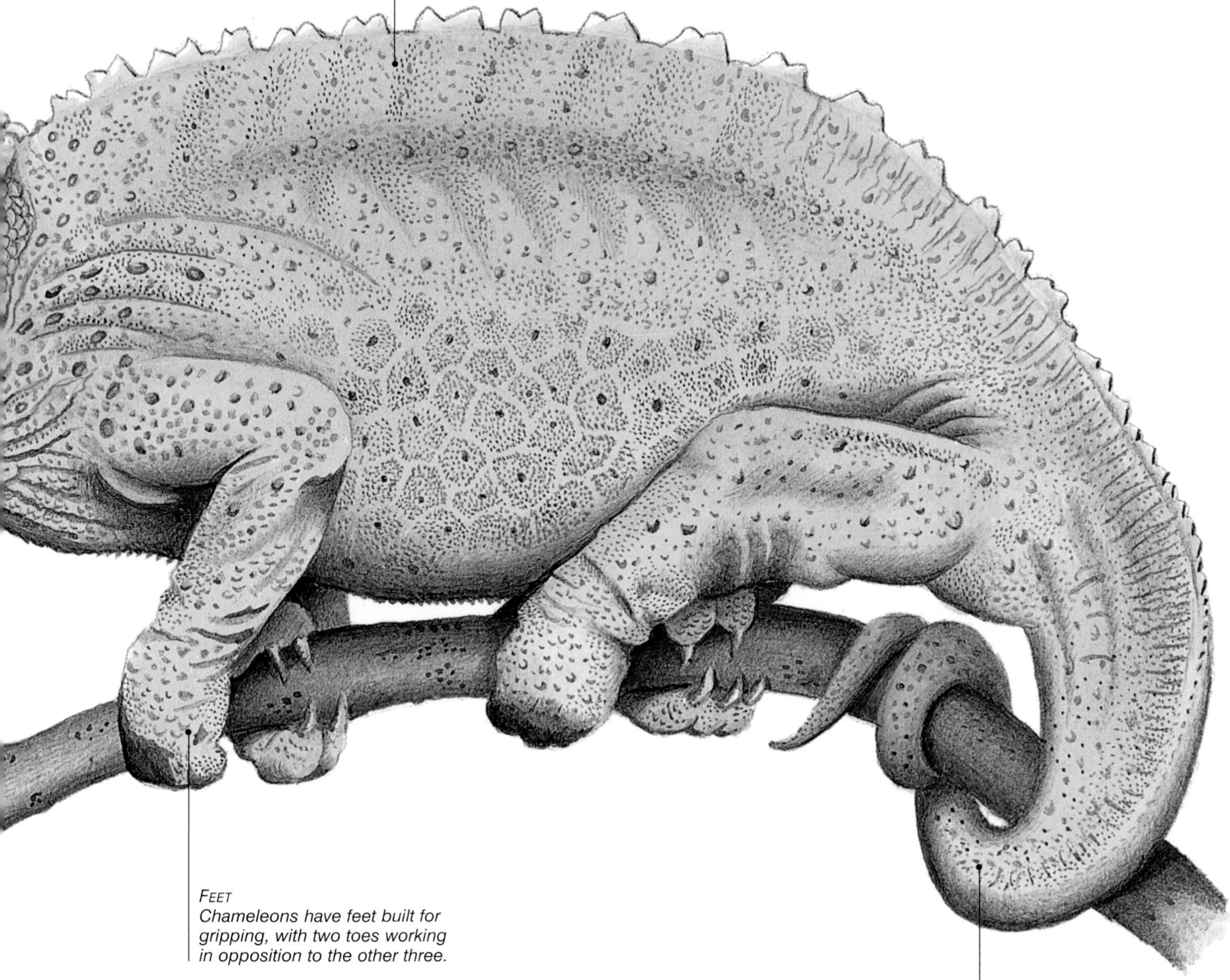

SKIN
The skin contains colour cells that can contract and expand to hide or show off a certain colour. There are three types of colour cells – red, yellow and blue – which combine to make the detailed skin patterns.

FEET
Chameleons have feet built for gripping, with two toes working in opposition to the other three.

TAIL
The long tail is prehensile, meaning it can wrap around branches, providing extra support on flimsy branches.

Geckos

There are just under 1000 species of gecko, forming the Geckonidae family of reptiles. They live across the tropical regions of the earth, and rarely stray far north. Geckos tend to be small and agile, using claws and sticky toes to climb just about anything. They cannot blink, but their eyes are protected by a transparent covering.

Leopard Gecko

Eublepharis macularius

Named after its dark, mottled spots, this gecko is nocturnal. By day, it shelters under rocks. At dusk, it uses its claws to scramble onto warm rocks and branches to absorb heat through its belly. It is a hunter with diverse tastes, tackling scorpions, beetles and spiders that it encounters on the ground.

FACT FILE	
Length:	22cm (8½in)
Distribution:	Western Asia
Habitat:	Semi-deserts
Diet:	Scorpions, spiders and insects
Reproduction:	2 eggs buried in damp ground
Status (IUCN Red List):	Least concern

Leaf-tailed Gecko

Phyllurus cornutus

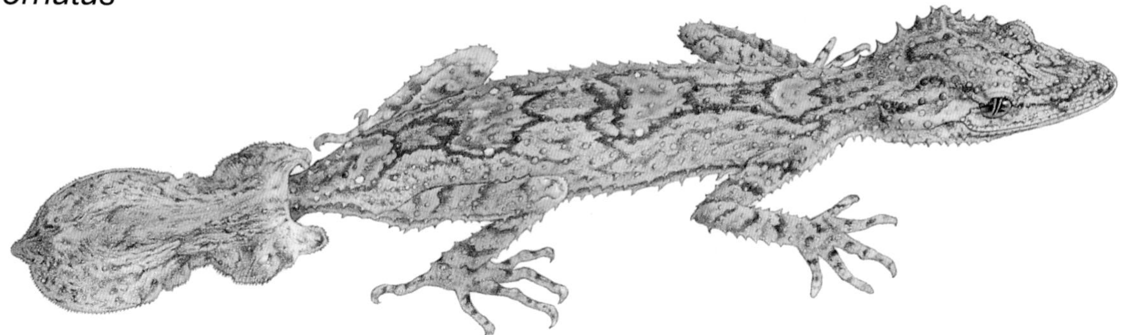

This is one of several leaf-tailed geckos that live in Australia. It rests during the day on tree trunks. The flat, leaf-shaped tail breaks up the tell-tale lizard shape against the bark. The gecko clings closely to the bark to reduce any shadows beneath the body that might highlight its presence.

FACT FILE	
Length:	16cm (6¼in)
Distribution:	Eastern Australia
Habitat:	Forests
Diet:	Insects
Reproduction:	Eggs buried in the ground
Status (IUCN Red List):	Least concern

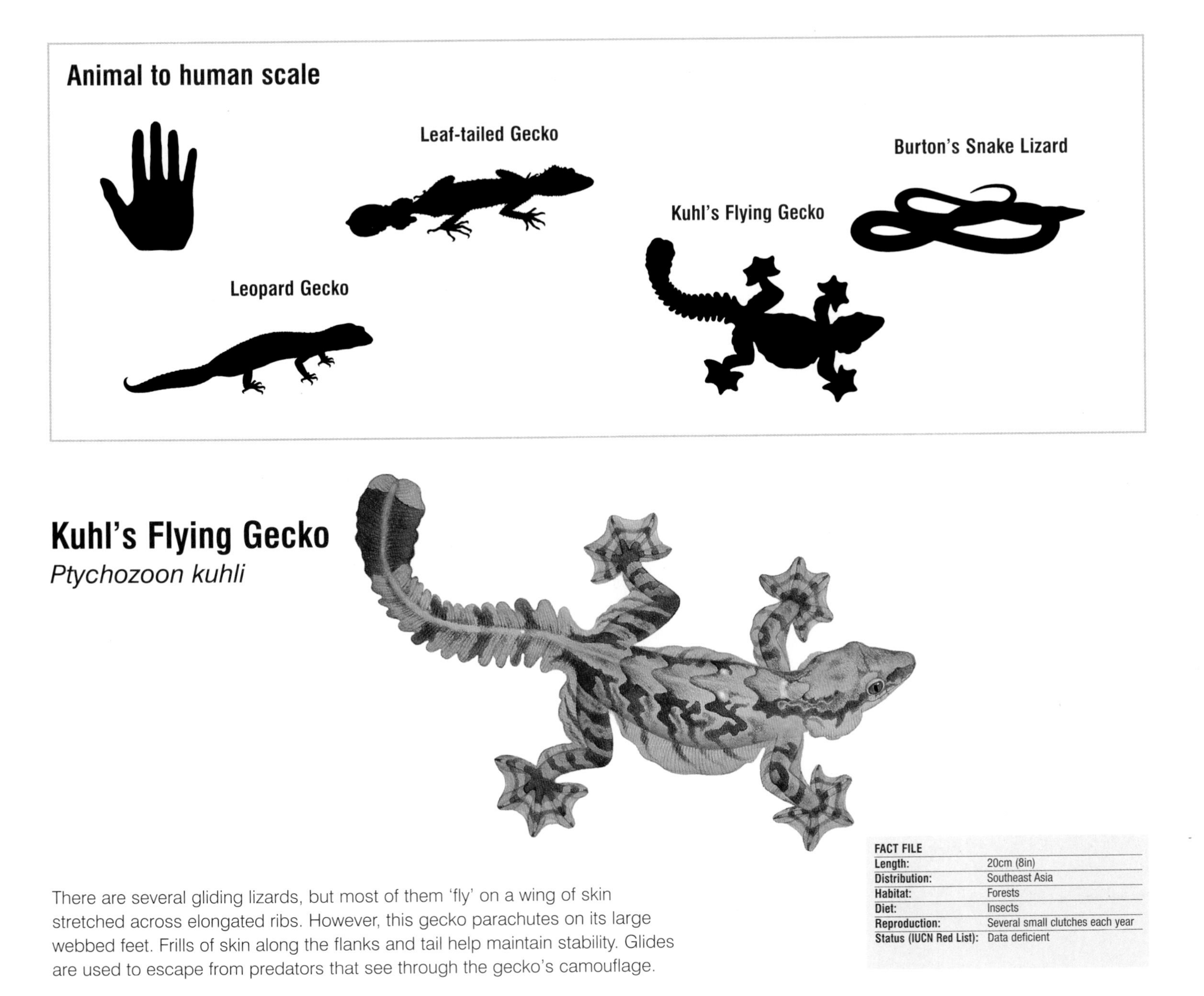

Kuhl's Flying Gecko

Ptychozoon kuhli

There are several gliding lizards, but most of them 'fly' on a wing of skin stretched across elongated ribs. However, this gecko parachutes on its large webbed feet. Frills of skin along the flanks and tail help maintain stability. Glides are used to escape from predators that see through the gecko's camouflage.

FACT FILE	
Length:	20cm (8in)
Distribution:	Southeast Asia
Habitat:	Forests
Diet:	Insects
Reproduction:	Several small clutches each year
Status (IUCN Red List):	Data deficient

Burton's Snake Lizard

Lialis burtonis

This may look like a snake but it is actually a lizard that does not have any legs. It is a relative of the geckos and so, like snakes, cannot blink – most legless lizards can blink. The giveaway here is that this species has eardrums behind the eyes; true snakes are more or less deaf.

FACT FILE	
Length:	60cm (23½in)
Distribution:	Australia and New Guinea
Habitat:	Forests to desert
Diet:	Lizards
Reproduction:	2 eggs laid per year
Status (IUCN Red List):	Least concern

Skinks and Relatives

The Scinidae family is the largest group of reptiles, containing about 1400 species. Unsurprisingly for such a large family, skinks come in all shapes and sizes, but they tend to be long, slender lizards. A larger suborder called the Scincomorpha contains another 500 related species, including the girdled lizards and whiptails.

Karoo Girdled Lizard

Cordylus polyzonus

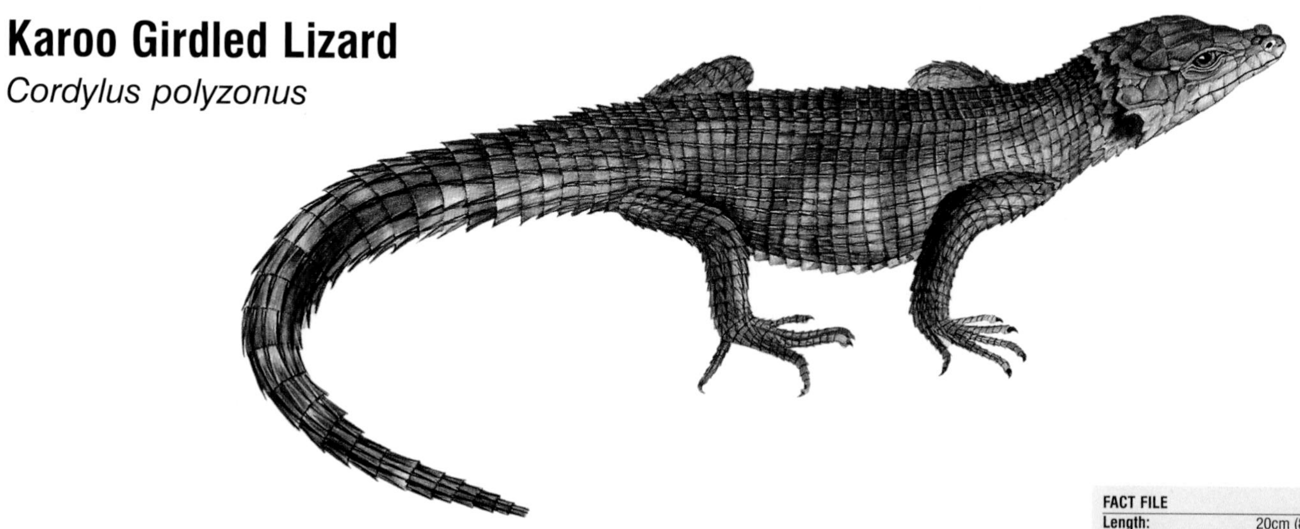

All girdled lizards live in southern and eastern Africa. This species is from the arid Karoo region of western South Africa. Its large scales give it the look of a miniature crocodile. The scales are arranged in rings or girdles around the body – hence the name – and make the lizard's skin very rough to the touch.

FACT FILE	
Length:	20cm (8in)
Distribution:	Karoo, South Africa
Habitat:	Rocky semi-desert
Diet:	Beetles and grasshoppers
Reproduction:	5 young born in summer
Status (IUCN Red List):	Endangered

Berber Skink

Eumeces schneideri

This desert skink spends a lot of time burrowing – almost swimming – through soft sand, to keep cool in the heat of the day. The long body is almost cylindrical and the short legs fold back against the body to reduce resistance as it wriggles underground. On the surface, its long, wide toes stop it sinking into the sand.

FACT FILE	
Length:	36cm (14in)
Distribution:	North Africa and west Asia
Habitat:	Deserts
Diet:	Beetles and ground insects
Reproduction:	Eggs laid in spring
Status (IUCN Red List):	Least concern

Milos Wall Lizard

Podarcis milensis

FACT FILE	
Length:	20cm (8in)
Distribution:	Aegean islands
Habitat:	Rocky areas
Diet:	Insects
Reproduction:	Lays several clutches
Status (IUCN Red List):	Vulnerable

Wall lizards are the small, scampering lizards seen around the Mediterranean region. This species lives on the Greek island of Milos and a few surrounding islets. Wherever they are seen, wall lizards are all very similar, which leads zoologists to think they all evolved very recently from a single ancestor.

Granite Night Lizard

Xantusia henshawi

FACT FILE	
Length:	14cm (5½in)
Distribution:	S. California and Baja, Mexico
Habitat:	Arid areas
Diet:	Insects and spiders
Reproduction:	Babies born tail first
Status (IUCN Red List):	Least concern

The night lizards are small scincomorphs that live mainly in the desert region of North America. They look similar to wall lizards, but are not closely related. As the name suggests, this species is strictly nocturnal. By day, it stays cool by squeezing into cracks in dry rocks.

Tenerife Lizard

Gallotia galloti

FACT FILE	
Length:	40cm (16in)
Distribution:	Tenerife and La Palma
Habitat:	Rocky areas
Diet:	Ripe fruits and insects
Reproduction:	Several clutches per year
Status (IUCN Red List):	Least concern

This species is a giant type of wall lizard that lives on a few of the Canary Islands. It is an example of island giganticism, where normally small animal types take on a large size in the absence of large mainland animals. However, the Tenerife species is outgrown by a lizard on neighbouring Hierro.

Gila Monster

Heloderma suspectum

The gila monster marauds through the rocky deserts of the southwestern United States and Mexico. It preys on rodents, birds' eggs and small birds, killing with its wide, powerful jaws. The jaws hold a secret weapon – there is venom in the saliva, which makes the gila monster one of perhaps just three venomous lizards.

FACT FILE	
Length:	55cm (21½in)
Distribution:	Southwest USA and Mexico
Habitat:	Grasslands, shrubs and desert
Diet:	Eggs, rodents and birds
Reproduction:	10 eggs laid each year
Status (IUCN Red List):	Near threatened

The gila monster belongs to a tiny reptile family, the Helodermatidae, or the beaded lizards. There is just one other member, the Mexican beaded lizard, which is slightly larger and also deploys poisonous saliva. Both give painful bites with their hooked teeth, although humans are rarely affected by the venom.

TEETH
The gila monster does not have fangs. The venom is produced by salivary glands and trickles along the teeth. The monster flips on its back after attacking to help the venom enter its victim's blood.

SCALES
The gila monster is a 'beaded' lizard, so named after the unusual round scales that cover the skin.

TAIL
The large tail stores fats for keeping the lizard alive during droughts and other times of famine.

TONGUE
Like many reptiles, the gila monster smells with its forked tongue. The tips pick up scent chemicals; these are detected by a smelling organ in the roof of the mouth.

Pythons and Boas

The boas and pythons are the largest snakes of all. The green anaconda, a South American boid, is the heaviest, weighing 250kg (551lb). The slightly more slender reticulated python of southern Asia is the longest; some specimens grow to 12m (39ft 4in) or more. No boas or pythons are venomous; they kill by constriction.

Cuban Boa

Epicrates angulifer

FACT FILE	
Length:	3.75m (12ft)
Distribution:	Cuba
Habitat:	Forests
Diet:	Rodents, including hutias
Reproduction:	Gives birth to young
Status (IUCN Red List):	Least concern

This rare boa lives only on the Cuban mainland and a few surrounding islands. It is the country's largest snake. Despite its large size, the boa is frequently seen hunting in trees as well as on the ground. Its forest habitat has been reduced in recent years, and many boas have been captured as pets.

Green Tree Python

Chondropython viridis

FACT FILE	
Length:	1.5m (5ft)
Distribution:	New Guinea and N. Australia
Habitat:	Tropical forest
Diet:	Reptiles, insects and rodents
Reproduction:	Up to 30 eggs laid in spring
Status (IUCN Red List):	Least concern

There are two big differences between pythons and boas. Boas generally give birth to their young, while pythons lay eggs. In addition, pythons use heat-sensitive pits on the face to track prey in the dark; boas do not. The tree python's pits are on the upper lip, helping it home in on warm-blooded targets.

Blood Python

Python curtus

This Asian python is not particularly long, but is very heavily built. It lays at least a dozen eggs each year, and the female wraps her thick body around them for protection. She also shivers her muscles to provide a little extra heat now and then. The female does not eat for many days as she broods the eggs.

FACT FILE	
Length:	2.5m (8ft 3in)
Distribution:	Southeast Asia
Habitat:	Forests with marshes and rivers
Diet:	Mammals and birds
Reproduction:	12 eggs brooded by female
Status (IUCN Red List):	Least concern

Royal Python

Python regius

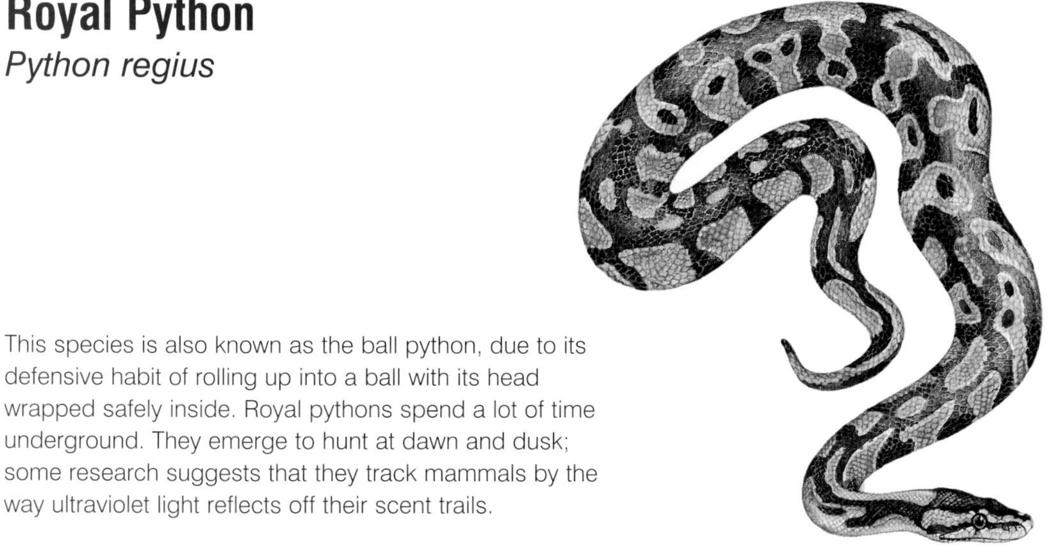

This species is also known as the ball python, due to its defensive habit of rolling up into a ball with its head wrapped safely inside. Royal pythons spend a lot of time underground. They emerge to hunt at dawn and dusk; some research suggests that they track mammals by the way ultraviolet light reflects off their scent trails.

FACT FILE	
Length:	1.8m (6ft)
Distribution:	West and Central Africa
Habitat:	Forests
Diet:	Rodents
Reproduction:	10 eggs brooded by mother
Status (IUCN Red List):	Least concern

Red-tailed Pipe Snake

Cylindrophis rufus

This species is also called the two-headed snake; the snake has a tube-shaped body with an indistinct head and a bright tail. It is difficult to tell which end is the head, and the snake makes the most of this confusion. When attacked, it hides its head and holds the tail up. Attackers normally aim for the wrong end.

FACT FILE	
Length:	1m (3ft 3in)
Distribution:	South China to Indonesia
Habitat:	Forest
Diet:	Snakes and eels
Reproduction:	2 young born per litter
Status (IUCN Red List):	Least concern

Non-deadly Snakes

Most snakes are not venomous, but they are all hunters. Many smaller snakes kill with the power of their bites, swallowing prey whole, perhaps while still alive. Larger species are constrictors. The largest family of snakes are colubrids. The majority are non-venomous, although some have chemicals in their saliva that stun prey.

Beauty Rat Snake

Orthriophis taeniurus

FACT FILE	
Length:	2.1m (6ft 10in)
Distribution:	East and Southeast Asia
Habitat:	Forest edges and rocky areas
Diet:	Bats, birds and rodents
Reproduction:	5–15 eggs laid
Status (IUCN Red List):	Least concern

This colourful colubrid snake has many subspecies and colour variants living all over eastern Asia. They all have a characteristic stripe along the flexible tail. They will wiggle the tail when threatened in an attempt to emulate a rattlesnake; if this fails, they squirt foul liquids onto attackers from an anal gland.

Kingsnake

Lampropeltis getula

FACT FILE	
Length:	1.3m (4ft 3in)
Distribution:	North America
Habitat:	Forests, grasslands and deserts
Diet:	Small snakes, birds and rodents
Reproduction:	Up to 24 eggs laid in nest
Status (IUCN Red List):	Least concern

There are at least half a dozen subspecies of kingsnake. Each displays an eye-boggling array of vibrant colour variants, which belies the fact that they are all the same species. Some colour morphs mimic the looks of deadly coral snakes, which they rub shoulders with in many parts of their range.

Grass Snake

Natrix natrix

This species is one of the most widespread reptiles on earth. Its range extends from the river valleys of the Welsh borders to the shores of Lake Baikal in Siberia. The snake is tied to water; most of its prey are aquatic animals like frogs, newts and fish. It incubates its eggs in heaps of rotting leaves.

FACT FILE	
Length:	76cm (30in)
Distribution:	Europe, Siberia, northwest Africa
Habitat:	Ponds, marshes and lakes
Diet:	Frogs, fish, rodents and birds
Reproduction:	Eggs laid in compost and manure
Status (IUCN Red List):	Least concern

Banded Water Snake

Nerodia fasciata

Water snakes often bask on rocks beside rivers and lakes during the day. They slide into the water when disturbed and they can bite if cornered. The saliva is not venomous, but it does contain an anticoagulant that makes prey bleed to death. The snakes hunt mainly at night.

FACT FILE	
Length:	1.2m (4ft)
Distribution:	Southern United States
Habitat:	Freshwater
Diet:	Fish and amphibians
Reproduction:	Young born in summer
Status (IUCN Red List):	Least concern

Painted Bronzeback

Dendrelaphis pictus

This slender snake is a common visitor to gardens in southern Asia. Its long body spreads its weight through the flimsiest branches and leaf fronds. When threatened, the snake inflates its body, stretching the scales apart to reveal an eerie bluish skin beneath.

FACT FILE	
Length:	1.2m (4ft)
Distribution:	South and southeast Asia
Habitat:	Shrubs and forest
Diet:	Frogs and lizards
Reproduction:	Lays eggs
Status (IUCN Red List):	Least concern

Venomous Snakes

Snake venom is produced in large modified salivary glands, meaning venom is just a very toxic form of spit. Many venomous snakes have arrow-shaped heads to accommodate the large glands. Snake venom kills in several ways, by attacking the nervous system and muscles. Most also digest the bite site, causing blood loss.

Black Mamba

Dendroaspis polylepis

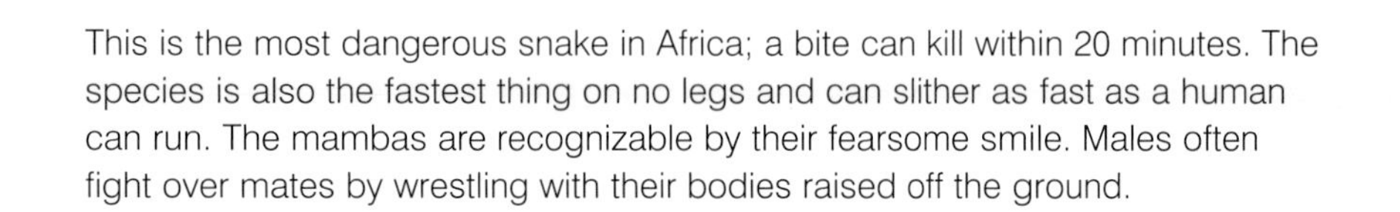

FACT FILE	
Length:	2.5m (8ft 3in)
Distribution:	South and East Africa
Habitat:	Wooded savannah
Diet:	Rodents
Reproduction:	6–17 eggs laid in spring
Status (IUCN Red List):	Least concern

This is the most dangerous snake in Africa; a bite can kill within 20 minutes. The species is also the fastest thing on no legs and can slither as fast as a human can run. The mambas are recognizable by their fearsome smile. Males often fight over mates by wrestling with their bodies raised off the ground.

Monocled Cobra

Naja kaouthia

FACT FILE	
Length:	1.7m (5ft 6in)
Distribution:	Central and South Asia
Habitat:	Swamps and mangroves
Diet:	Rodents and snakes
Reproduction:	25–45 eggs
Status (IUCN Red List):	Least concern

The monocled cobra is named after the diamond-shaped marking on its hood. This is in contrast to the spectacled cobra, which lives further east, and has a 'two-eyed' mark. This cobra is one of the species used by snake charmers. The deaf snakes rise out of their basket in response to light, not the sound.

Eastern Coral Snake

Micrurus fulvius

FACT FILE	
Length:	76cm (30in)
Distribution:	Southern USA and Mexico
Habitat:	Soil and leaf litter
Diet:	Snakes
Reproduction:	5–7 eggs laid in summer
Status (IUCN Red List):	Least concern

The coral snakes are the most venomous snakes in North America, although bites are less common than those from rattlesnakes. Many non-venomous snakes mimic its banded colours. A rhyme is used to identify the killer: 'Red touches yellow, you're a dead fellow. Red touches black, you're OK Jack.'

Turtle-headed Seasnake

Emydocephalus annulatus

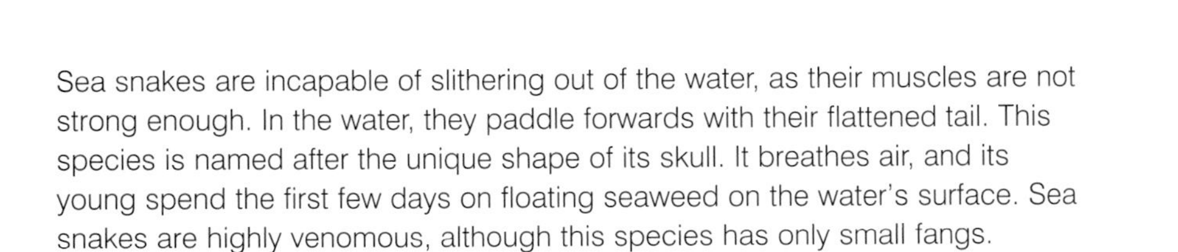

FACT FILE	
Length:	90cm (35in)
Distribution:	Western Pacific
Habitat:	Coral reefs
Diet:	Fish eggs
Reproduction:	2 young born at surface
Status (IUCN Red List):	Least concern

Sea snakes are incapable of slithering out of the water, as their muscles are not strong enough. In the water, they paddle forwards with their flattened tail. This species is named after the unique shape of its skull. It breathes air, and its young spend the first few days on floating seaweed on the water's surface. Sea snakes are highly venomous, although this species has only small fangs.

Russell's Viper

Daboia russelii

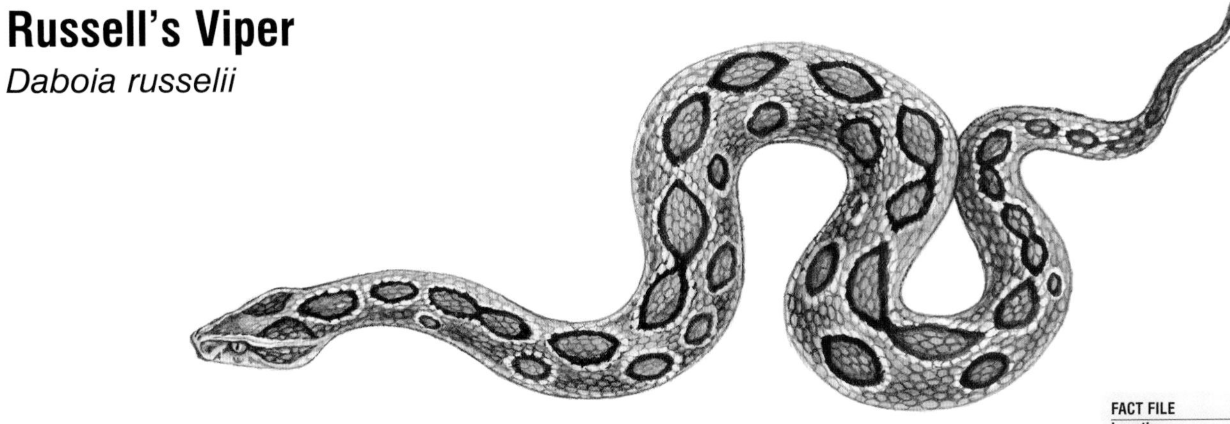

FACT FILE	
Length:	1.2m (4ft)
Distribution:	South and East Asia
Habitat:	Grassy and bushy areas
Diet:	Rodents
Reproduction:	20–40 babies in each litter
Status (IUCN Red List):	Least concern

The Russell's viper is one of the 'Big Four' snakes in India, which together are responsible for hundreds of thousands of potentially fatal bites – thousands of people do die each year. The other three snakes are the spectacled cobra, the krait and the saw-scaled viper.

King Cobra

Ophiophagus hannah

The king cobra is the largest venomous snake in the world. Its venom is also one of the most potent, although bites are rare because the snake tends to stay out of sight in the deep jungle. This cobra preys exclusively on other snakes and is largely immune to their venom.

FACT FILE	
Length:	4.9m (16ft)
Distribution:	South and southeast Asia
Habitat:	Dense forest
Diet:	Snakes
Reproduction:	Eggs laid in nest
Status (IUCN Red List):	Vulnerable

YELLOW BANDS
The most obvious features of a king cobra are the yellow and black bands that run across its throat.

The king cobra is the only snake species to build a nest for its eggs. The nest is a mound of leaves; the eggs are laid in a lower chamber while the female sits in the upper section. The male patrols nearby. The parents leave the area as soon as the eggs begin to hatch and so avoid preying on their own young.

FANGS
Unlike vipers and rattlesnakes, a cobra's fangs are positioned near the back of the mouth. They have a hollow centre for pumping venom into victims.

THREAT DISPLAY
A king cobra can raise the first third of its body off the ground and so stand eye to eye with a human. This threat display is accompanied by a deep hiss.

Hood
A king cobra has a smaller hood than many cobras, but it is built in the same way; it has long ribs that can articulate outwards.

AMPHIBIANS

Amphibian means 'between two worlds'. In general, these animals live a double life, with the early days spent underwater, before the adults move onto dry land.

There are about 5500 species of amphibian. Most of them are frogs, those familiar big-mouth, tailless leapers. However, there are also a few hundred newts, salamanders and other similarly tailed amphibians. The most unusual amphibians are the little-known caecilians. At first glance often mistaken for fat worms or blind snakes, these strange hunting amphibians live in tropical rivers or in deep burrows.

Left: The fire salamander lives across southern Europe. It stores milky toxins in glands on its neck, which burn the skin of attackers.

Great Crested Newt

Triturus cristatus

Newts and salamanders are amphibians with tails. There is no strict difference between the two types of animal, although newts tend to be more associated with water than the ground-living salamanders. The great crested newt is one of the largest newt species – although salamanders grow to ten times the size. The species is named after the distinctive crest on the back of the males.

TAIL
The tail is flattened into a paddle, and is swung from side to side to push the newt through the water.

FACT FILE	
Length:	17cm (6¾in)
Distribution:	Europe
Habitat:	Freshwater
Diet:	Tadpoles and aquatic insects
Reproduction:	300 eggs laid in summer
Status (IUCN Red List):	Least concern

Newts start their lives in water, breathing through gills. By around four months old, they have lost the gills and grown legs, and now emerge from the water to hibernate on land. In spring, the newts return to the water to hunt and breed, gluing eggs to water plants. A great crested newt can repeat this cycle for ten years.

FEMALE
Females do not develop a crest of vibrant breeding colours, but they are usually slightly longer than the males.

WARTS
Lumpy mucous glands keep the skin moist when the newt leaves the water.

CREST
The jagged crest running down the spine develops on males during the breeding season as a signal of dominance. The males with the largest crests get the most mates.

UNDERPARTS
Both sexes have blotchy underparts, but the male's belly takes on a vibrant orange colour in the breeding season.

True Frogs

There are 28 families of frogs, living on all land masses except Antarctica. The most widespread family – although not quite the largest – is the Ranidae, known as the true frogs. This family includes the edible frogs served in haute cuisine restaurants, the burly bullfrogs, and many of the tree-living frogs of Africa and Asia.

African Bullfrog

Pyxicephalus adspersus

This species is one of the biggest frogs, with a male weighing 2kg (4lb 6oz). Males have a yellow throat and are about twice the size of females, but both sexes are olive green with bumpy skin folds along the back. In the wild, African bullfrogs bury themselves during the dry season. A cocoon of loose skin and mucus stops them drying out.

FACT FILE	
Length:	24cm (9½in)
Distribution:	Central and southern Africa
Habitat:	Grassland
Diet:	Insects and fish
Reproduction:	3000–4000 eggs at a time
Status (IUCN Red List):	Least concern

American Bullfrog

Rana catesbeiana

The largest North American member of the true frog family, this bullfrog is a largely aquatic species. Males have a visible eardrum larger than their eyes, while in females the eardrum is the same size as the eyes. Male American bullfrogs attract females with their loud call, similar to the roar of a bull.

FACT FILE	
Length:	20cm (8in)
Distribution:	North America
Habitat:	Permanent bodies of water
Diet:	Insects, worms and fish
Reproduction:	20,000 eggs at a time
Status (IUCN Red List):	Least concern

Pickerel Frog

Rana palustris

This species is a North American type of leopard frog, so-called because of the prominent dark spots on the green skin. The other frogs within this group have circular spots, but the pickerel has rectangular spots. The pickerel frog secretes irritants from its skin, so pet owners should wash their hands after handling.

FACT FILE	
Length:	10cm (4in)
Distribution:	United States and SE Canada
Habitat:	Close to water
Diet:	Crickets, maggots and worms
Reproduction:	3000 eggs at a time
Status (IUCN Red List):	Least concern

Marsh Frog

Rana ridibunda

The largest European frog, the marsh frog lives in lakes and marshes. The males make a duck-like croak using two grey vocal sacs that inflate on either side of the throat. The edible frogs eaten in some parts of Europe are a hybrid of the marsh frog and the slightly smaller, but very similar, pool frog.

FACT FILE	
Length:	18cm (7in)
Distribution:	S.W. Europe to west China
Habitat:	Close to still water
Diet:	Crickets, maggots and worms
Reproduction:	1000–4000 eggs
Status (IUCN Red List):	Least concern

Common Sand Frog

Tomopterna cryptotis

This species is sometimes called the cryptic sand frog because its colouring keeps it hidden among the mossy pebbles of its savannah habitat. The back feet have a spade-like structure on the heel for digging into soft sand. The frog spends the dry season buried underground, emerging only when the rains arrive.

FACT FILE	
Length:	6cm (2¼in)
Distribution:	Sub-Saharan Africa
Habitat:	Dry grasslands
Diet:	Termites and beetles
Reproduction:	Eggs laid in temporary pool
Status (IUCN Red List):	Least concern

Marine Toad

Bufo marinus

This enormous toad is one of the few amphibian species to survive in coastal waters. However, they can live pretty much anywhere with enough water. They eat just about anything and so the toads have been exported around the world as pest controllers. However, these experiments have often failed, with the toads becoming pests themselves – most notably in Australia, where they are known as cane toads.

FACT FILE	
Length:	24cm (9½in)
Distribution:	Central and South America
Habitat:	Coasts, grasslands and forests
Diet:	Insects, rodents and snakes
Reproduction:	20,000 eggs laid all year around
Status (IUCN Red List):	Least concern

A marine toad will eat whatever it can fit in its large mouth. It is known as the cane toad in Australia because it was introduced there in the 1930s to tackle beetle pests that were destroying sugar cane crops. However, few of the toads set up home in the plantations and instead now live wild across the east of the country.

HIND FEET
Toads tend to crawl more than frogs, which move by leaping. The back feet are only slightly webbed to help with covering rough ground, but are of less use when swimming.

WARTY SKIN
Toads are known for their warty skin. They secrete waterproofing mucus; this liquid also contains toxins that can cause hallucinations in humans if ingested.

TOXIN GLAND
Large swellings behind the ear are called parotid glands. They contain milky toxins that squirt over attackers when the toad is handled roughly.

TONGUE
The sticky tongue is attached at the front of the mouth, not the back, and extends a long way to ensnare smaller prey.

VOCAL SAC
All frogs and toads breathe by pulsating the throat rather than using chest muscles. The toad's flexible throat sac is inflated to produce a trilling call.

Tree Frogs

The largest group of frogs is the Hylidae family, with the more unwieldy common name of the Austro-American tree frogs. Although many species of ranid true frogs have also adapted to life in the trees in a similar way, the hylids tend to be lanky frogs with bulbous fingertips used to clamber through the branches.

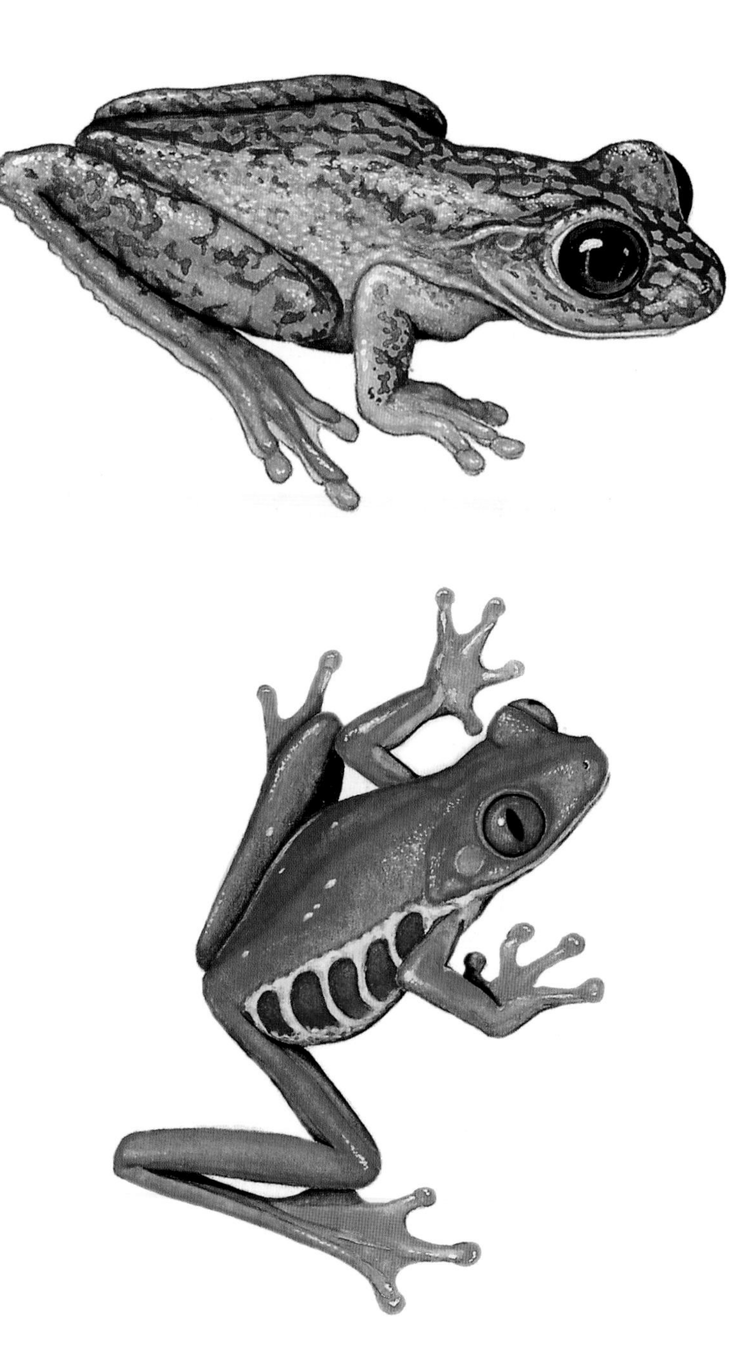

Australian Lace-lid

Nyctimystes dayi

This is the only Australian representative of a tree frog group that is common in New Guinea and parts of Indonesia. It lives in the bushes around fast-flowing streams in the rugged bush of northeast Australia. Its tadpoles have sucker-shaped mouths, which they use to cling to rocks to avoid being washed downstream.

FACT FILE	
Length:	5cm (2in)
Distribution:	N.E. Queensland, Australia
Habitat:	Mountain creeks
Diet:	Insects
Reproduction:	100 eggs laid in streams
Status (IUCN Red List):	Endangered

Red-eyed Tree Frog

Agalychnis callidrias

One of the most iconic of tree frogs, this species rests on leaves during the day, employing the disc-shaped suckers on its toes to cling to flat surfaces. It hunts at night. Females lay their eggs on a leaf overhanging water, where the male then fertilizes them. When the eggs hatch, the tadpoles fall into the water beneath.

FACT FILE	
Length:	7cm (2¾in)
Distribution:	Central America
Habitat:	Tropical forest
Diet:	Insects
Reproduction:	Eggs laid on leaves in summer
Status (IUCN Red List):	Least concern

Blue-webbed Gliding Tree Frog

Rhacophorus reinwardtii

This frog belongs to the Rhacophoridae family, a smaller group of tree frogs found in Africa and Asia. It makes great leaps between branches, splaying its deeply webbed feet to form a parachute. Frogs have been seen to make glides of 12m (39ft) – a useful method of getting clean away from predators.

FACT FILE	
Length:	7cm (2¾in)
Distribution:	Southeast Asia and Indonesia
Habitat:	Rainforest
Diet:	Insects
Reproduction:	800 eggs laid in foam nests
Status (IUCN Red List):	Near threatened

Clown Tree Frog

Hyla leucophyllata

These tiny tree frogs have a dark and slender body dabbed with irregular blobs of yellow or cream. The undersides of their legs are orange, as is the webbing between their toes. As the wide circular iris shows, they are nocturnal and hunt in the dark. During the day they find a hiding place to sleep.

FACT FILE	
Length:	2.5cm (1in)
Distribution:	Amazon Basin
Habitat:	Lowland rainforest
Diet:	Moths and tiny insects
Reproduction:	600 eggs at a time
Status (IUCN Red List):	Least concern

Higher Frogs

All land vertebrates evolved from amphibian ancestors. However, today's frogs were something of an offshoot from these ancient animals, evolving about 230 million years ago. A handful of species have retained primitive features from this period, but 95 per cent are higher frogs, or neobatrachians.

Table Mountain Ghost Frog

Heleophryne rosei

This rare and endangered frog lives only on the fynbos heathlands of Table Mountain above Cape Town in South Africa. Out of the breeding season, it makes long journeys across land to find new streams. It lays its eggs at the time of year when the water is at its lowest, thus ensuring the young will hatch just when the mountain is receiving more rain.

FACT FILE	
Length:	6cm (2¼in)
Distribution:	Table Mountain, Cape Province
Habitat:	Fynbos heathland
Diet:	Insects
Reproduction:	Eggs laid in stream
Status (IUCN Red List):	Critically endangered

Turtle Frog

Myobatrachus gouldii

The turtle frog is a burrowing species that breaks into termite mounds to feed. It is named after the way it burrows head first – most frogs dig with their back feet – and almost swims like a turtle into the ground. The frog's eggs are laid underground; the young bypass the tadpole stage and hatch out as little froglets.

FACT FILE	
Length:	4.5cm (1¾in)
Distribution:	Western Australia
Habitat:	Semi-desert
Diet:	Insects
Reproduction:	Large eggs laid underground
Status (IUCN Red List):	Least concern

Emerald Glass Frog

Centrolene prosoblepon

Glass frogs are named after their translucent skin, which is so thin that you can see eggs and internal organs inside. The see-through skin makes them hard to spot on leaves – the green colour shows through from underneath. The males of this species have spines on their upper arms, which are used in fights over mates.

FACT FILE	
Length:	8cm (3in)
Distribution:	Colombia to Nicaragua
Habitat:	Tropical forests
Diet:	Insects
Reproduction:	Egg masses dropped in stream
Status (IUCN Red List):	Least concern

Blue Poison Dart Frog

Dendrobates azureus

The bright blue skin is a warning; it says, 'do not touch'. Poison dart frogs produce the strongest toxins of any vertebrate. It is manufactured from poisons collected from ants and other prey. Just touching the frog can cause pain (although pet frogs are not poisonous). The frog's toxins are used to tip traditional hunting darts.

FACT FILE	
Length:	6cm (2¼in)
Distribution:	Suriname
Habitat:	Rainforest, rocks near streams
Diet:	Tiny insects
Reproduction:	10 eggs laid in bromeliads
Status (IUCN Red List):	Least concern

Desert Rain Frog

Breviceps macrops

The desert rain frog is a narrow-mouth frog with a small pointed snout for digging through sand. It spends the dry season deep underground, emerging when the rains come. The round body helps with burrowing but makes mating tricky, so the male secretes a glue that sticks him to his intended.

FACT FILE	
Length:	6cm (2¼in)
Distribution:	Namaqualand, South Africa
Habitat:	Sandy dunes
Diet:	Insects
Reproduction:	Eggs laid underground
Status (IUCN Red List):	Vulnerable

Suriname Toad

Pipa pipa

This is one of the most outlandish amphibian species – a South American member of a primitive family called the Pipidae, which also includes the clawed frogs of Africa. Despite being an air-breathing amphibian, this animal never leaves the water. It is known for the extraordinary way in which mothers brood their eggs.

FACT FILE	
Length:	18cm (7in)
Distribution:	Tropical South America
Habitat:	Forest pools
Diet:	Fish and invertebrates
Reproduction:	Eggs brood on back
Status (IUCN Red List):	Least concern

The Suriname toad is not confined to Suriname but lives in murky forest pools and slow-flowing waterways across the Amazon and Orinoco basins. The toads have very flat bodies that allow them to slide in crevices or creep beneath water plants to avoid detection by predators.

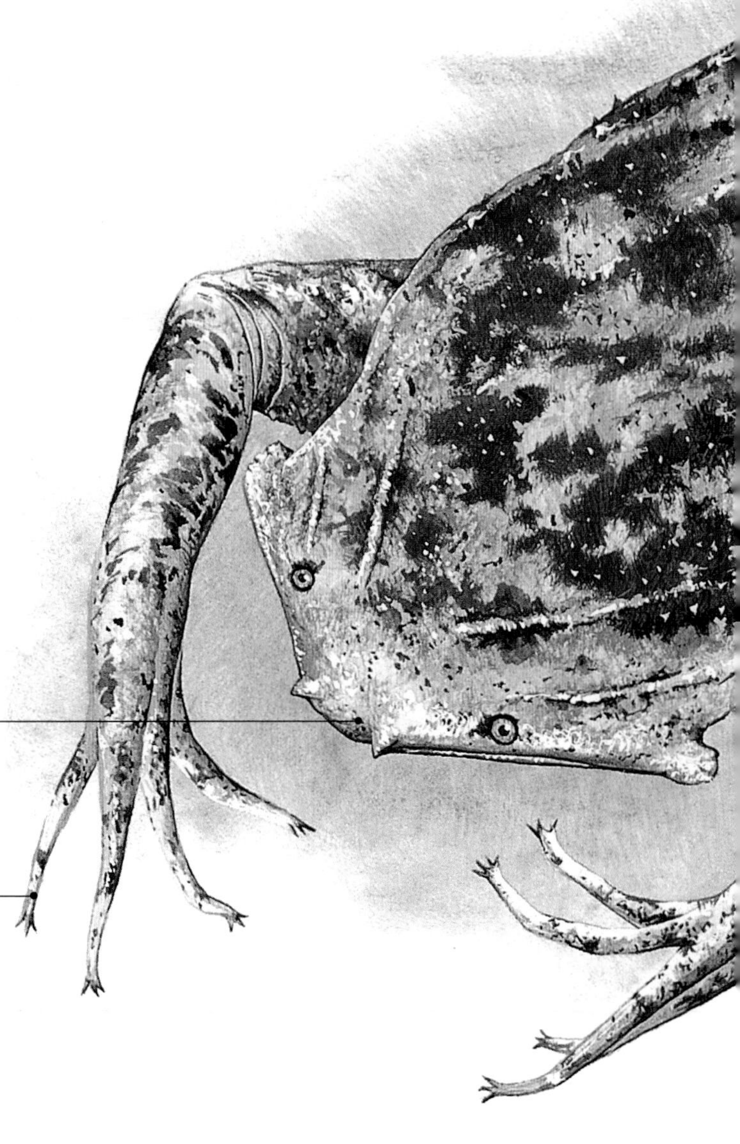

PITS
During mating, the male sweeps eggs onto the mother's back, where they embed themselves for three months. The tiny froglets emerge from pits in their mother's back.

NOSTRILS
The toad has long nostrils that function like snorkels, so the animal can breathe while hardly breaking the surface of the water.

FINGERS
The long fingers are used as feelers for finding prey in mud or in murky water. Each fingertip has several super-sensitive filaments.

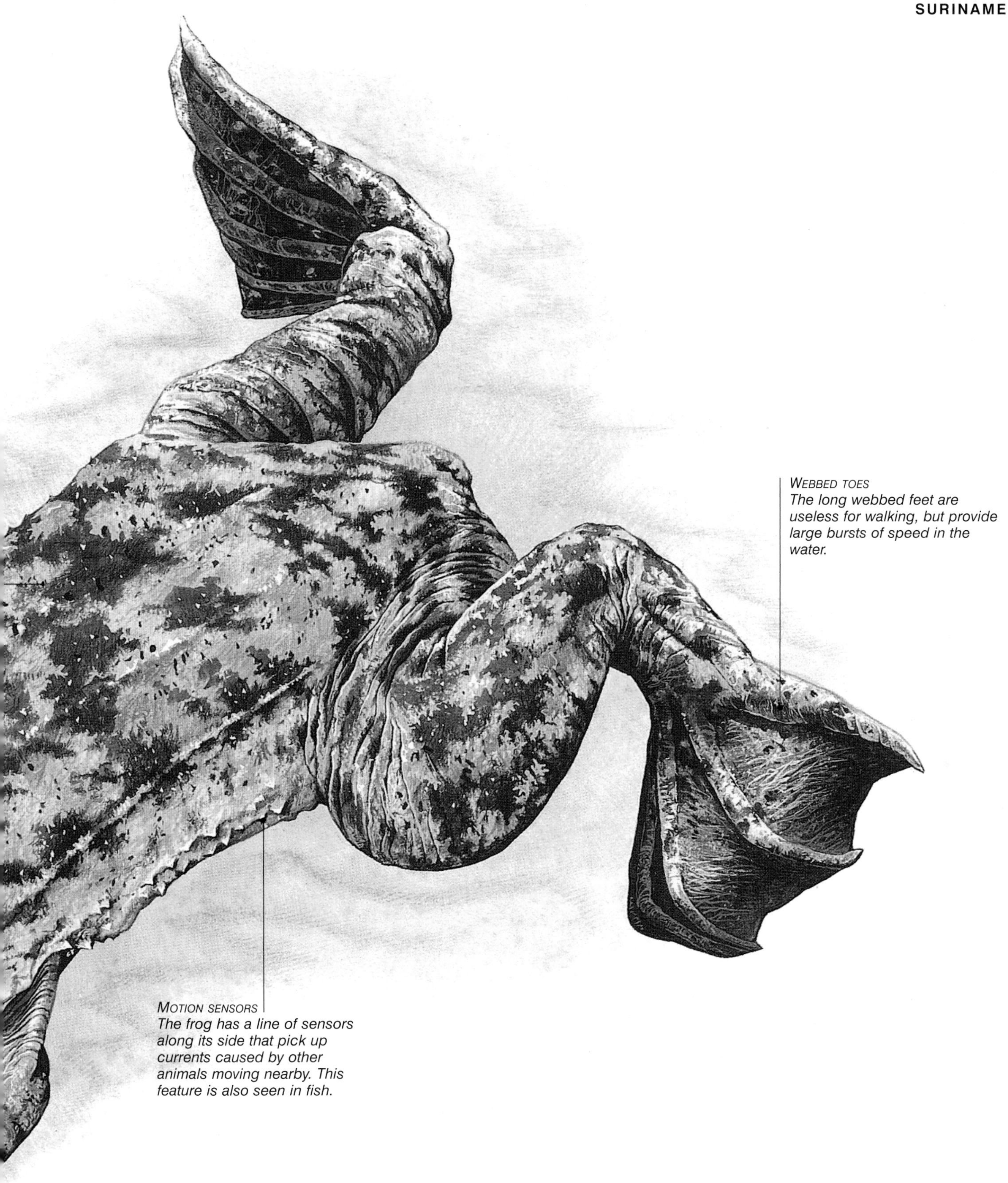

WEBBED TOES
The long webbed feet are useless for walking, but provide large bursts of speed in the water.

MOTION SENSORS
The frog has a line of sensors along its side that pick up currents caused by other animals moving nearby. This feature is also seen in fish.

FISH

One out of every two vertebrate species is a fish. These were the first backboned animals to appear on Earth, evolving more than half a billion years ago.

Today's fish are divided into three groups. The largest group are the bony fish, which contains the great majority of today's species. The second group, the cartilaginous fish, includes the sharks and rays, predating the first. The third group is the earliest of all. It is made up of jawless species, such as lancelets and hagfish, which have spiral-shaped mouths for sucking and grinding their food.

Left: All fish use gills to extract oxygen from the water. This whale shark also uses its gills as filters for sieving tiny bits of food.

Sharks

Including the largest and fiercest fish in the sea, there are more than 300 species of shark. They belong to an ancient group of fish that had skeletons made from flexible cartilage instead of bone. Most sharks live in warm ocean waters, but some hunt in cold and deep waters and a few species swim into large river systems.

Whale Shark

Rhincodon typus

The whale shark is the biggest known fish, but it poses little threat to people. It sucks in seawater and filters the food out of it using stacks of spongy tissue in the gills. The whale shark's mouth is so big that it often takes in fish – mainly small sardines and anchovies, but sometimes species as big as tuna.

FACT FILE	
Length:	18m (60ft)
Distribution:	Tropical oceans
Diet:	Plankton and fish
Reproduction:	Gives birth to young
Status (IUCN Red List):	Vulnerable

Tiger Shark

Galeocerdo cuvier

Named after the stripes on its flanks, especially when young, the tiger shark is not the largest fish in the sea, but it is responsible for more deadly attacks on humans than the great white. The species is regarded as something of a swimming dustbin, with specimens found with outlandish stomach contents.

FACT FILE	
Length:	4.3m (14ft)
Distribution:	Warm waters worldwide
Diet:	Fish, turtles and dolphins
Reproduction:	Around a dozen pups born
Status (IUCN Red List):	Near threatened

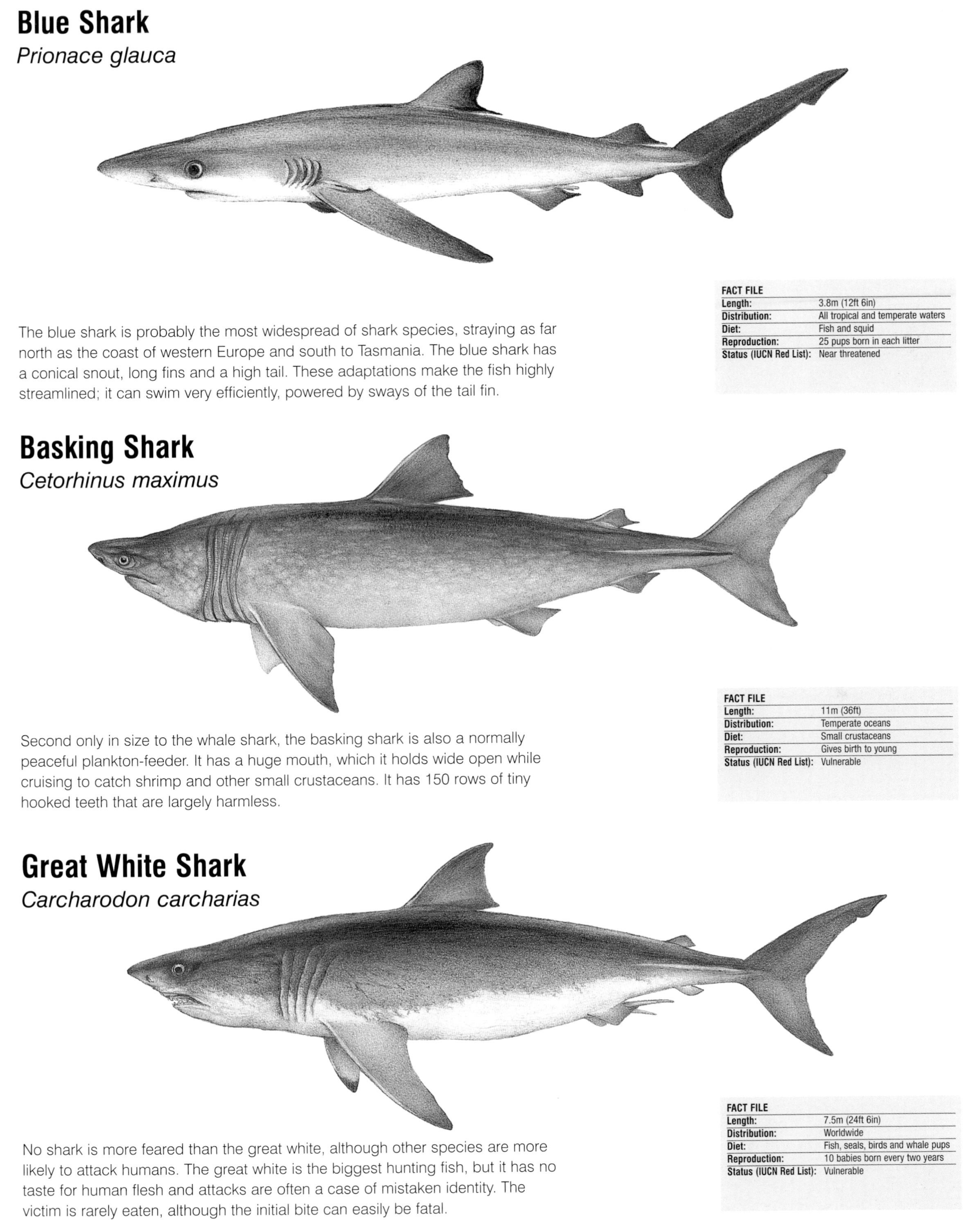

Blue Shark

Prionace glauca

The blue shark is probably the most widespread of shark species, straying as far north as the coast of western Europe and south to Tasmania. The blue shark has a conical snout, long fins and a high tail. These adaptations make the fish highly streamlined; it can swim very efficiently, powered by sways of the tail fin.

FACT FILE	
Length:	3.8m (12ft 6in)
Distribution:	All tropical and temperate waters
Diet:	Fish and squid
Reproduction:	25 pups born in each litter
Status (IUCN Red List):	Near threatened

Basking Shark

Cetorhinus maximus

Second only in size to the whale shark, the basking shark is also a normally peaceful plankton-feeder. It has a huge mouth, which it holds wide open while cruising to catch shrimp and other small crustaceans. It has 150 rows of tiny hooked teeth that are largely harmless.

FACT FILE	
Length:	11m (36ft)
Distribution:	Temperate oceans
Diet:	Small crustaceans
Reproduction:	Gives birth to young
Status (IUCN Red List):	Vulnerable

Great White Shark

Carcharodon carcharias

No shark is more feared than the great white, although other species are more likely to attack humans. The great white is the biggest hunting fish, but it has no taste for human flesh and attacks are often a case of mistaken identity. The victim is rarely eaten, although the initial bite can easily be fatal.

FACT FILE	
Length:	7.5m (24ft 6in)
Distribution:	Worldwide
Diet:	Fish, seals, birds and whale pups
Reproduction:	10 babies born every two years
Status (IUCN Red List):	Vulnerable

Hammerhead Shark

Sphyrna mokarran

No one is certain why hammerheads have their wide heads. It is probably for at least two reasons. First, the hammerhead provides extra lift as the shark swims slowly through the water. Second, the wide head is bristling with sensors, making it an accurate scanner for prey.

FACT FILE	
Length:	4.8m (15ft 7in)
Distribution:	Tropical oceans
Diet:	Fish, squid and crabs
Reproduction:	Embryos nourished by placenta
Status (IUCN Red List):	Endangered

ELECTRORECEPTORS
Tiny pits on the underside of the head are filled with gel that picks up the electric pulses produced by the muscles of prey.

This species is the largest of all the hammerheads. It lives in all oceans, but is confined to warmer waters. It often hunts in shallower waters, where its scanning equipment can be used to locate prey hiding on the seabed.

SENSORS
The shark's eyes and nostrils are located at the ends of the hammerhead. The broad distance between them makes the sensors more effective: the eyes scan a wider area, and scents arrive at the nostrils at slightly different times, making it easier to pinpoint their source.

SKIN
The shark's skin is covered in tiny hooks, or denticles, which are made from the same material as its teeth.

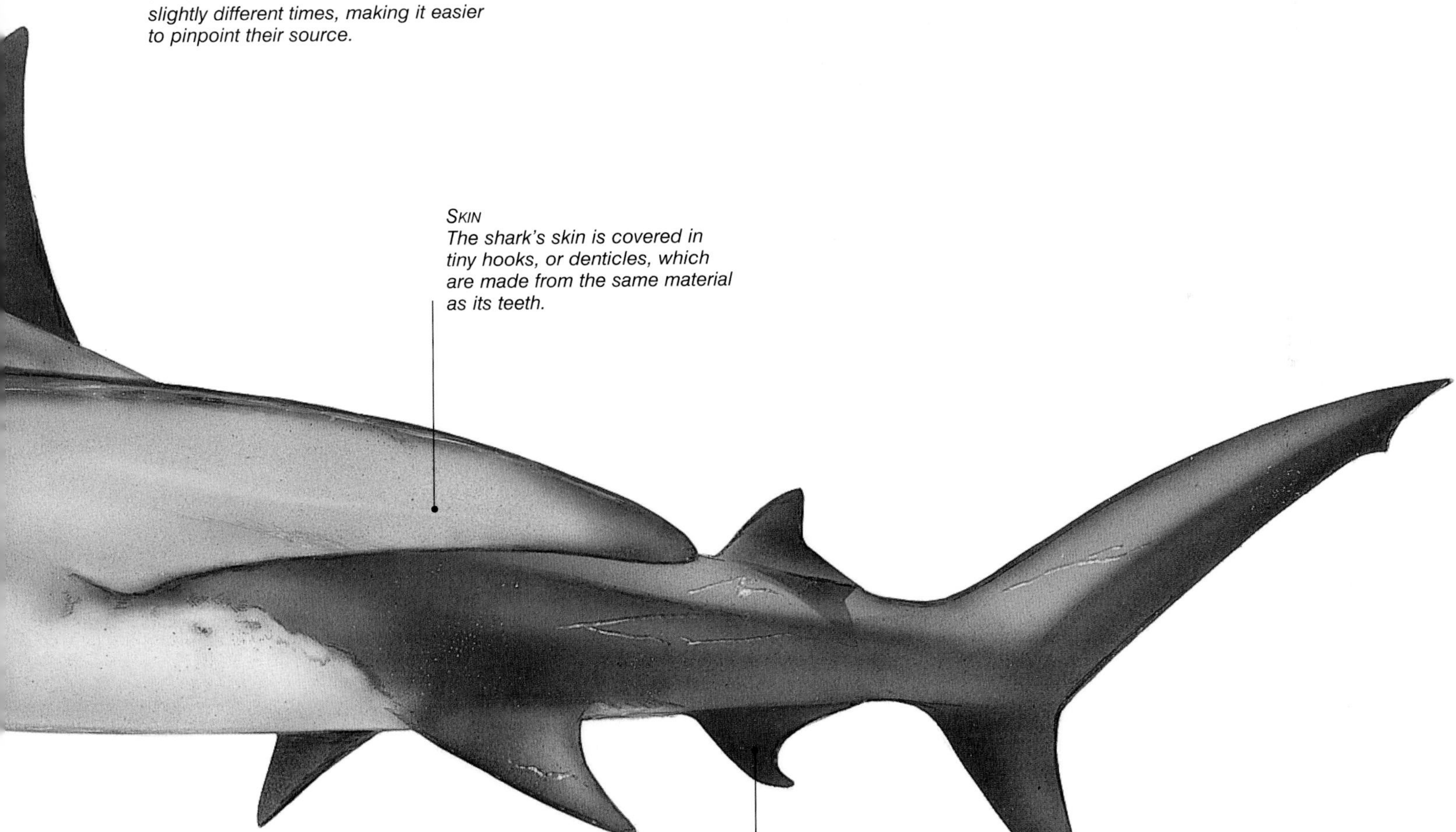

FINS
The pectoral fins work like the hydroplane of a submarine. They are angled to steer the shark up or down in the water.

Rays

The rays and skates are the cousins of sharks. Like their bigger and meaner relatives, these fish do not have any bones, only a skeleton of cartilage. There are about 450 species; most have a flat body with wing-like fins that flap the fish through the water.

Electric Ray

Torpedo torpedo

Electric rays have a kidney-shaped organ on each side of their body that, when contracted, can generate an electrical discharge. This species can inflict a shock of up to 200 volts. The electricity is used to defend the ray against attack, and also to stun or kill its prey.

FACT FILE	
Length:	60cm (23½in)
Distribution:	Eastern Atlantic; Mediterranean
Diet:	Mainly small fish
Reproduction:	About 20 pups born each year
Status (IUCN Red List):	Data deficient

Common Stingray

Dasyatis pastinaca

Slightly more rounded in outline than skates and true rays, the common stingray lives in shallow water. A saw-toothed poisonous barb, up to 35cm (13¾in) long, projects from the top of its tail. If disturbed, it will lash with its tail and may stab or cut its victim seriously. Poison on the barb causes pain, but deaths are rare.

FACT FILE	
Length:	1.5m (5ft)
Distribution:	Eastern Atlantic; Mediterranean
Diet:	Fish, crustaceans and molluscs
Reproduction:	6 pups born every year
Status (IUCN Red List):	Data deficient

Spotted Eagle Ray

Aetobatus narinari

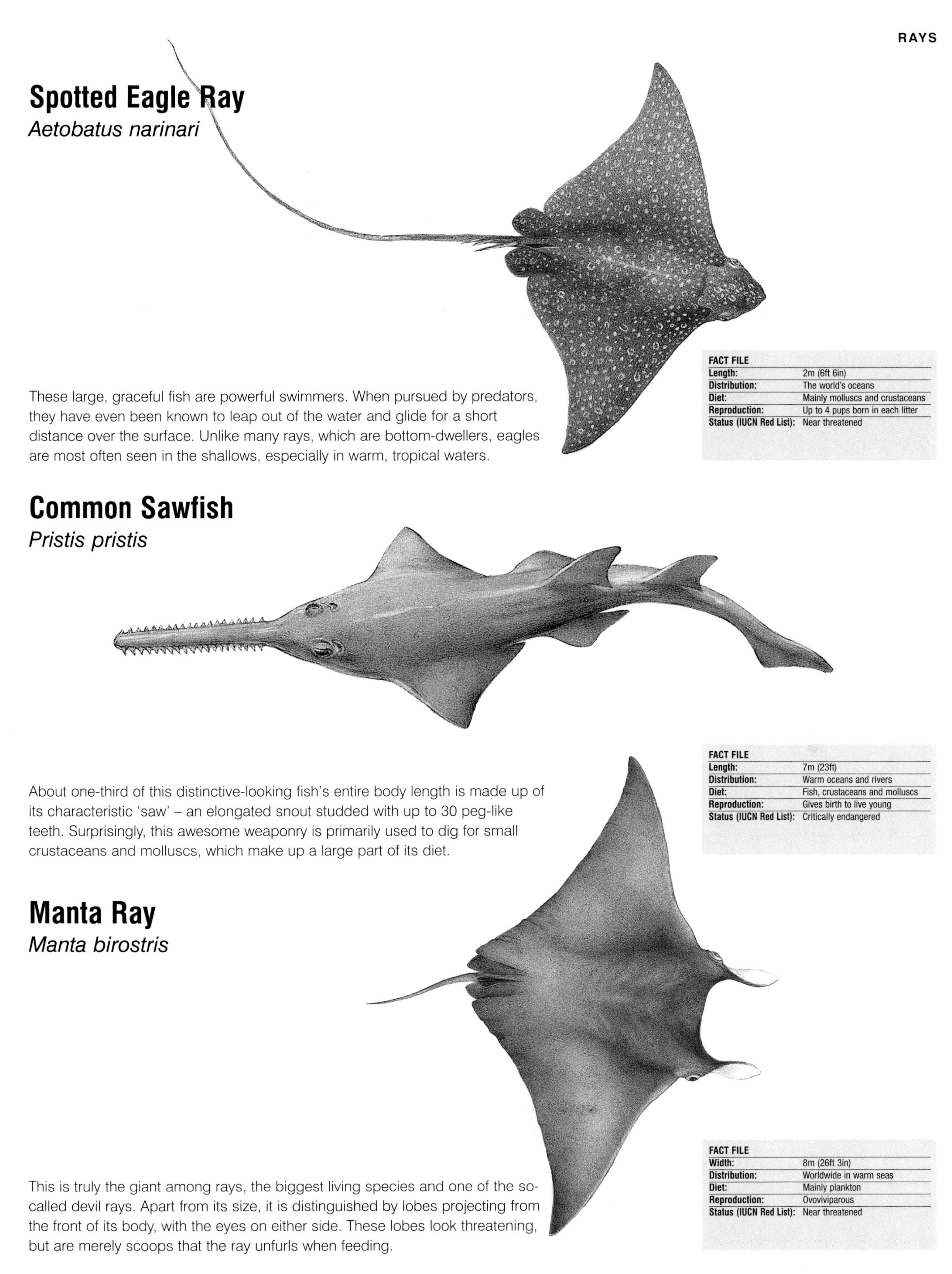

These large, graceful fish are powerful swimmers. When pursued by predators, they have even been known to leap out of the water and glide for a short distance over the surface. Unlike many rays, which are bottom-dwellers, eagles are most often seen in the shallows, especially in warm, tropical waters.

FACT FILE	
Length:	2m (6ft 6in)
Distribution:	The world's oceans
Diet:	Mainly molluscs and crustaceans
Reproduction:	Up to 4 pups born in each litter
Status (IUCN Red List):	Near threatened

Common Sawfish

Pristis pristis

About one-third of this distinctive-looking fish's entire body length is made up of its characteristic 'saw' – an elongated snout studded with up to 30 peg-like teeth. Surprisingly, this awesome weaponry is primarily used to dig for small crustaceans and molluscs, which make up a large part of its diet.

FACT FILE	
Length:	7m (23ft)
Distribution:	Warm oceans and rivers
Diet:	Fish, crustaceans and molluscs
Reproduction:	Gives birth to live young
Status (IUCN Red List):	Critically endangered

Manta Ray

Manta birostris

This is truly the giant among rays, the biggest living species and one of the so-called devil rays. Apart from its size, it is distinguished by lobes projecting from the front of its body, with the eyes on either side. These lobes look threatening, but are merely scoops that the ray unfurls when feeding.

FACT FILE	
Width:	8m (26ft 3in)
Distribution:	Worldwide in warm seas
Diet:	Mainly plankton
Reproduction:	Ovoviviparous
Status (IUCN Red List):	Near threatened

European Sturgeon

Acipenser sturio

Sturgeons are best known as the source of caviar, their immature eggs, which are salted to make a luxury food. These may be cut from the female's body, killing her, or may be stripped and the female returned to the water. However, the sturgeon flesh is also eaten, and it is now an endangered species.

FACT FILE	
Length:	3.5m (11ft 5in)
Distribution:	Eastern Atlantic and its rivers
Diet:	Worms, crustaceans and molluscs
Reproduction:	Spawns in spring
Status (IUCN Red List):	Critically endangered

The sturgeon is a primitive fish that has rows of bony plates along its body. It breeds in freshwater; the young stay in the river of their birth for up to three years before returning to the sea. A similar (perhaps identical) species, *Acipenser oxyrhynchus*, lives along the North American Atlantic coast.

MOUTH
The small mouth is positioned under the head. The jaws are pushed outward to grab food.

BARBELS
Four flexible barbels taste the surrounding water as well as feeling the riverbed for food.

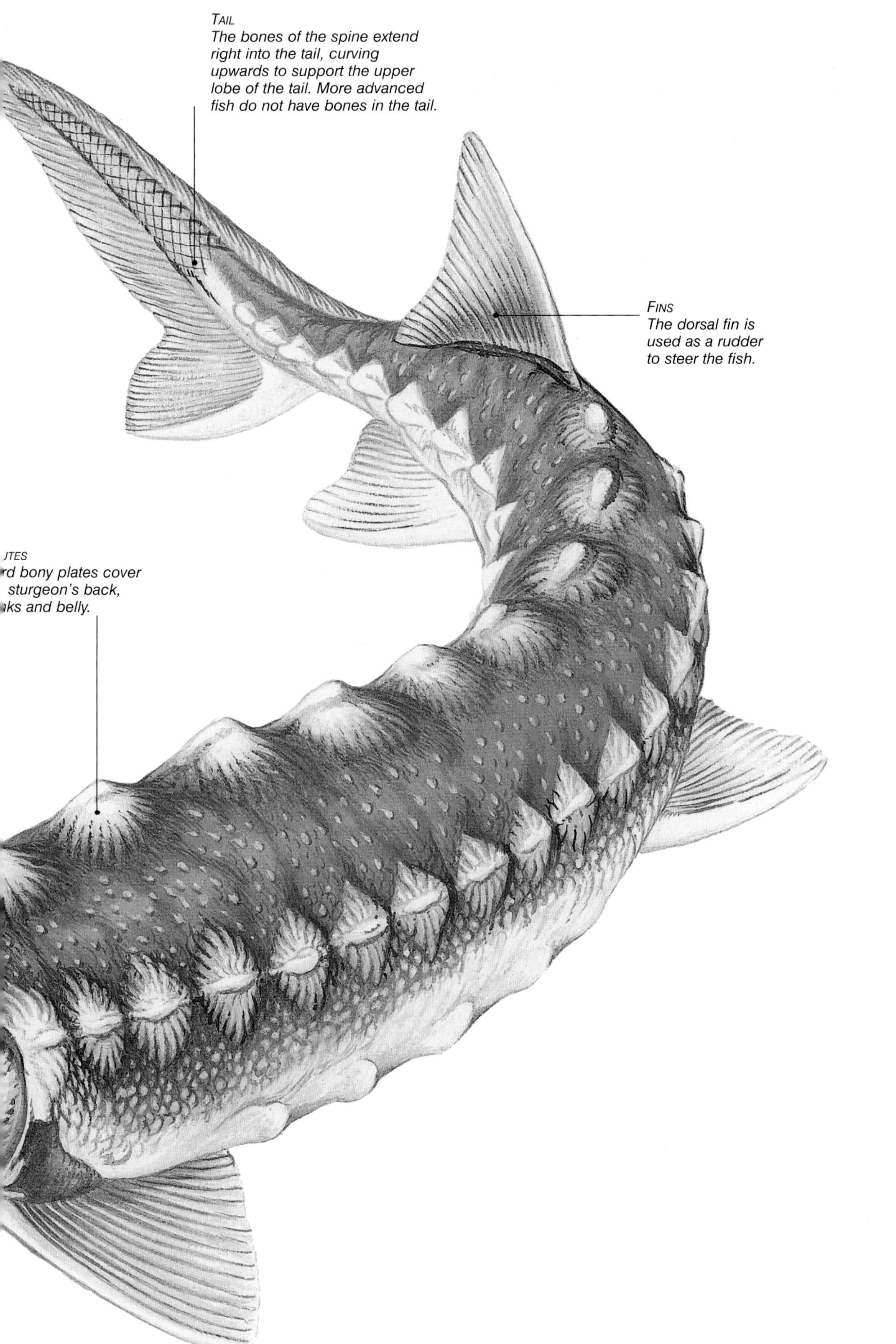
TAIL
The bones of the spine extend right into the tail, curving upwards to support the upper lobe of the tail. More advanced fish do not have bones in the tail.
FINS
The dorsal fin is used as a rudder to steer the fish.
JTES
rd bony plates cover
sturgeon's back,
ks and belly.

Primitive Bony Fish

More than 95 per cent of fish species have bony skeletons. Their ancestors were also the ancestors of all land vertebrates, including humans. While most of today's fish have fins supported by thin bones radiating outwards, some fish have fins containing sturdier bones, from which legs, toes, fingers and arms evolved.

Coelacanth

Latimeria chalumnae

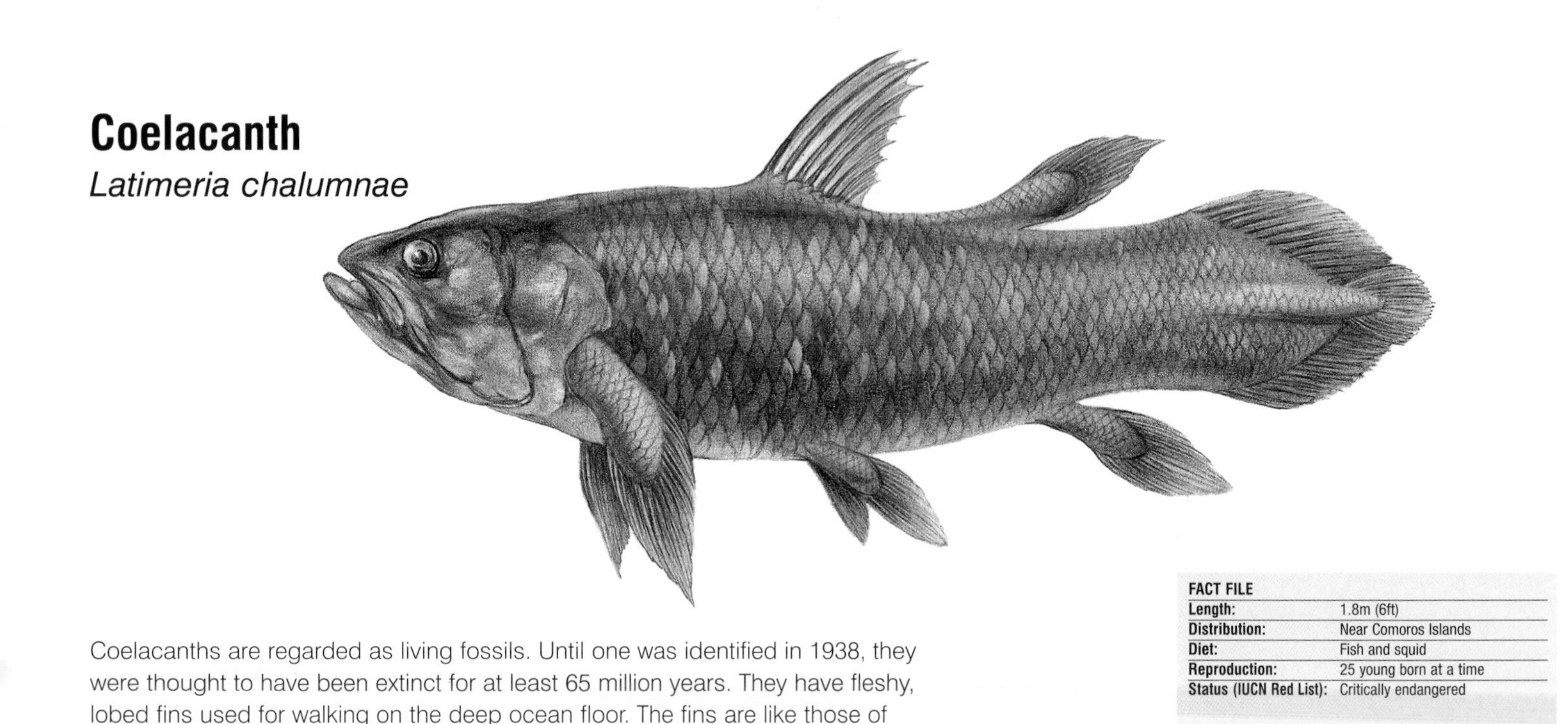

Coelacanths are regarded as living fossils. Until one was identified in 1938, they were thought to have been extinct for at least 65 million years. They have fleshy, lobed fins used for walking on the deep ocean floor. The fins are like those of the fish that evolved into the amphibians, the first land animals.

FACT FILE	
Length:	1.8m (6ft)
Distribution:	Near Comoros Islands
Diet:	Fish and squid
Reproduction:	25 young born at a time
Status (IUCN Red List):	Critically endangered

Chinese Paddlefish

Psephurus gladius

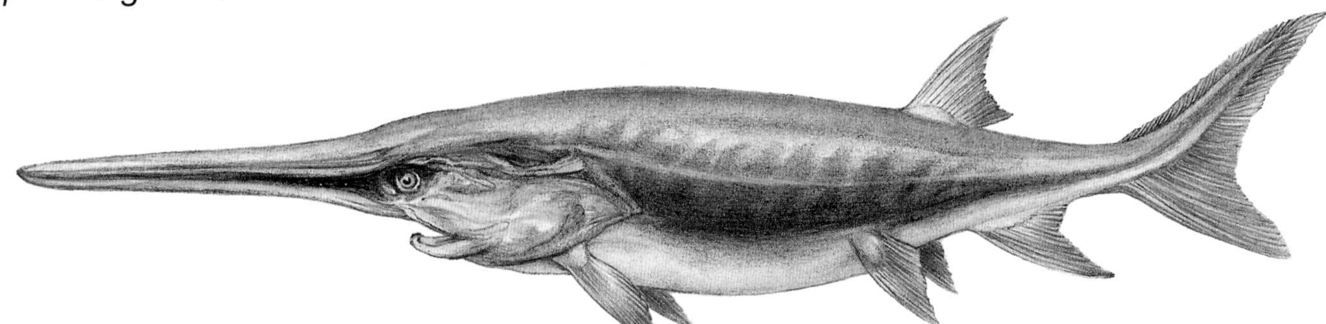

This East Asian paddlefish is one of two surviving species; the other lives in North America. The fish is not related to sharks, although it has similar pointed tail fins, the upper one supported by the spine. Much of the skeleton is cartilage. The long snout is believed to contain electroreceptors for detecting prey.

FACT FILE	
Length:	2m (6ft 6in)
Distribution:	Lower Yangtze
Diet:	Fish, crabs and crayfish
Reproduction:	9000 eggs laid in spring
Status (IUCN Red List):	Critically endangered

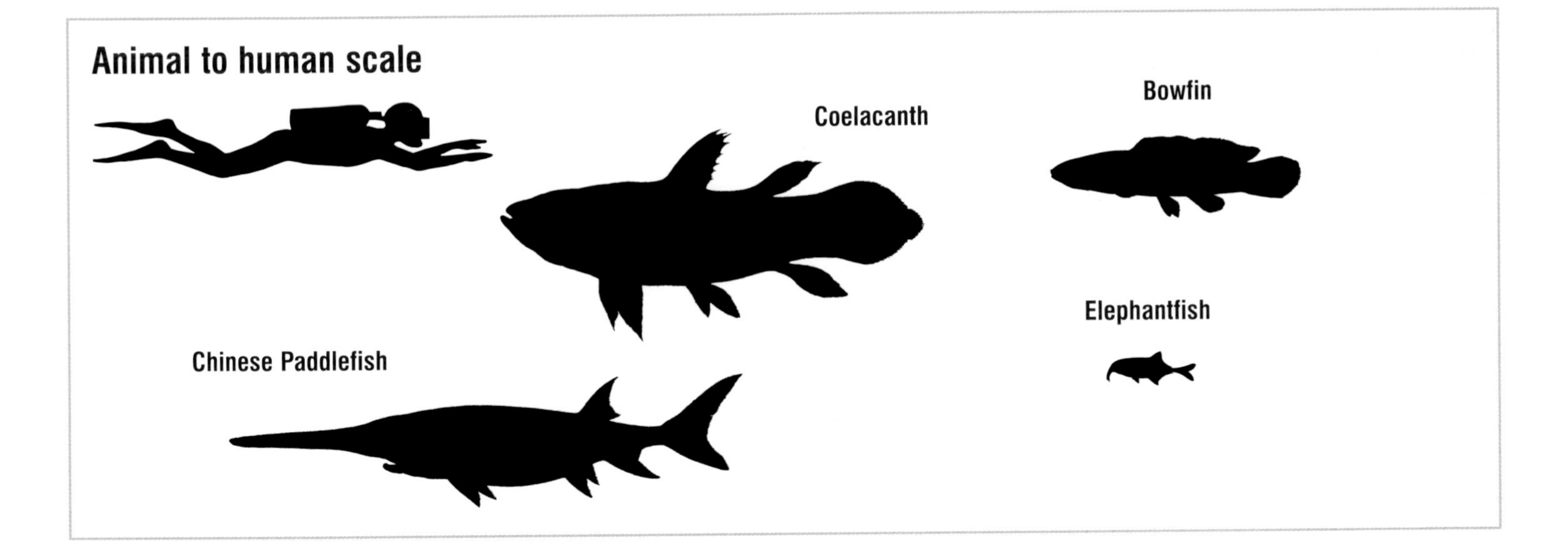

Bowfin

Amia calva

FACT FILE	
Length:	1.1m (3ft 7in)
Distribution:	Eastern North America
Diet:	Insects, crayfish and frogs
Reproduction:	Male protects eggs in mud nest
Status (IUCN Red List):	Not evaluated

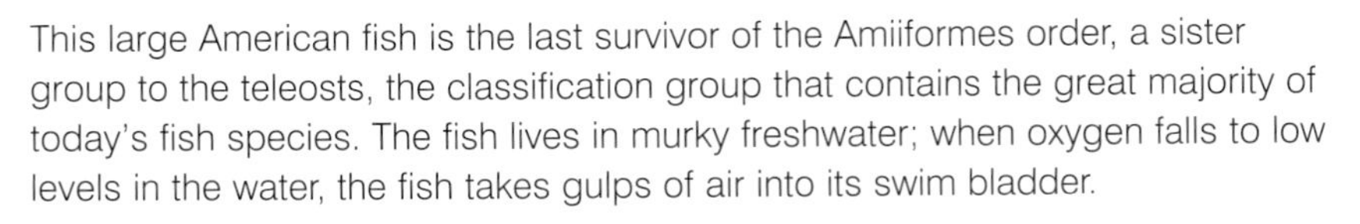

This large American fish is the last survivor of the Amiiformes order, a sister group to the teleosts, the classification group that contains the great majority of today's fish species. The fish lives in murky freshwater; when oxygen falls to low levels in the water, the fish takes gulps of air into its swim bladder.

Elephantfish

Latimeria chalumnae

FACT FILE	
Length:	23cm (9in)
Distribution:	West Africa
Diet:	Shellfish and insects
Reproduction:	Lays eggs
Status (IUCN Red List):	Least concern

Obviously named after its long fleshy snout, this species belongs to a group called the bony-tongued fish. The fish uses a fleshy probe on the shin to search muddy riverbeds, and emits electric pulses to detect hidden animals. The fish has a huge brain for its size and can be taught tricks in captivity.

Eels and Relatives

An eel is a long fish that swims using an undulating motion. Some eels have more than 100 vertebrae in their spines. Most eels live in the sea, although edible eels breed in deep water before travelling up rivers far inland to feed, part of one of the animal kingdom's great migrations.

Atlantic Tarpon

Megalops atlanticus

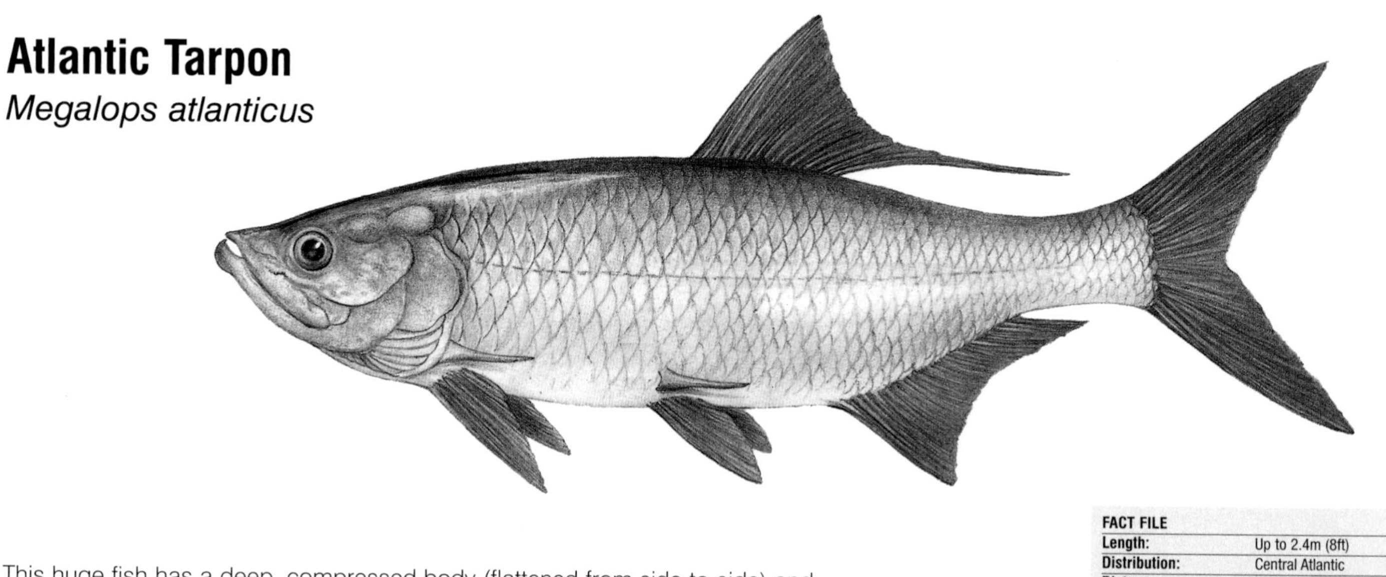

FACT FILE	
Length:	Up to 2.4m (8ft)
Distribution:	Central Atlantic
Diet:	Mainly schooling fish and crabs
Reproduction:	Spawns in spring and summer
Status (IUCN Red List):	Not evaluated

This huge fish has a deep, compressed body (flattened from side to side) and large scales. It is regarded by biologists as one of the most primitive of the ray-finned bony fish, but its link to the eels becomes clear when its young hatch out. These eel-like fry feed in river mouths and inland waterways.

Mediterranean Moray

Muraena helena

FACT FILE	
Length:	Up to 1.3m (4ft 3in)
Distribution:	Mediterranean
Diet:	Mainly fish, squid and cuttlefish
Reproduction:	Spawns in summer, eggs float
Status (IUCN Red List):	Not evaluated

Moray eels live in rocky crevices and reefs in warm seas. They are voracious predators, lunging from their lair (where they lurk with only their head showing) to snatch prey. They have a large mouth and sharp teeth, and can give divers a nasty bite – perhaps mistaking their fingers for the tentacles of a tasty octopus.

European Conger

Conger conger

FACT FILE	
Length:	3m (9ft 9in)
Distribution:	North Atlantic and Mediterranean
Diet:	Fish and shellfish
Reproduction:	Spawns at 4km (2½ miles)
Status (IUCN Red List):	Not evaluated

Conger eels are powerful predators that hunt mainly at night for fish. By day, they hide among rocks. Divers exploring wrecks often find them inhabited by many large congers. They are distinguished from moray eels by the fact that they have pectoral fins. They breed in deep water like the edible eels.

Swallower

Saccopharynx ampulaceus

FACT FILE	
Length:	Up to 1m (3ft 3in)
Distribution:	Worldwide
Diet:	Crustaceans, fish and squid
Reproduction:	Eggs develop in shallower water
Status (IUCN Red List):	Not evaluated

Discounting its whip-like tail, the large head and mouth of this deep-sea hunter make up more than half of its body length. Its gape is formed by a highly elastic membrane. It has a flashing luminous organ at the tip of its tail, used either to lure prey or attract mates.

Snipe Eel

Serrivomer beani

FACT FILE	
Length:	1.3m (4ft 3in)
Distribution:	Worldwide
Diet:	Small crustaceans, some fish
Reproduction:	Eggs hatch into planktonic larvae
Status (IUCN Red List):	Not evaluated

This eel is named after its long, beak-like jaws, which resemble the beak of the snipe (a wading bird). The fish feeds by swimming along with its mouth open, using its sharp, backward-facing teeth to trap shrimp and other small creatures that swim into its gape. The eels are believed to die after breeding.

Common Carp

Cyprinus carpio

This chunky freshwater fish was one of the first fish to be raised in captivity. It was originally from the river systems of Europe and Asia, but has since spread all over the world. The fish is a valuable source of food in Eastern Europe and Central Asia, and many ornamental varieties have been bred over the centuries.

FACT FILE	
Length:	45cm (17¾in)
Distribution:	Europe and Asia
Diet:	Insects, snails and worms
Reproduction:	Spawns in spring and summer
Status (IUCN Red List):	Vulnerable

The carp is an omnivore. It ruffles through the muddy riverbed to unearth molluscs, insect larvae and worms in the sediment. It then slurps them up using its protrusible lips. The mud-based diet does tend to affect the flavour of the fish's flesh, and cultures with easy access to sea fish generally eschew a meal of carp.

THROAT BONES
The carp has no teeth in its jaw. Food is sucked in whole and then crushed by a pair of pharyngeal bones as it is swallowed.

BARBELS
Two pairs of sensitive feelers grow above and below the flexible lips. They detect food items as the fish roots through the muddy riverbed.

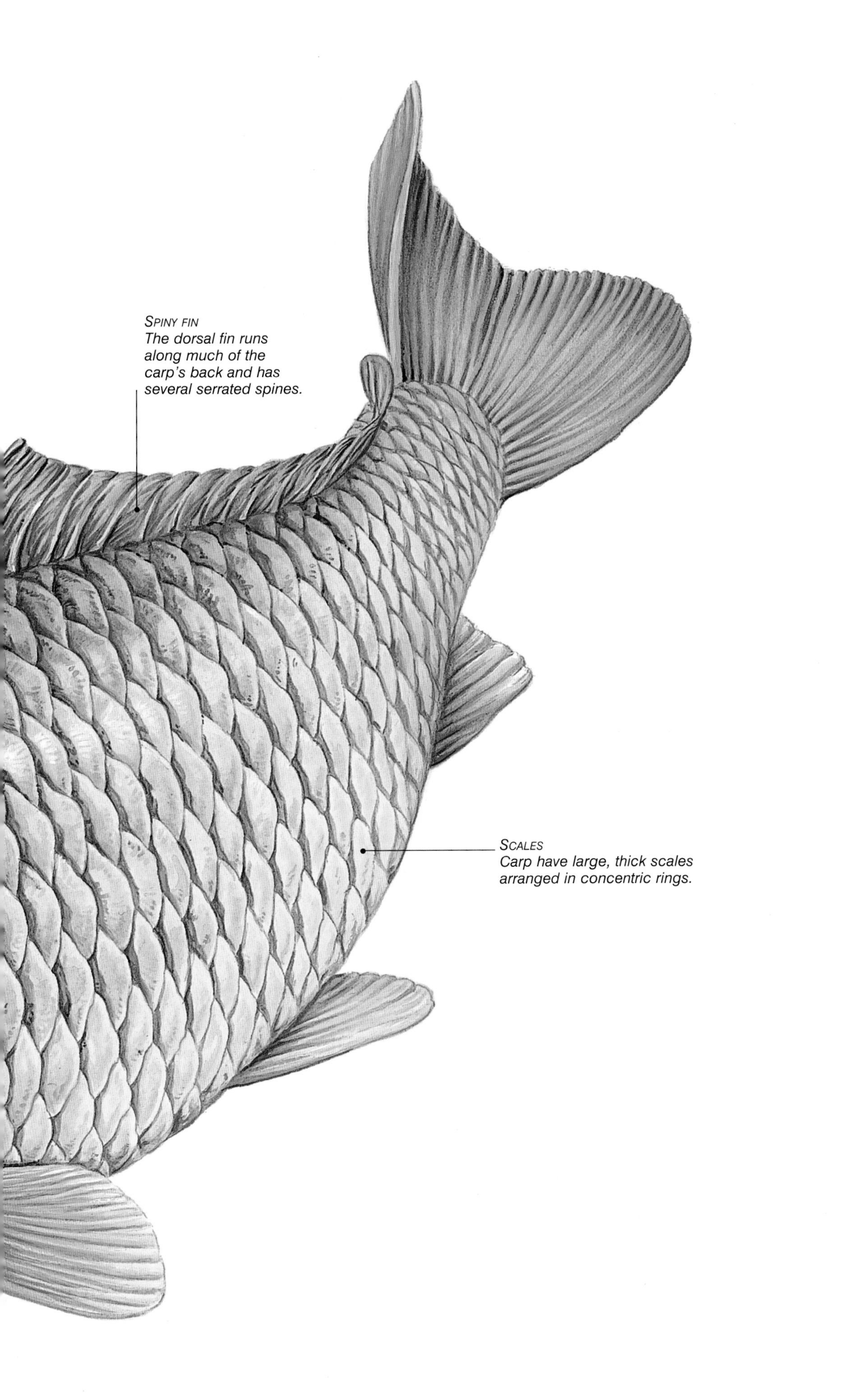
SPINY FIN
The dorsal fin runs along much of the carp's back and has several serrated spines.
SCALES
Carp have large, thick scales arranged in concentric rings.

Carp and Relatives

The Cypriniformes form an order of bony fish that includes the cyprinids – the true carps – as well as the loaches, minnows and suckers. There are well over 3000 species, mostly freshwater, and they live in all continents except South America and Australia. Many smaller Cypriniformes are popular aquarium fish.

Tench

Tinca tinca

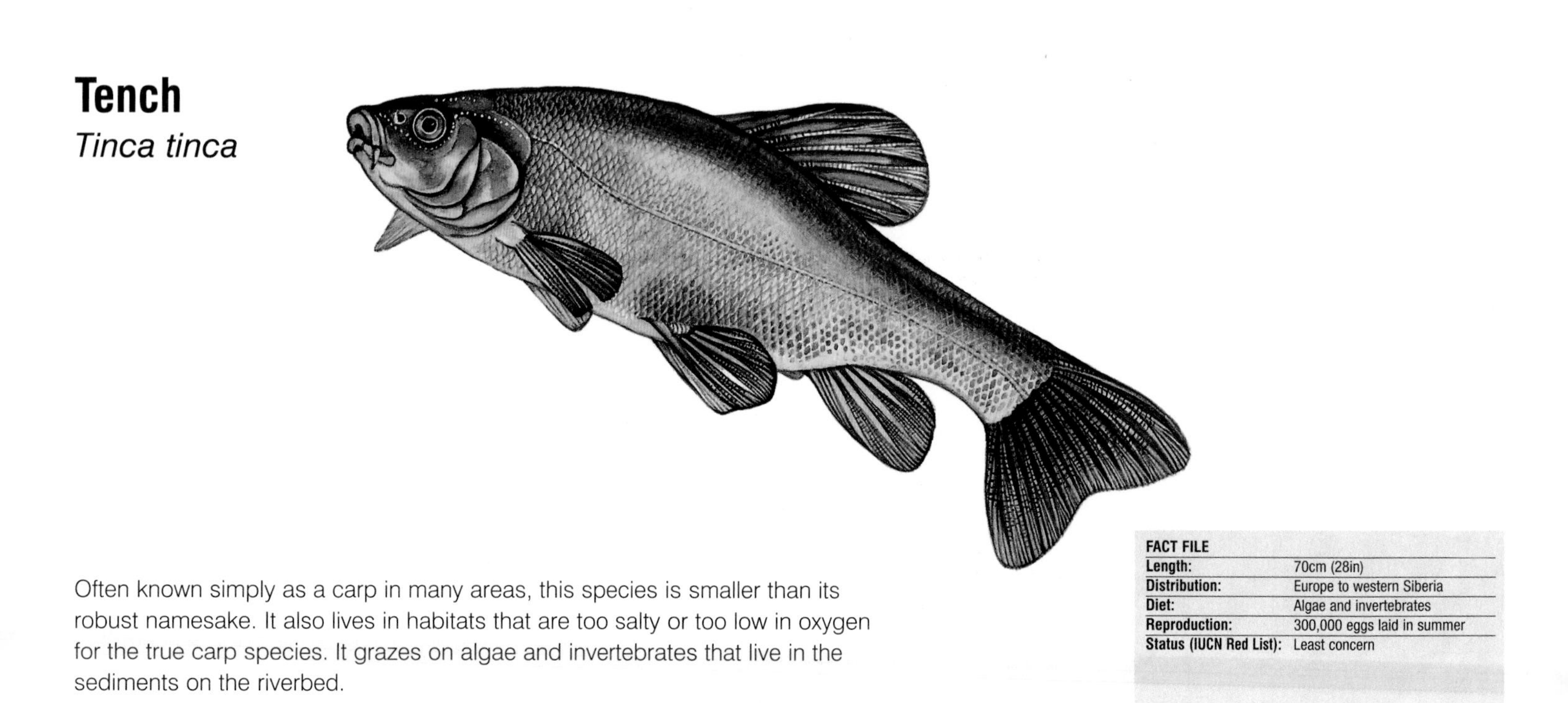

Often known simply as a carp in many areas, this species is smaller than its robust namesake. It also lives in habitats that are too salty or too low in oxygen for the true carp species. It grazes on algae and invertebrates that live in the sediments on the riverbed.

FACT FILE	
Length:	70cm (28in)
Distribution:	Europe to western Siberia
Diet:	Algae and invertebrates
Reproduction:	300,000 eggs laid in summer
Status (IUCN Red List):	Least concern

Harlequin Rasbora

Rasbora heteromorpha

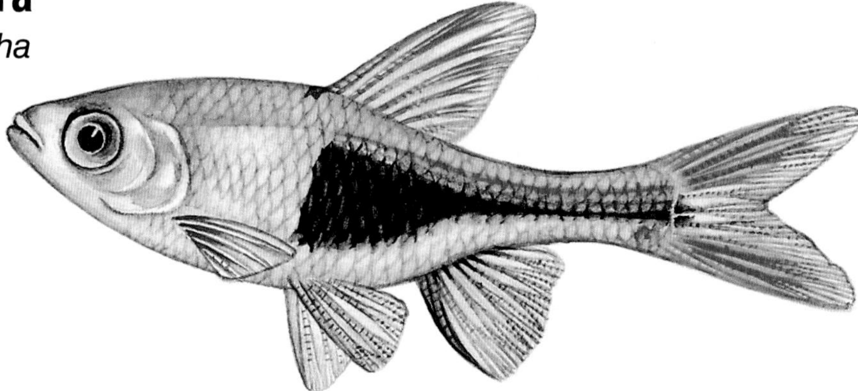

This popular aquarium fish's name refers to the triangular black patch on the fish's orange-pink body, resembling a harlequin's costume. In the wild, the fish lives in warm water with a thick cover of water plants. The females lay up to 100 eggs on the underside of large leaves.

FACT FILE	
Length:	5cm (2in)
Distribution:	Southeast Asia
Diet:	Insect larvae
Reproduction:	Eggs deposited on water plants
Status (IUCN Red List):	Not evaluated

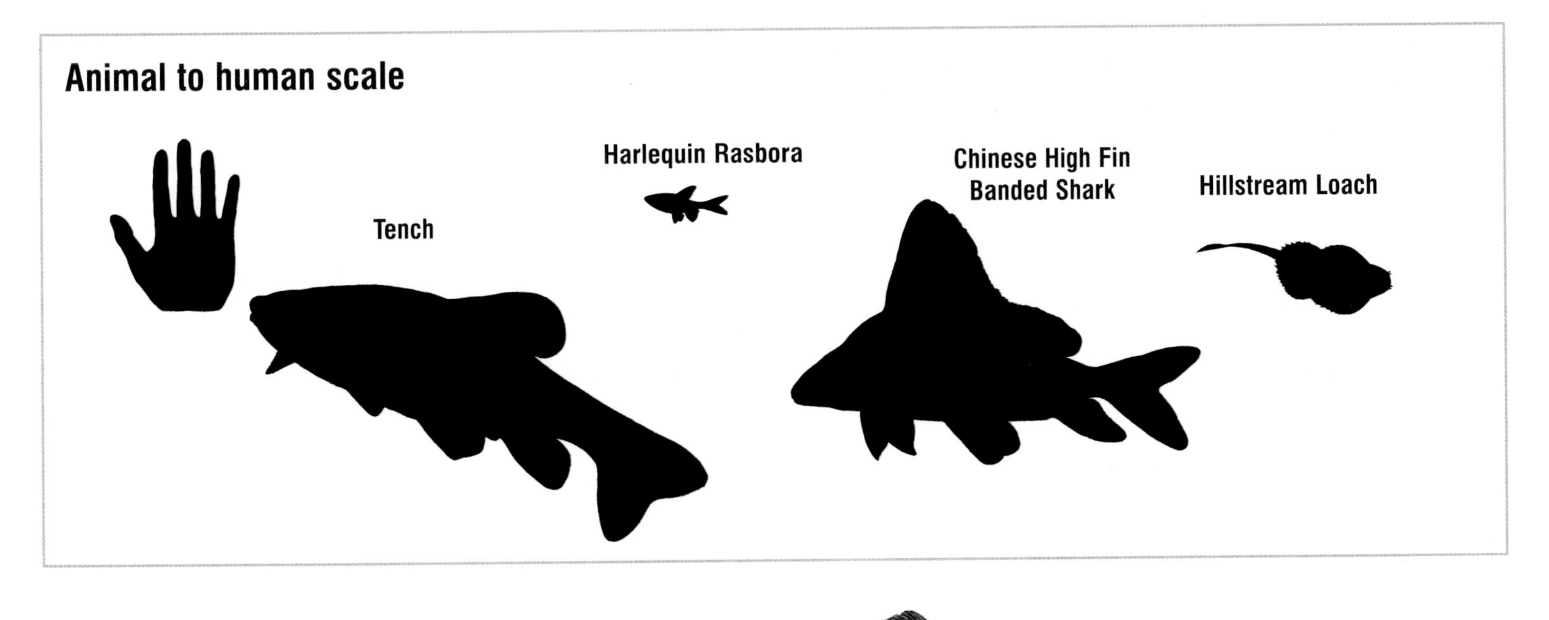

Chinese High Fin Banded Shark

Myxocyprinus asiaticus

FACT FILE	
Length:	60cm (23½in)
Distribution:	Eastern China
Diet:	Insects and shellfish
Reproduction:	Eggs scattered on riverbed
Status (IUCN Red List):	Not evaluated

Also known as the Chinese sucker, this fish uses its flexible lips to slurp up animals from the riverbed. Its body looks triangular when seen from the front. It faces into the current as it feeds, and the water flowing over it pushes it down onto the riverbed rather than washing it downstream.

Hillstream Loach

Gastromyzon sp.

FACT FILE	
Length:	15cm (6in)
Distribution:	Southeast Asia
Diet:	Algae
Reproduction:	4000 eggs laid in sand
Status (IUCN Red List):	Data deficient

There are about 600 species of hillstream loaches in 60 genera. The genus Gastromyzon is one of the largest. These fish live in clean, fast-flowing water, which is packed with oxygen. They cling to rocks using their wide fins and graze on algae growing on the rocky stream bed. Wild fish defend feeding territories.

Tetras and Relatives

The tetras are small, often colourful, freshwater fish. They are close relatives of the carps and catfish. Along with other species, including the piranhas, the tetras form the Characiformes order. This group includes about 1600 species, most of which are found in Central and South America.

Sixbar Distichodus

Distichodus sexfasciatus

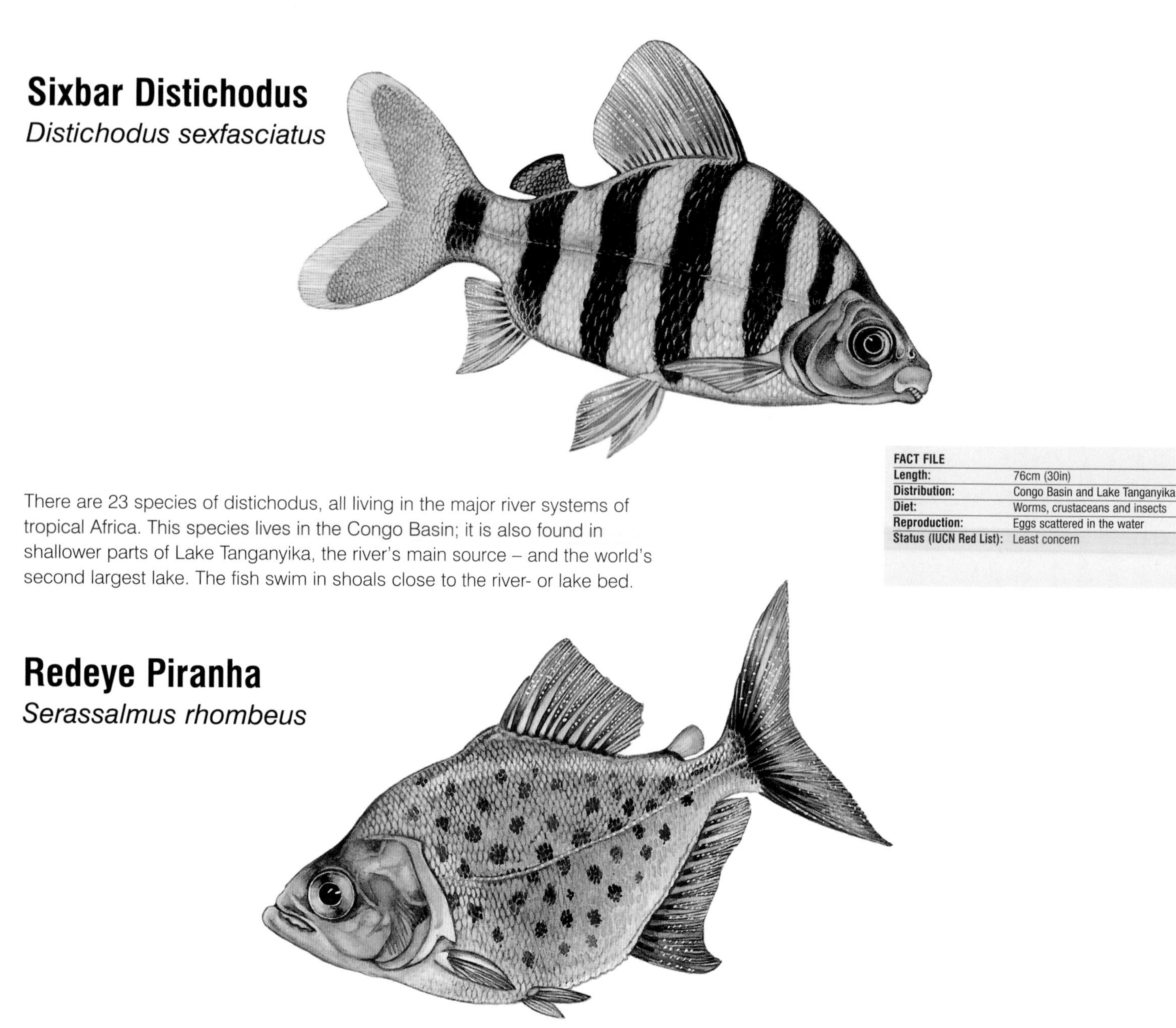

There are 23 species of distichodus, all living in the major river systems of tropical Africa. This species lives in the Congo Basin; it is also found in shallower parts of Lake Tanganyika, the river's main source – and the world's second largest lake. The fish swim in shoals close to the river- or lake bed.

FACT FILE	
Length:	76cm (30in)
Distribution:	Congo Basin and Lake Tanganyika
Diet:	Worms, crustaceans and insects
Reproduction:	Eggs scattered in the water
Status (IUCN Red List):	Least concern

Redeye Piranha

Serassalmus rhombeus

The redeye piranha, also known as the black piranha, has razor-sharp teeth. The meat-eating fish is generally non-aggressive in deep water, but in the dry season, when fish become concentrated in pools, hungry piranhas feed in a frenzy on animals that enter the water.

FACT FILE	
Length:	38cm (15in)
Distribution:	Amazon and Orinoco river basins
Diet:	Insects, fish and fruits
Reproduction:	Eggs laid on water plants
Status (IUCN Red List):	Not evaluated

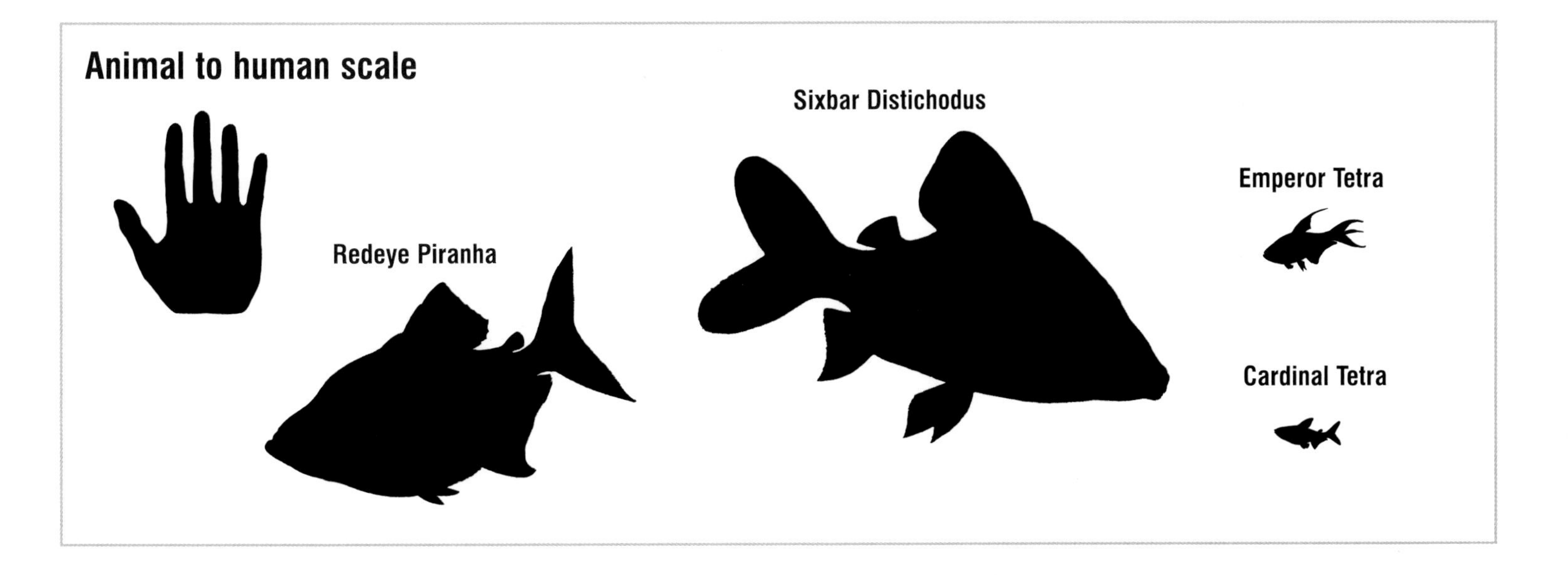

Emperor Tetra

Nematobrycon palmeri

FACT FILE	
Length:	5cm (2in)
Distribution:	Western Colombia
Diet:	Worms, crustaceans and insects
Reproduction:	One egg laid at a time
Status (IUCN Red List):	Not evaluated

This colourful species lives wild in the warm streams of western Colombia. It swims in large schools as a defensive strategy. When crowded together, the little fish appear to be a single iridescent mass, and predators find it hard to distinguish the shape of any individual fish.

Cardinal Tetra

Paracheirodon axelrodi

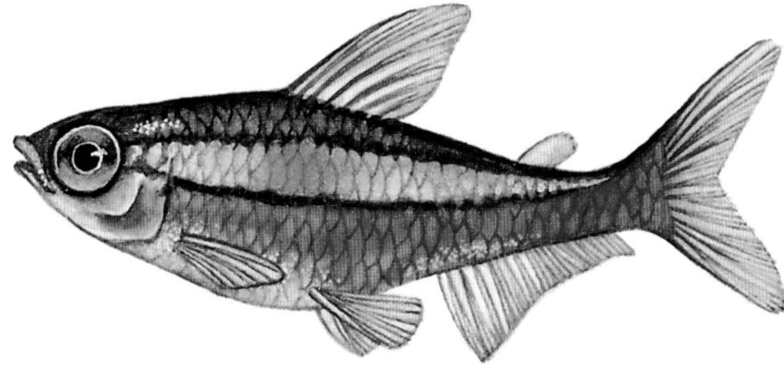

FACT FILE	
Length:	3cm (1¼in)
Distribution:	Upper Orinoco and Negro rivers
Diet:	Worms, insects and crustaceans
Reproduction:	500 eggs laid in shaded water
Status (IUCN Red List):	Not evaluated

A popular aquarium fish, the cardinal tetra sports an iridescent blue line midway down its sides, with the body below this line being cardinal red. The closely related neon tetra looks identical, but only the back portion of its body is red. The fish is harvested for the pet trade from the Negro River in Brazil.

Red-bellied Piranha

Pygocentrus nattereri

As the largest piranha, this species is also the most dangerous. There are around 18 species of piranha found throughout the river systems of South America. The red piranha is found as far south as the River Plate. While the fish is not the man-eater of modern myth, it can give a deep bite, and large shoals can feed in a frenzy.

FACT FILE	
Length:	60cm (23½in)
Distribution:	River systems of South America
Diet:	Fish, small mammals, insects, fruit
Reproduction:	Males guard young
Status (IUCN Red List):	Least concern

The piranha is a lone predator, lurking in the shadows ready to dash out and grab small prey. In shallow, shrinking pools, however, they attack in groups. A shoal of piranhas could take less than one minute to reduce to bone an animal the size of a fully grown pig and weighing 45kg (99lb). They are particularly aggressive during the breeding season, when any unusual movement in the water may trigger an attack.

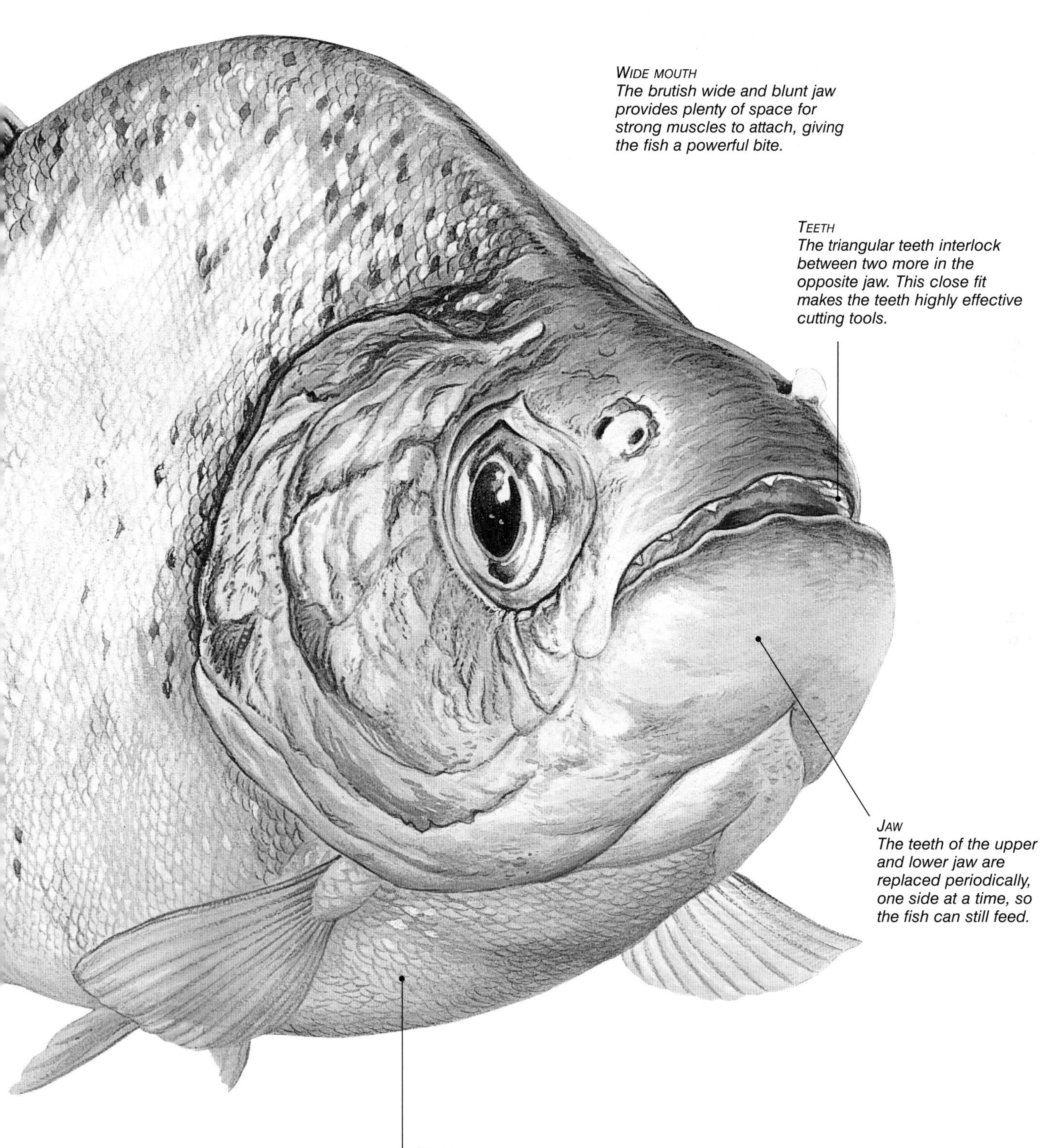
WIDE MOUTH
The brutish wide and blunt jaw provides plenty of space for strong muscles to attach, giving the fish a powerful bite.
TEETH
The triangular teeth interlock between two more in the opposite jaw. This close fit makes the teeth highly effective cutting tools.
JAW
The teeth of the upper and lower jaw are replaced periodically, one side at a time, so the fish can still feed.
COLOURING
Most piranha species are silvery, dark grey or even black. However, this large species has a conspicuous red underside.

Catfish

The catfish are named after the long fleshy whiskers, or barbels, that protrude from around the mouth. These are not just feelers but are also covered in taste buds. The catfish form the Siluriformes order, which contains a total of 3025 species. Most of the species live in freshwater, although some live in shallow coastal seas, too.

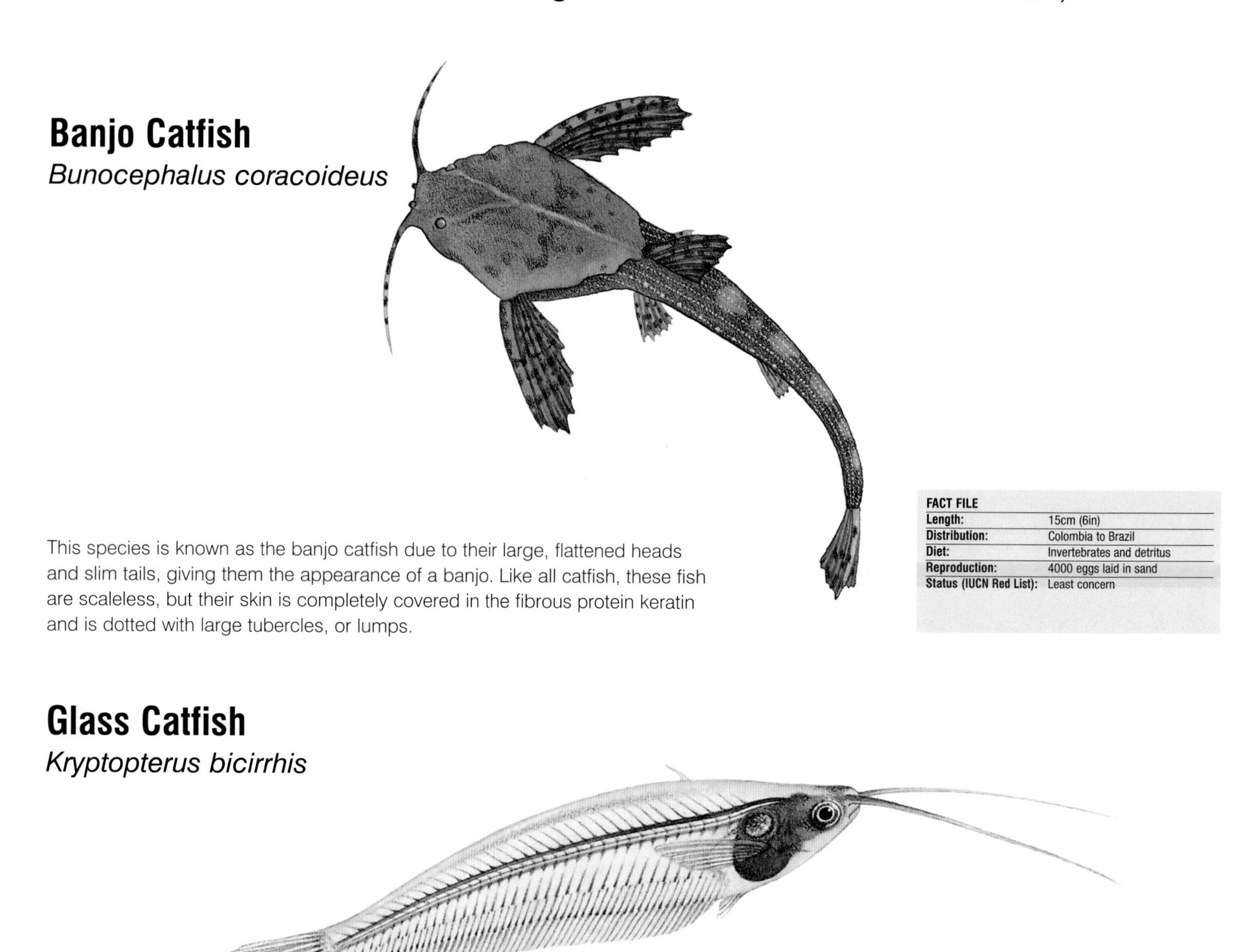

Banjo Catfish

Bunocephalus coracoideus

This species is known as the banjo catfish due to their large, flattened heads and slim tails, giving them the appearance of a banjo. Like all catfish, these fish are scaleless, but their skin is completely covered in the fibrous protein keratin and is dotted with large tubercles, or lumps.

FACT FILE	
Length:	15cm (6in)
Distribution:	Colombia to Brazil
Diet:	Invertebrates and detritus
Reproduction:	4000 eggs laid in sand
Status (IUCN Red List):	Least concern

Glass Catfish

Kryptopterus bicirrhis

Since this fish has no scales and no body pigment, it is transparent, earning it the alternative common name of ghost fish. If you look closely enough, the fish's heart is visible. In the clear streams and rivers that are this catfish's home, its transparency serves as camouflage.

FACT FILE	
Length:	15cm (6in)
Distribution:	Southeast Asia
Diet:	Larvae and small worms
Reproduction:	Rarely bred in aquariums
Status (IUCN Red List):	Not evaluated

Electric Catfish

Malapterurus electricus

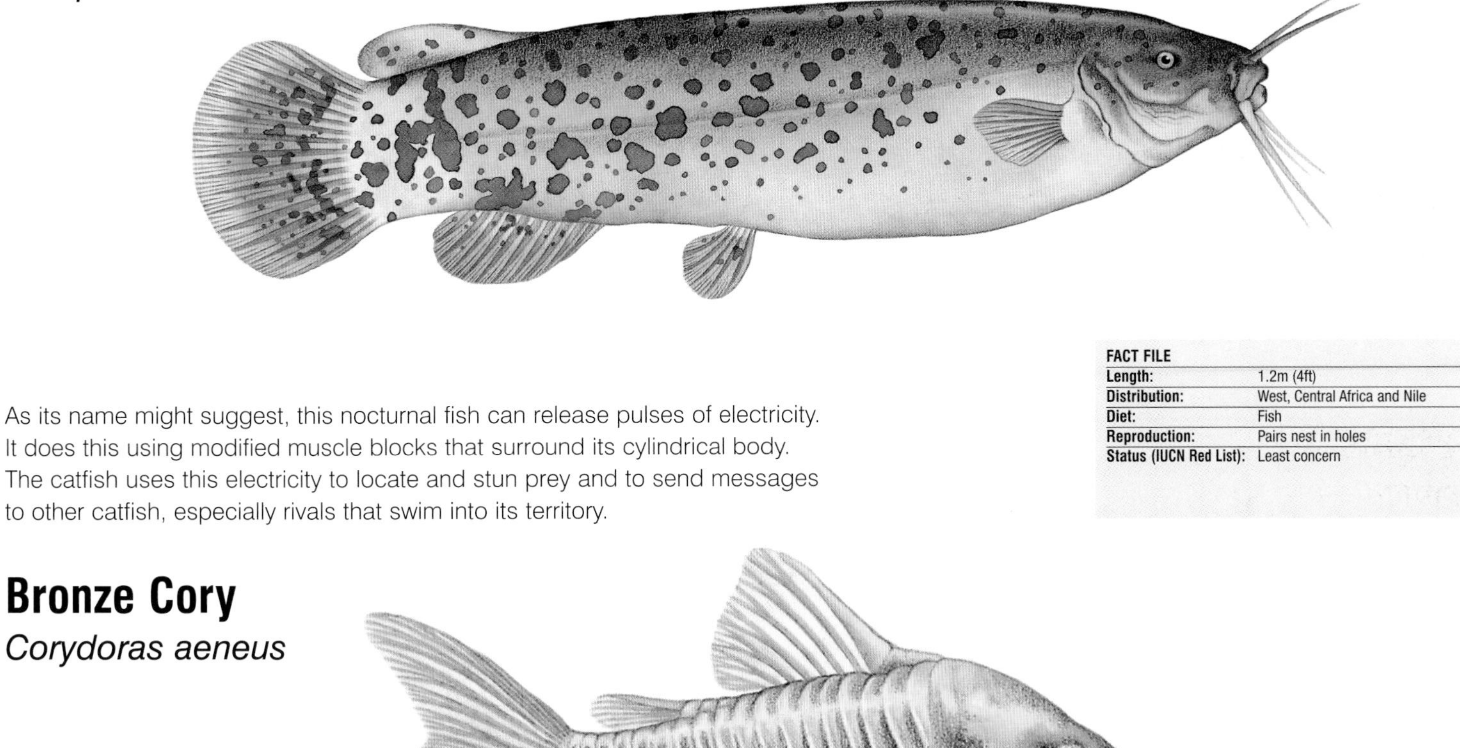

FACT FILE	
Length:	1.2m (4ft)
Distribution:	West, Central Africa and Nile
Diet:	Fish
Reproduction:	Pairs nest in holes
Status (IUCN Red List):	Least concern

As its name might suggest, this nocturnal fish can release pulses of electricity. It does this using modified muscle blocks that surround its cylindrical body. The catfish uses this electricity to locate and stun prey and to send messages to other catfish, especially rivals that swim into its territory.

Bronze Cory

Corydoras aeneus

FACT FILE	
Length:	8cm (3in)
Distribution:	Colombia to northern Argentina
Diet:	Worms and water fleas
Reproduction:	200 eggs laid on plant leaves
Status (IUCN Red List):	Not evaluated

Belonging to the armoured catfish family, this hardy fish is a popular aquarium species. It is not as beautiful as many freshwater aquarium fish, yet this catfish is liked by many aquarium owners because it is constantly active and has the habit of foraging along the bottom of the aquarium, disturbing clouds of sand.

Raphael Catfish

Platydoras costatus

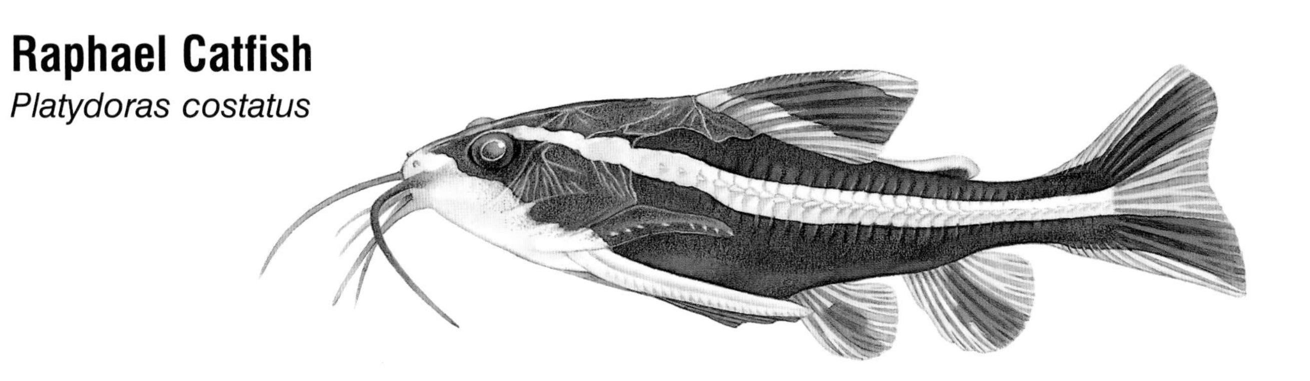

FACT FILE	
Length:	23cm (9in)
Distribution:	French Guiana and Suriname
Diet:	Molluscs and crustaceans
Reproduction:	Eggs laid on sandy beds
Status (IUCN Red List):	Not evaluated

Also known as the talking catfish, this species is popular for its sociability in a community aquarium, living happily alongside other catfish and similarly docile species. This distinctly striped fish has rigid pectoral fin spines, which it sticks out even more firmly when stressed.

Wels Catfish

Silurus glanis

Also known as the sheathfish, this species is one of the largest river fish in Europe and Asia, with some extreme examples reaching 3m (9ft 9in) and weighing 220kg (485lb). Few exclusively freshwater fish anywhere reach this kind of size, and most wels are considerably smaller.

FACT FILE	
Length:	1.45m (4ft 9in)
Distribution:	Eastern Europe and Asia
Diet:	Fish, mammals, birds and frogs
Reproduction:	Millions of eggs on riverbed
Status (IUCN Red List):	Least concern

Wels catfish can live for several years; they adjust the size of their prey accordingly as they grow. The young prey on insect larvae and move up to aquatic mammals, ducks and large fish as adult. Large specimens have been known to clear small lakes of fish.

Barbels
The fish have six whisker-like barbels: two long ones on the upper jaw, and four shorter ones on the chin. These feelers can detect currents in the water created by prey.

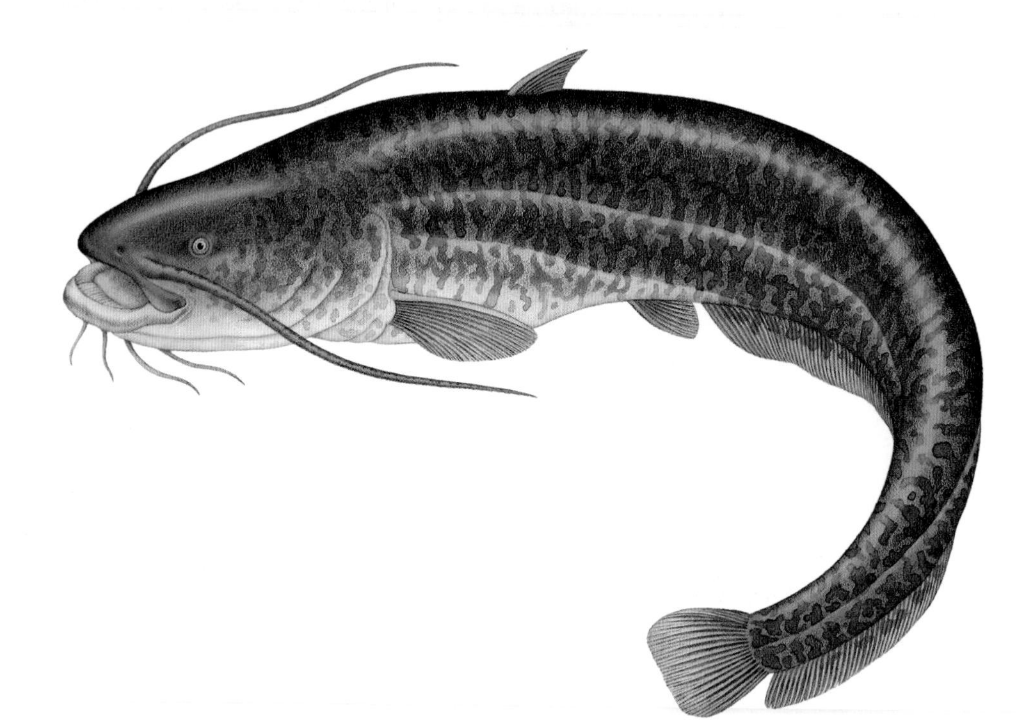

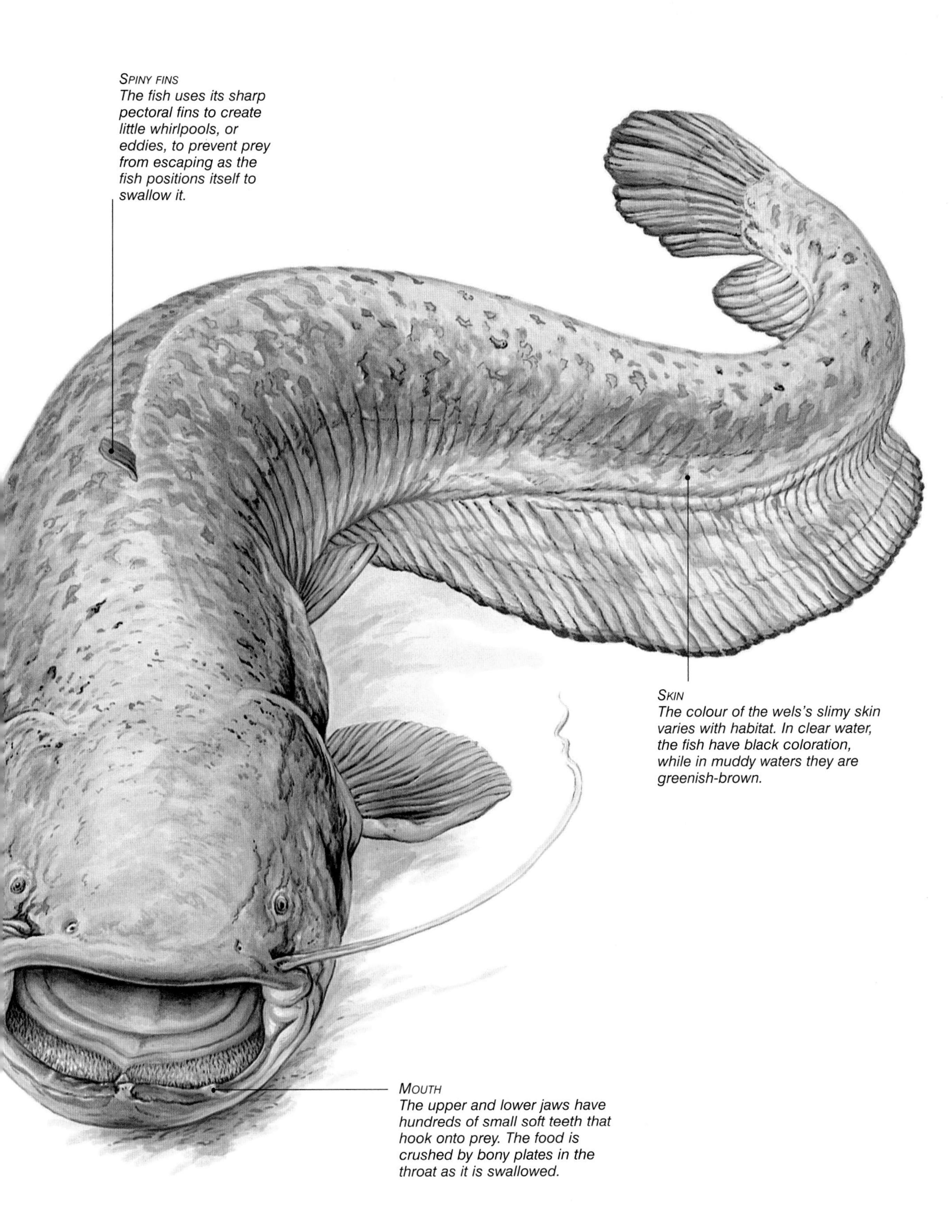
SPINY FINS
The fish uses its sharp pectoral fins to create little whirlpools, or eddies, to prevent prey from escaping as the fish positions itself to swallow it.
SKIN
The colour of the wels's slimy skin varies with habitat. In clear water, the fish have black coloration, while in muddy waters they are greenish-brown.
MOUTH
The upper and lower jaws have hundreds of small soft teeth that hook onto prey. The food is crushed by bony plates in the throat as it is swallowed.

Deep-sea Fish

Scientists estimate that there is 300 times more living space in the oceans than on dry land. Most of that is far below the surface, where light never reaches – even at midday – and it is largely empty, save for a few creatures capable of surviving in the extreme cold and pressures easily high enough to crush a human body.

Pacific Viperfish

Chauliodus macouni

With its distendible jaws and massive fangs that reach over its head, the viperfish is a fearsome sight. Yet few people see this predator close up, as it lives about 1000m (3280ft) down. Food is scarce in this region; to attract prey, the viperfish's dorsal fin is elongated and tipped with a luminous lure.

FACT FILE	
Length:	35cm (13¾in)
Distribution:	Worldwide
Diet:	Fish and crustaceans
Reproduction:	Eggs float to the surface
Status (IUCN Red List):	Not evaluated

Deep-sea Hatchetfish

Argyropelecus olfersi

The hatchetfish has a huge, gaping mouth, which it uses to scoop up food that falls from above. The fish has light-producing organs along its axe-shaped underbelly, which matches the sunlight shining from above. This helps the fish blend with its surroundings and become virtually invisible.

FACT FILE	
Length:	40cm (16in)
Distribution:	Worldwide
Diet:	Varies with species
Reproduction:	1000s of eggs in a floating 'raft'
Status (IUCN Red List):	Not evaluated

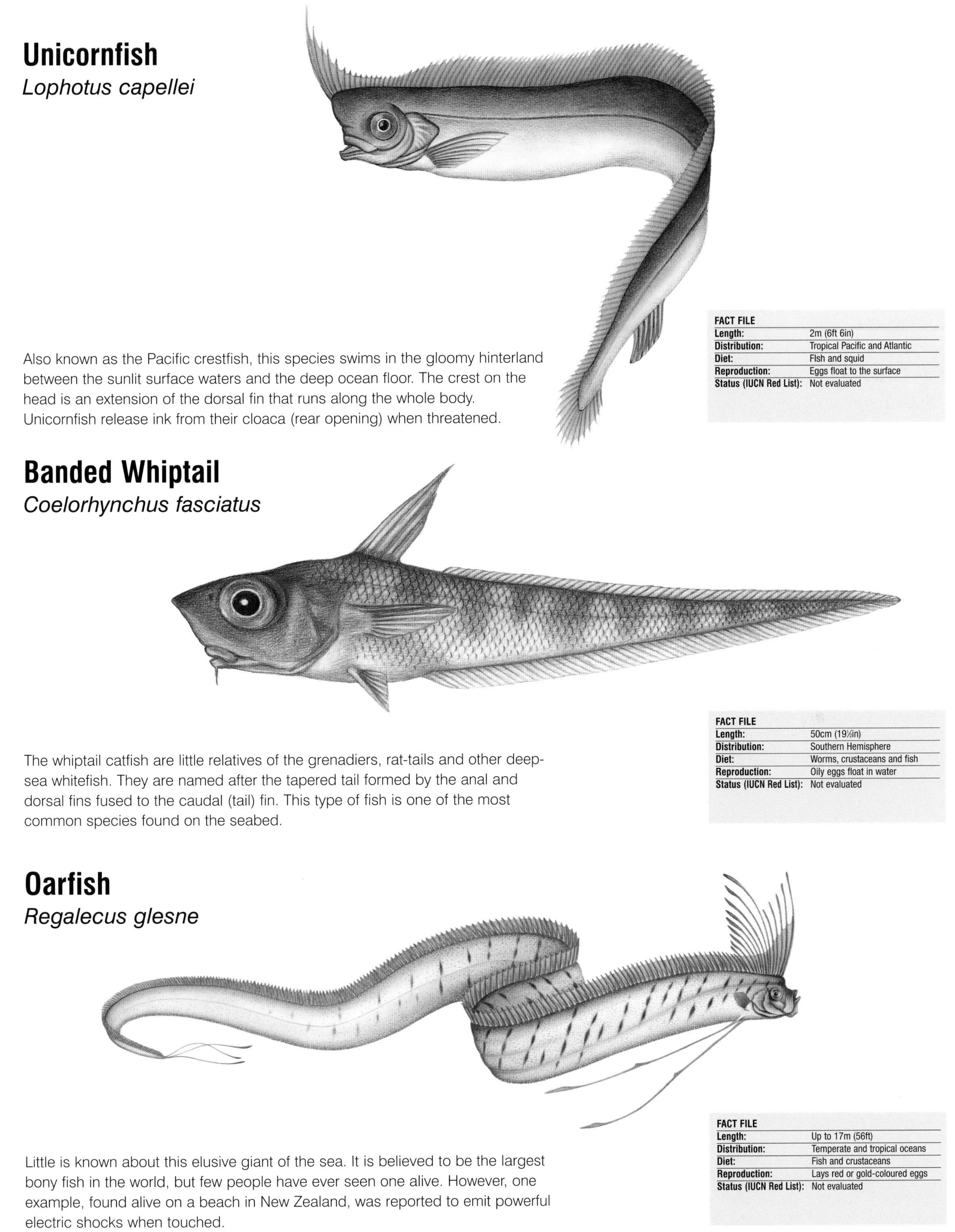

Unicornfish

Lophotus capellei

Also known as the Pacific crestfish, this species swims in the gloomy hinterland between the sunlit surface waters and the deep ocean floor. The crest on the head is an extension of the dorsal fin that runs along the whole body. Unicornfish release ink from their cloaca (rear opening) when threatened.

FACT FILE	
Length:	2m (6ft 6in)
Distribution:	Tropical Pacific and Atlantic
Diet:	Fish and squid
Reproduction:	Eggs float to the surface
Status (IUCN Red List):	Not evaluated

Banded Whiptail

Coelorhynchus fasciatus

The whiptail catfish are little relatives of the grenadiers, rat-tails and other deep-sea whitefish. They are named after the tapered tail formed by the anal and dorsal fins fused to the caudal (tail) fin. This type of fish is one of the most common species found on the seabed.

FACT FILE	
Length:	50cm (19½in)
Distribution:	Southern Hemisphere
Diet:	Worms, crustaceans and fish
Reproduction:	Oily eggs float in water
Status (IUCN Red List):	Not evaluated

Oarfish

Regalecus glesne

Little is known about this elusive giant of the sea. It is believed to be the largest bony fish in the world, but few people have ever seen one alive. However, one example, found alive on a beach in New Zealand, was reported to emit powerful electric shocks when touched.

FACT FILE	
Length:	Up to 17m (56ft)
Distribution:	Temperate and tropical oceans
Diet:	Fish and crustaceans
Reproduction:	Lays red or gold-coloured eggs
Status (IUCN Red List):	Not evaluated

Salmon and Trout

There are 66 species of salmon and trout, making up the Salmonidae family. Many of them are important food fish. Salmon divide their lives between freshwater rivers, where they gather to breed, and the ocean, where young fish feed in shallow coastal water. Trouts generally stay in freshwater all their lives.

Atlantic Salmon

Salmo salar

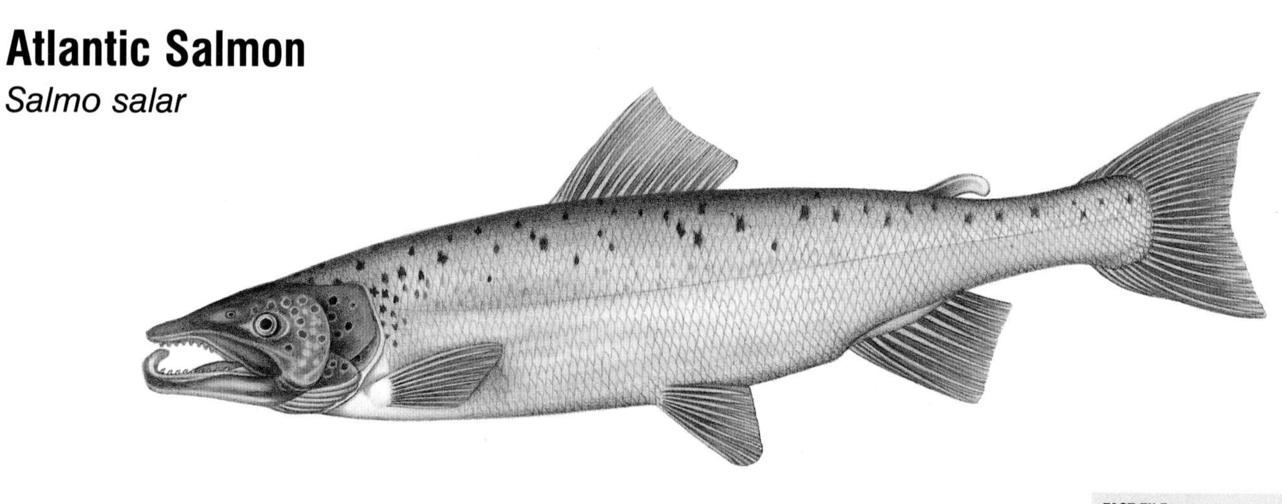

Often called the 'king of fish', the Atlantic salmon is prized for its delicate pink meat. It hatches out in shallow rivers and lives there for about three years. Now known as a smolt, it swims to the sea, where it stays for several more years. To breed, adults smell their way back to the river where they were born.

FACT FILE	
Length:	Up to 1.5m (5ft)
Distribution:	North Atlantic
Diet:	Squid, crustaceans and fish
Reproduction:	Spawns in river of birth
Status (IUCN Red List):	Least concern

Brown Trout

Salmo trutta fario

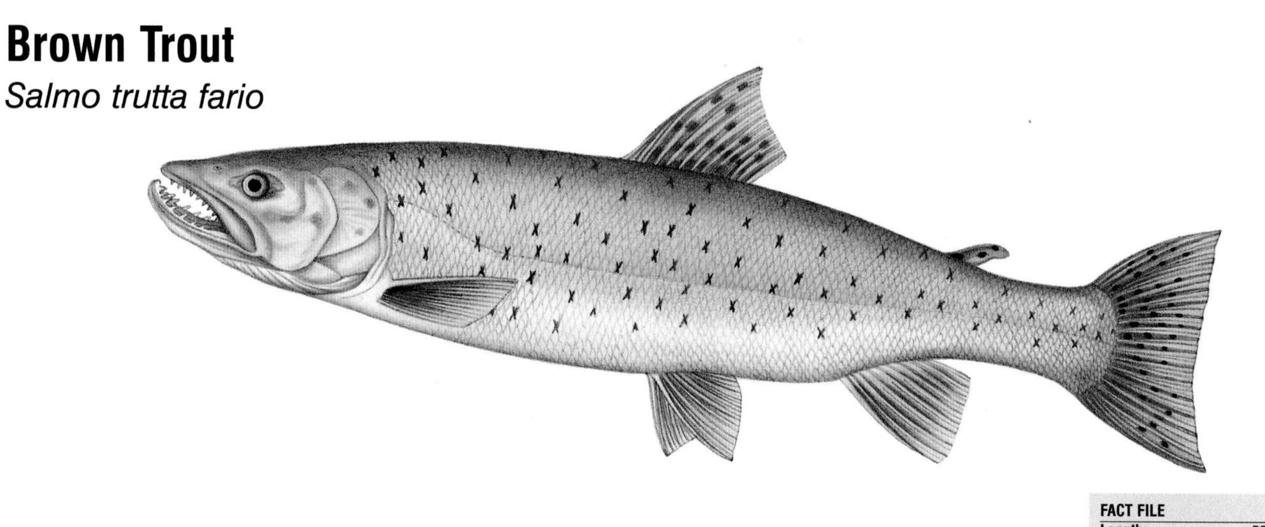

Despite being a close relative of the ocean-going salmon, this species spends its entire life in freshwater – although it may stray into brackish estuaries occasionally and, like salmon, the fish migrate to their home streams to spawn. Trout meat is browner than salmon because they eat fewer crustaceans.

FACT FILE	
Length:	50cm (19½in)
Distribution:	Europe
Diet:	Insects, snails and frogs
Reproduction:	Eggs buried in gravel
Status (IUCN Red List):	Least concern

Cutthroat Trout

Oncorhynchus clarkii

These fish are named after the pink-orange slash on the lower jaw. They live in the rivers of the American West, with several subspecies found in the various river systems between California and Alaska. The fish head upstream to breed after several years devoted to growth. Most fish die after breeding once.

FACT FILE	
Length:	30cm (12in)
Distribution:	West coast of North America
Diet:	Crustaceans and algae
Reproduction:	Eggs laid in a redd (gravel nest)
Status (IUCN Red List):	Not evaluated

Chinook Salmon

Oncorhynchus tshawytscha

This is one of the most widespread salmon species in the Pacific. Like its Atlantic cousins, the fish spends its first and last days in freshwater, while living its middle age out at sea. The fish is named after the Native American people that traditionally live in the Pacific Northwest.

FACT FILE	
Length:	90cm (35in)
Distribution:	Coasts of northern Pacific
Diet:	Squid, crustaceans and fish
Reproduction:	Spawns in river of birth
Status (IUCN Red List):	Not evaluated

Rainbow Trout

Oncorhynchus mykiss

Rainbow trout are named for the fine colouring of adult fish that spawn in fast-flowing streams. Those living in still lakes are a more uniform silver colour. The species originated in the American northwest, where populations that migrate to the sea are known as steelheads. However, most stay in freshwater.

FACT FILE	
Length:	1.2m (4ft)
Distribution:	E. Pacific, introduced worldwide
Diet:	Various invertebrates, small fish
Reproduction:	Breed in shallow water
Status (IUCN Red List):	Not evaluated

Pike

Esox lucius

The pike is a large freshwater fish related to salmon, trout and grayling. It is a voracious hunter, known by some as the 'freshwater shark'. Pikes are not a popular food fish, but they are highly sought by anglers, who relish the challenge of outwitting this powerful yet sly fish.

FACT FILE	
Length:	1.5m (5ft); males smaller
Distribution:	Northern Hemisphere
Diet:	Fish, birds and water mammals
Reproduction:	Up to 70,000 eggs laid
Status (IUCN Red List):	Least concern

The pike is one of the most widespread freshwater fish in the world. It is known as a jackfish in North America. The fish lurks in thick vegetation and ambushes prey with a rapid forward surge. Pikes breed in early summer, when the fish gather in shallow water. Once fertilized, the sticky eggs cling to water plants.

MOUTH
The jaw takes up about 20 per cent of the whole body length and is lined with hooked teeth. The lower jaw overbites the upper one.

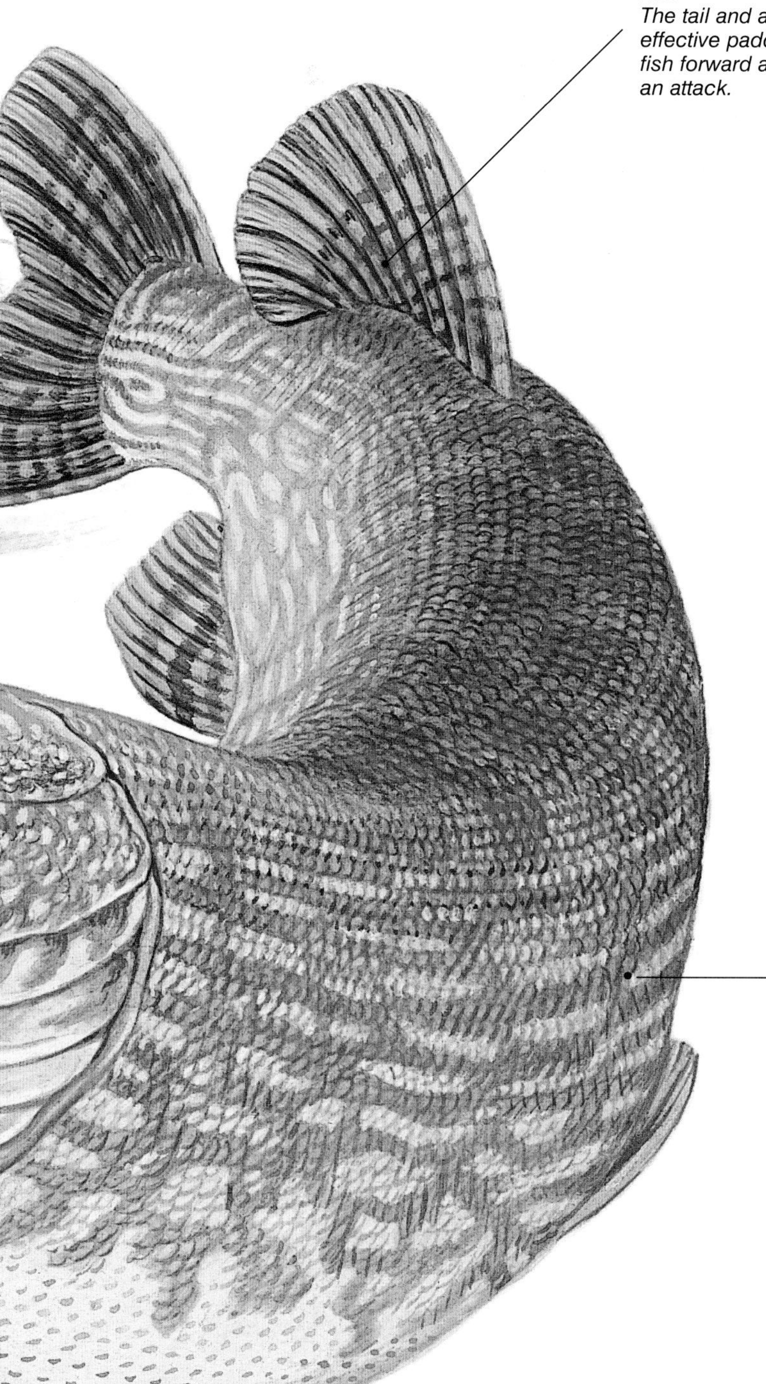

FINS
The tail and anal fins make an effective paddle for pushing the fish forward as it surges in for an attack.

SKIN
The upper body is a dark green, while the underbelly is cream. Pikes that live in brackish waters, where rivers mix with tidal seawater, tend to be yellower.

Whitefish

Many of the fish harvested from the seas destined for the dinner table are the so-called whitefish, named after the colour of their succulent flesh. There are about 475 species, forming the order Gadiformes. The most familiar is the Atlantic cod, a 2m (6ft 6in) monster that is now quite rare due to overfishing.

European Hake

Merluccius merluccius

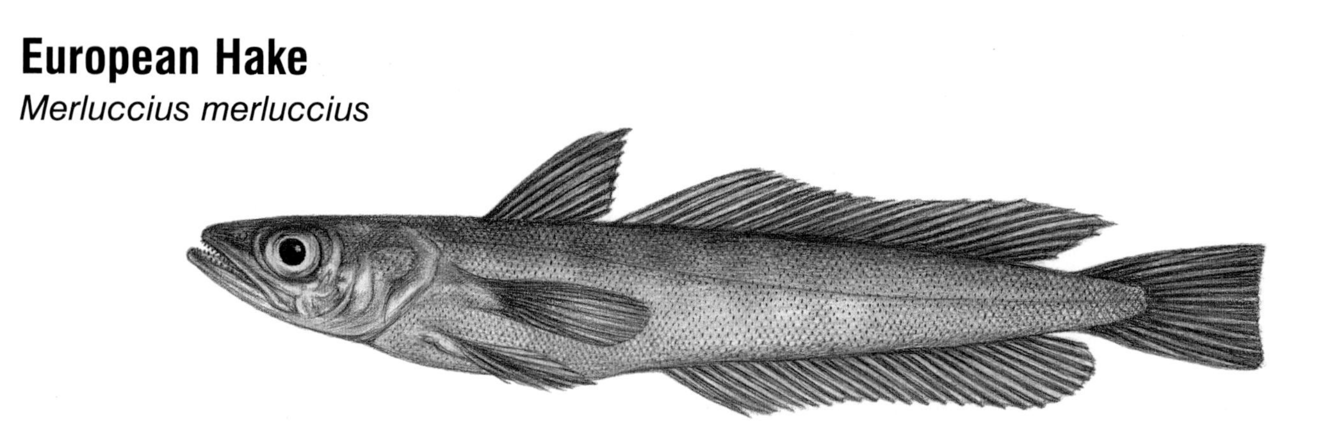

The hakes are similar to cod, but slightly more slender. By day, adults lurk at the bottom of the ocean. When it gets darker up top, they rise up the water column. The shoals spawn in spring, with males hastily fertilizing millions of eggs released by females. The eggs float to the surface and are dispersed by ocean currents.

FACT FILE	
Length:	1.4m (4ft 6in)
Distribution:	Eastern North Atlantic
Diet:	Shellfish, fish and cephalopods
Reproduction:	Spawns in spring
Status (IUCN Red List):	Not evaluated

Cusk

Brosme brosme

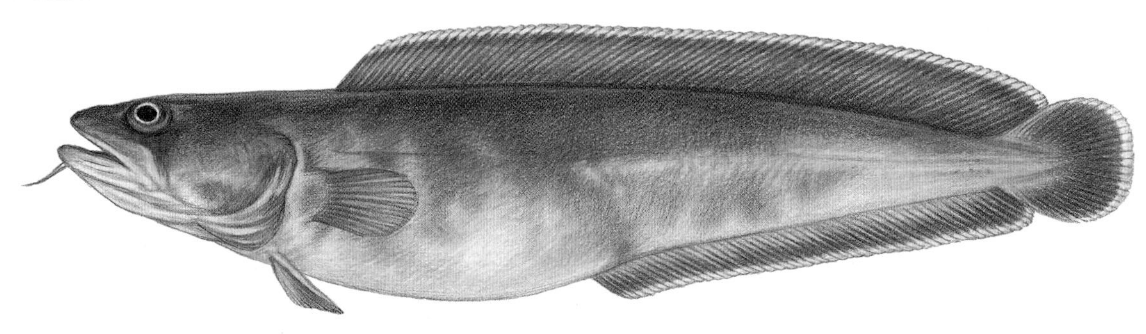

This Atlantic whitefish is variously known as the moonfish or tusk. Its rounded tail fin differentiates it from other sea-going whitefish. The fish stays on the bottom, using the fleshy barbels on its lower lip to search for crustaceans and bivalves. Young hatch from eggs at the surface and the head of rocky seabeds.

FACT FILE	
Length:	1m (3ft 3in)
Distribution:	North Atlantic coasts
Diet:	Shellfish
Reproduction:	Floating eggs laid in spring
Status (IUCN Red List):	Not evaluated

Burbot

Lota lota

FACT FILE	
Length:	1.5m (5ft)
Distribution:	Northern Hemisphere
Diet:	Fish and shellfish
Reproduction:	Spawns in winter
Status (IUCN Red List):	Least concern

The burbot is the only cod-like fish that spends its entire life in freshwater. It is most common in cold northern waterways. By day, it lurks out of sight in tangles of roots and water plants; it emerges at night to hunt for fish and shellfish in shallow water.

Haddock

Melanogrammus aeglefinus

FACT FILE	
Length:	1m (3ft 3in)
Distribution:	North Atlantic
Diet:	Bottom-living animals
Reproduction:	Spawns in spring
Status (IUCN Red List):	Vulnerable

Like the cod, this is an important North Atlantic fish, although it does not grow as big. Haddock are easily distinguished by their sharply pointed first dorsal fin (the cod's is rounded). Young haddock live at first near the surface, protected among the tentacles of a large jellyfish before heading for deep waters.

Tadpole Cod

Raniceps raninus

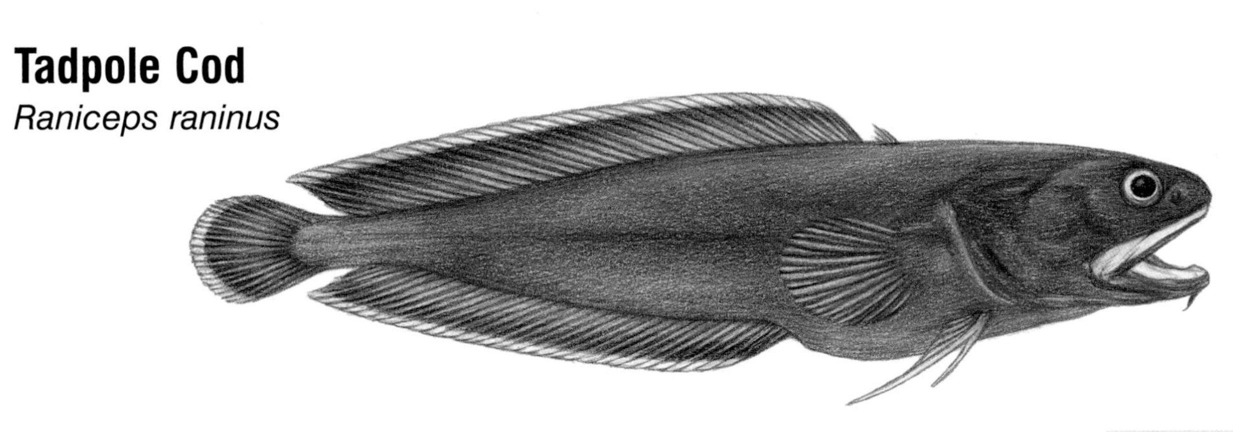

FACT FILE	
Length:	27cm (10½in)
Distribution:	Northeast Atlantic
Diet:	Worms, fish and shellfish
Reproduction:	Spawns near shore in autumn
Status (IUCN Red List):	Not evaluated

Also known as the tadpole fish, this species lives in the coastal water around Britain and Scandinavia. The forward section of the body is more rounded than the flattened hindquarters, so the fish really does look like a giant tadpole when seen from above.

Anglerfish and Relatives

The anglerfish belong to the Lophiiformes order, a group of benthic (bottom-living) or deep-sea fish, characterized by their large mouths and luminescent lures, which they use to attract prey. The anglerfish are close relatives of the cod; their meat is also highly prized. Another related group is the Batrachoididae, or toadfish.

Midshipman Fish

Porichthys notatus

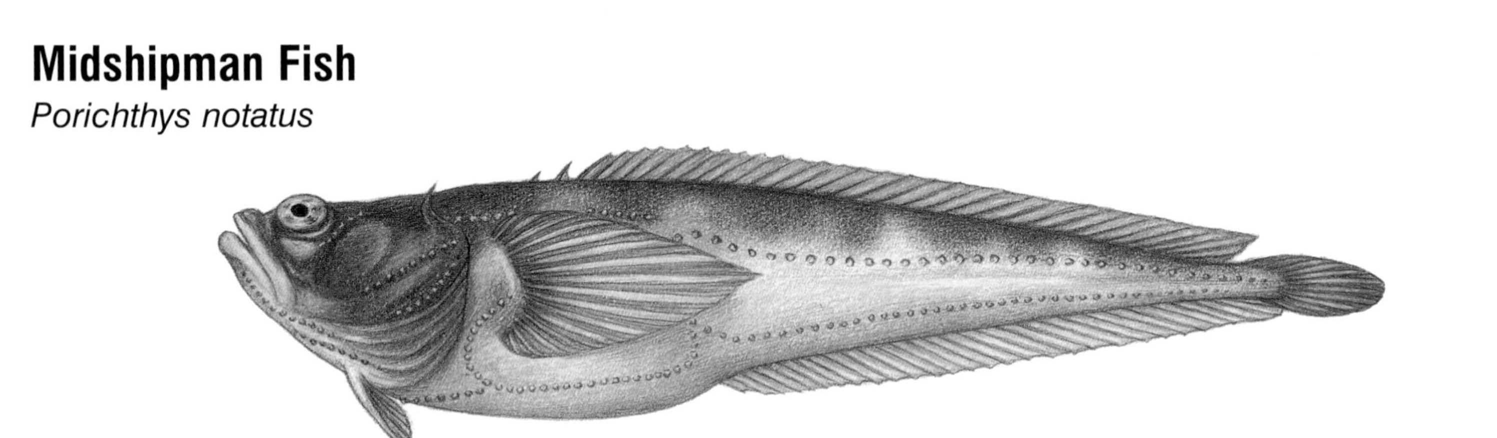

FACT FILE	
Length:	38cm (15in)
Distribution:	West coast of North America
Diet:	Crustaceans and fish
Reproduction:	Males call for mates
Status (IUCN Red List):	Least concern

The midshipman fish is a toadfish. It is one of the few species that uses sounds to attract mates. During the breeding season, males broadcast a hum produced by vibrating their swim bladders. The frequency of the hum is often amplified by the hull of a ship and can become rather intrusive in cabins below the water line.

Anglerfish

Lophius piscatorius

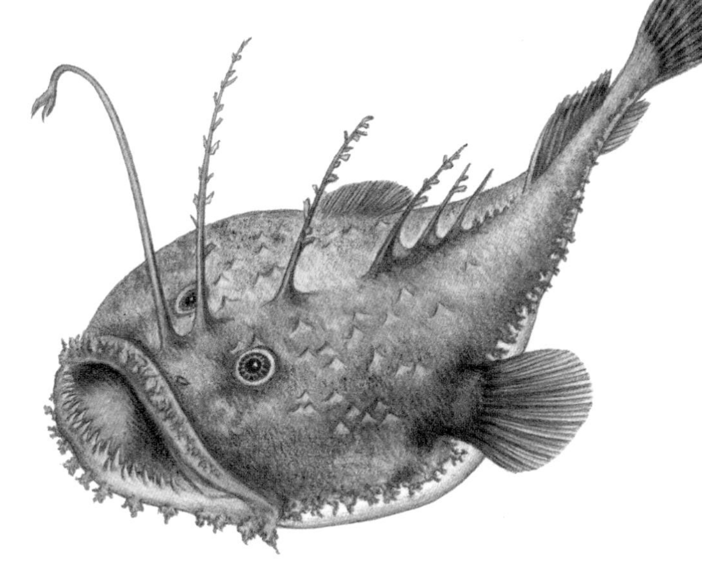

FACT FILE	
Length:	2m (6ft 6in)
Distribution:	E. Atlantic, Mediterranean, Black Sea
Diet:	Fish and larger invertebrates
Reproduction:	Spawns on beach at high tide
Status (IUCN Red List):	Not evaluated

The name anglerfish is very apt, since this fish has a 'fishing rod' – a long, flexible spine properly called the illicium – growing from its head; this spine ends in a fleshy lure called the esca. The fish lies on the bottom and the slightest touch on the esca provokes a snapping reflex from its huge jaws.

Monkfish

Lophius americanus

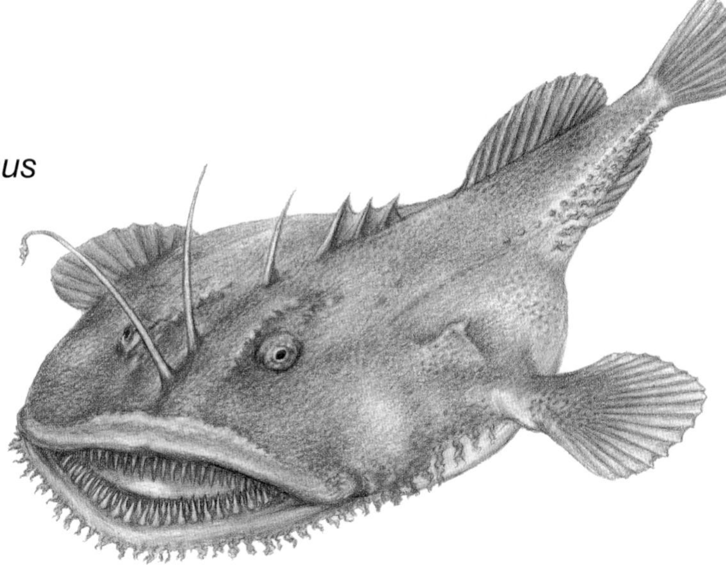

FACT FILE	
Length:	1.5m (5ft)
Distribution:	Western North Atlantic
Diet:	Fish and larger invertebrates
Reproduction:	Spawns on beach at high tide
Status (IUCN Red List):	Not evaluated

Perhaps understandably, this species is rarely described using its alternative common names of goosefish or American anglerfish. As a highly prized food fish, restaurant-goers prefer to order monkfish, an altogether more attractive-sounding dish.

Starry Handfish

Halieutaea stellata

FACT FILE	
Length:	30cm (12in)
Distribution:	Indian and Pacific ocean coasts
Diet:	Invertebrates
Reproduction:	Jelly eggs laid in rafts
Status (IUCN Red List):	Not evaluated

The starry handfish is a species of batfish. It is a very poor swimmer and usually walks on the seabed instead, using thickened, limb-like pectoral and pelvic fins. It lives in shallow coastal waters, preying on invertebrates including worms, molluscs and crustaceans.

Illuminated Netdevil

Linophryne arborifera

FACT FILE	
Length:	8cm (3in)
Distribution:	All warm oceans
Diet:	Fish and crustaceans
Reproduction:	Males parasitic on females
Status (IUCN Red List):	Not evaluated

One lure is not enough for this deep-sea angler. It also has a branched barbel that glows in the dark. As is the norm with anglerfish, only females of this species grow and feed. The male is a tiny parasite that sucks the blood of a female, releasing sperm onto the egg masses produced by his mate.

Rivulids, Killifish and Live Bearers

This mixed group of small freshwater fish form the order Cyprinodontiformes, which is translated into the common name toothcarps (although they are not related to carps). Many members do not lay eggs but give birth to, or bear, live young.

Killifish

Fundulopanchax gardneri

The name 'killifish' is derived from the Dutch for puddle, because many of these fish live in highly seasonal waters that shrink and swell with the season and can even survive out of water for a short while. However, this species, also known as the blue lyretail by the pet trade, lives in a more stable river habitat.

FACT FILE	
Length:	6.5cm (2½in)
Distribution:	Africa
Diet:	Algae and small invertebrates
Reproduction:	Spawns on river bottom
Status (IUCN Red List):	Near threatened

American Flag Fish

Jordanella floridae

This American killifish species bears a fair resemblance to the Stars and Stripes flag. The male's body displays a large blue-black dot with alternating red and blue-black stripes. Females are much less colourful, although they also sport an eyespot in the centre of their side, and another in the rear base of the dorsal fin.

FACT FILE	
Length:	5cm (2in)
Distribution:	Florida to the Yucatán
Diet:	Algae and small invertebrates
Reproduction:	100 eggs laid in a nest
Status (IUCN Red List):	Not evaluated

Four-eyed Fish

Anableps anableps

FACT FILE	
Length:	32cm (12½in)
Distribution:	Central and N. South America
Diet:	Insects
Reproduction:	Bears live young
Status (IUCN Red List):	Not evaluated

No vertebrate has more than two image-forming eyes, and this fish is named after the way each of its eyes is divided in two, with one half looking above the water and the other looking below. The fish also have one-sided genitals; this means that right-sided fish can mate only with left-sided ones, and vice versa.

Guppy

Poecilia reticulata

FACT FILE	
Length:	6.5cm (2½in)
Distribution:	Caribbean and South America
Diet:	Invertebrates
Reproduction:	Bears up to 100 young
Status (IUCN Red List):	Not evaluated

The guppy is perhaps the most common freshwater aquarium fish. It is named after the nineteenth-century British naturalist Robert Guppy. Male guppies have spots or stripes on their flanks, while females have grey bodies. Pet guppies are highly inbred and weak.They frequently die from congenital problems or shock.

Mosquitofish

Gambusia affinis

FACT FILE	
Length:	7cm (2¾in)
Distribution:	River systems of Gulf of Mexico
Diet:	Mosquito larvae
Reproduction:	Broods of up to 100 young
Status (IUCN Red List):	Not evaluated

As its name suggests, this fish feeds on the larvae and pupae of mosquitoes. These insect larvae live in stagnant waters, with little oxygen mixed into them. The mosquitofish can survive these harsh conditions, and have been introduced across the world to tackle mosquito problems, although with limited success.

Strange-shaped Fish

Fish tend to conform to a certain shape, with a flattened body, generally from side to side, but also from top to bottom in the case of flat fish. This shape is ideal for swimming and cutting through water. However, the bodies of some fish are adapted for more unusual purposes.

Lumpsucker

Cyclopterus lumpus

FACT FILE	
Length:	60cm (23½in)
Distribution:	North Atlantic
Diet:	Jellyfish, worms and crustaceans
Reproduction:	Sticky eggs laid on rocks
Status (IUCN Red List):	Not evaluated

The lumpsucker, or lumpfish, has a round sucker disc – actually modified pelvic fins – on its underside. The male fish uses this sucker to attach itself to a rock while guarding the masses of sticky eggs laid by the female in the shallows in the summer. The guarding male fans water over the eggs with his fins.

Razorfish

Aeoliscus strigatus

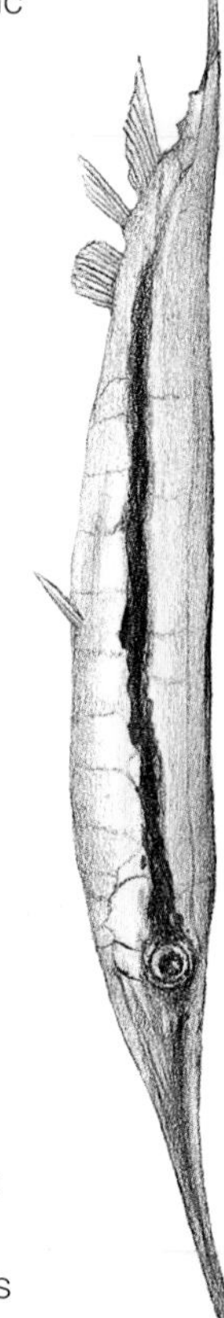

FACT FILE	
Length:	15cm (6in)
Distribution:	Indian and Pacific oceans
Diet:	Brine shrimps
Reproduction:	Eggs laid in masses
Status (IUCN Red List):	Not evaluated

This fish lives among sea urchins, sea grass and corals. In an effort to stay out of sight, it has evolved a unique head-down swimming style, so its long, knife-shaped body blends in with all the upright structures around it. The fish uses its long snout to pick off small crustaceans that feed on sea urchins.

Leafy Sea Dragon

Phycodurus eques

FACT FILE	
Length:	Up to 44cm (17in)
Distribution:	Southern coast of Australia
Diet:	Small crustaceans and plankton
Reproduction:	Male carries eggs until they hatch
Status (IUCN Red List):	Near threatened

Sea dragons are close relatives of seahorses, but with distinctive characteristic 'leaf' adornments covering their bodies. This spectacular natural camouflage enables them to pass virtually unnoticed amid the beds of seaweed where they make their homes.

Long-snouted Seahorse

Hippocampus ramulosus

FACT FILE	
Length:	21cm (8¼in)
Distribution:	Eastern Atlantic, Mediterranean
Diet:	Small shrimp and plankton
Reproduction:	Male carries eggs in tail pouch
Status (IUCN Red List):	Data deficient

This iconic species makes its home in eel grass and seaweed beds, often using their prehensile tails to anchor themselves to vegetation. Juveniles anchor themselves in a similar way, tail-to-tail with other seahorses for safety. Unlike most fish, a seahorse can moves its eyes independently of its head.

Reef Stonefish

Synanceia verrucosa

FACT FILE	
Length:	40cm (16in)
Distribution:	Indo-Pacific waters
Diet:	Small fish and crustaceans
Reproduction:	Egg-laying
Status (IUCN Red List):	Not evaluated

The reef stonefish has a large, gaping mouth. When opened quickly, the mouth creates a vacuum that sucks in prey. On the seabed, these lumpy, grey-brown fish are easily mistaken for a piece of rock. Anyone standing on the fish by mistake will find three stout spines on the fish's back injecting them with venom.

Lionfish

Pterois radiata

Lionfish are extraordinary-looking, brightly coloured fish. Their colouring is a warning to other reef-dwellers: the lionfish is highly venomous; it has poison glands at the base of its extremely sharp dorsal spines. Anyone disturbing the fish with their hands or feet is liable to get an extremely painful, although rarely fatal, sting.

FACT FILE	
Length:	40cm (16in)
Distribution:	Indian and Pacific oceans
Diet:	Small fish and crustaceans
Reproduction:	Egg-laying
Status (IUCN Red List):	Not evaluated

Lionfish are also known as turkeyfish, dragonfish and firefish, due to their rather ostentatious appearance. When young, lionfish are almost transparent, but as they mature they develop their distinctive bold stripes and feather-like fins. If threatened, the lionfish will dip its head towards an attacker, displaying its venomous spikes menacingly.

TAIL POWER
The lionfish is a slow swimmer, but its rounded caudal fin – or tail – is used to provide rapid bursts of speed over short distances as the fish lunges forward to grab prey.

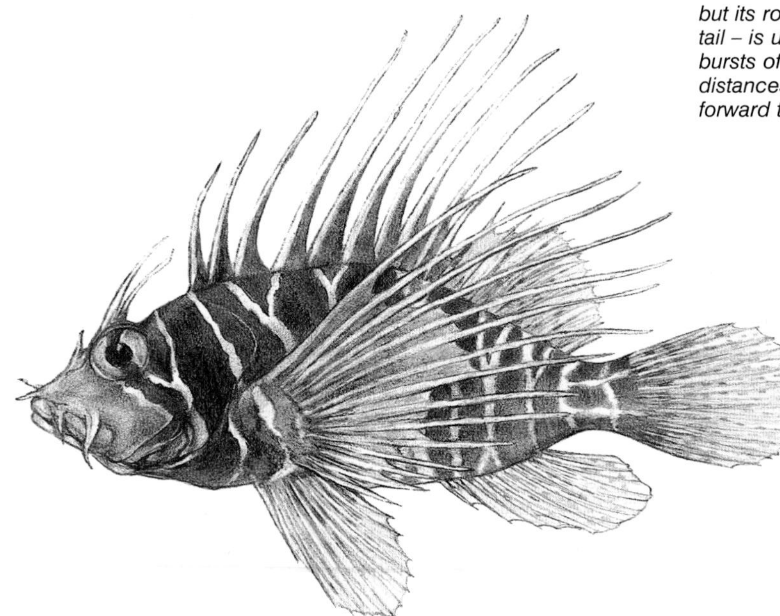

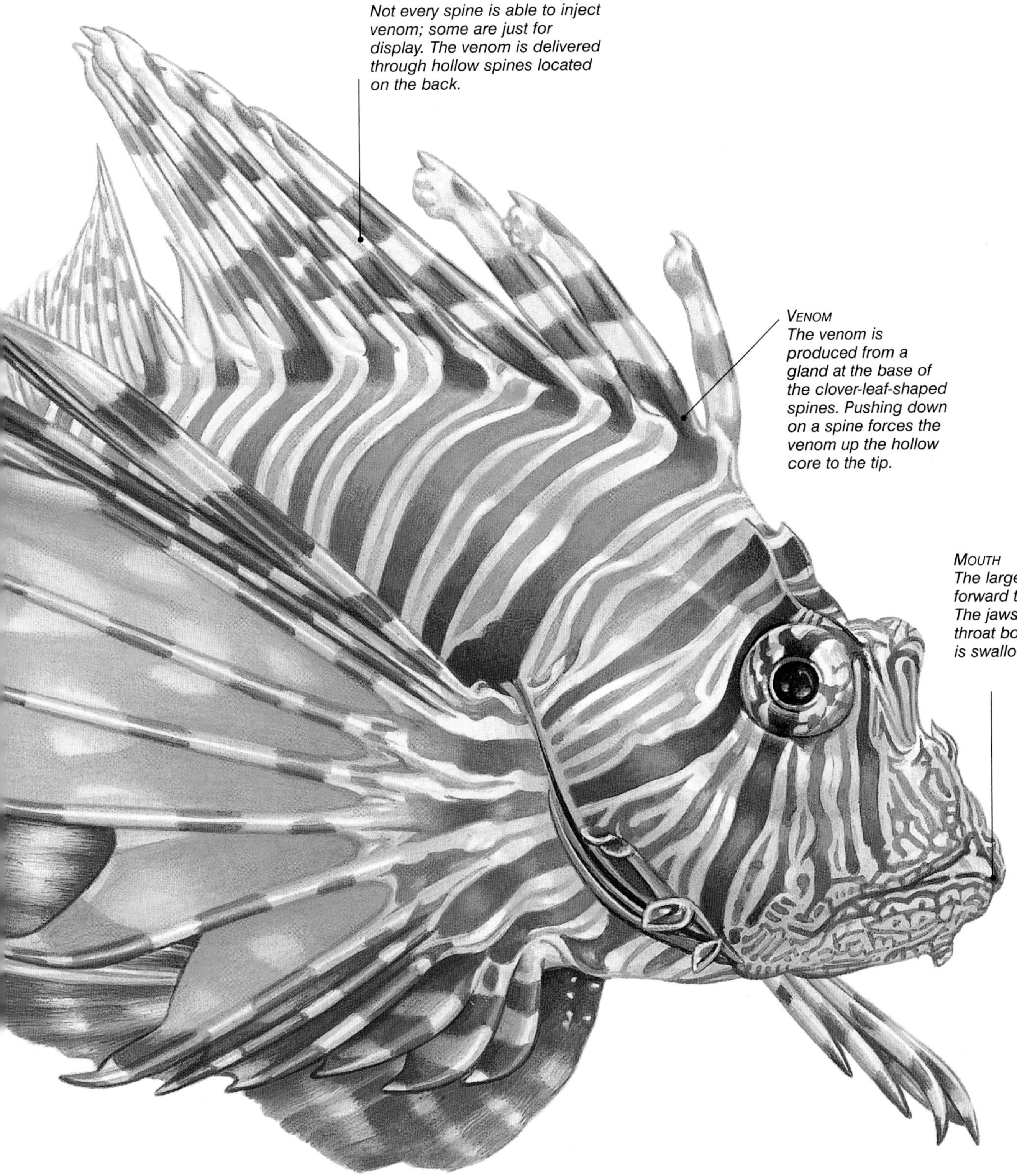

SPINES
Not every spine is able to inject venom; some are just for display. The venom is delivered through hollow spines located on the back.

VENOM
The venom is produced from a gland at the base of the clover-leaf-shaped spines. Pushing down on a spine forces the venom up the hollow core to the tip.

MOUTH
The large mouth is extended forward to envelope prey. The jaws are toothless, but throat bones crush food as it is swallowed.

Perch and Relatives

The perches lend their name to a huge order of fish called the Perciformes (perch-like fish). The order comprises at least 7000 species, about 40 per cent of all fish, and includes some familiar names, such as blennies, gobies, darters and whitings. Perches are found in all habitats, from lakes to coral reefs.

Crevalle Jack

Caranx hippos

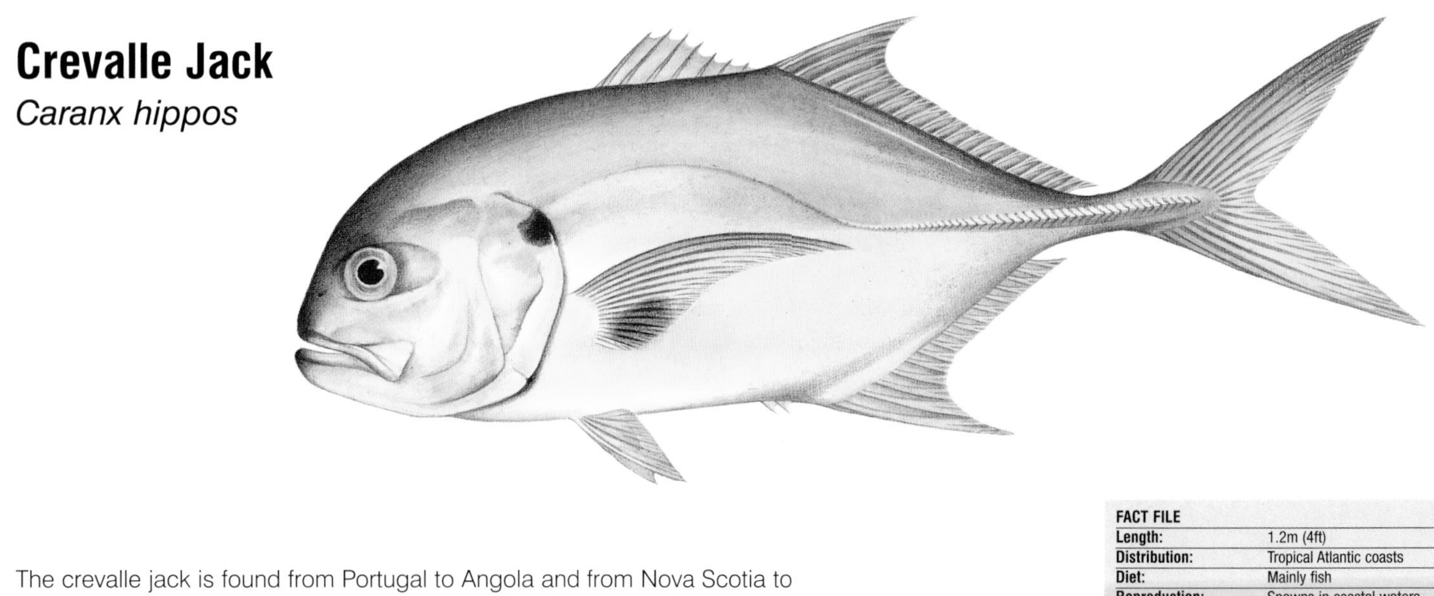

The crevalle jack is found from Portugal to Angola and from Nova Scotia to Uruguay. The Pacific crevalle jack (*C. caninus*) is probably the same species, but it is unable to breed with its Atlantic cousins. Crevalle jacks form fast-swimming schools. They often grunt when captured.

FACT FILE	
Length:	1.2m (4ft)
Distribution:	Tropical Atlantic coasts
Diet:	Mainly fish
Reproduction:	Spawns in coastal waters
Status (IUCN Red List):	Least concern

Comet

Calloplesiops altivelis

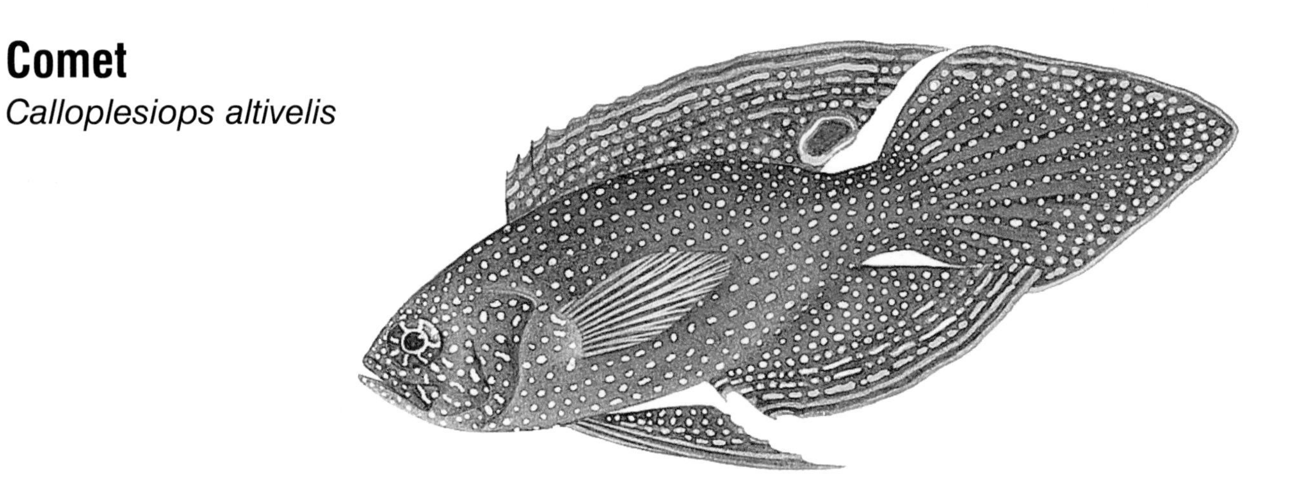

The white spots on the comet's body become smaller and more numerous as the fish ages. When threatened, the comet mimics the fierce whitemouth moray. It swims into a crevice, leaving its back portion exposed. An eyespot on the dorsal fin makes the fish's posterior resemble the face of the eel.

FACT FILE	
Length:	20cm (8in)
Distribution:	Indo-Pacific reefs
Diet:	Invertebrates
Reproduction:	300 eggs laid in crevice
Status (IUCN Red List):	Not evaluated

Honey Gourami

Trichogaster chuna

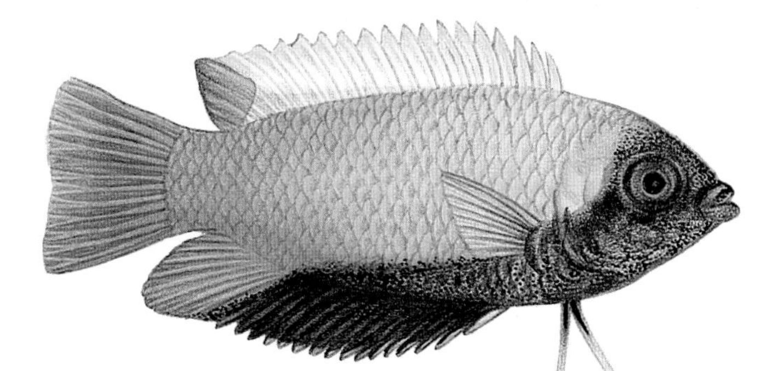

Despite its colourful name, the honey gourami looks a deceptively drab russet, until the male takes on his vibrant red, yellow and deep blue breeding colours. After spawning, the male builds a nest of bubbles, held together with saliva and plants, in which to house the eggs.

FACT FILE	
Length:	6cm (2¼in)
Distribution:	India and Bangladesh
Diet:	Worms and other invertebrates
Reproduction:	Eggs deposited in bubble nests
Status (IUCN Red List):	Least concern

Siamese Fighting Fish

Betta splendens

Also known as the betta, the Siamese fighting fish is renowned for its bright colours and flowing fins. These features are the product of selective breeding in captivity. In the wild, the betta has short fins and displays strong colours only when excited. Males kept in one tank will fight during the breeding season.

FACT FILE	
Length:	8cm (3in)
Distribution:	Mekong River basin
Diet:	Invertebrates
Reproduction:	300 eggs laid in bubble nests
Status (IUCN Red List):	Not evaluated

Kissing Gourami

Helostoma temmincki

This fish earns its name from its protruding lips, which are lined with horny teeth. These lips are used to rasp algae from stones and other surfaces in a 'kissing' action. Rival males sometimes lock lips in wrestling competitions over territory. The fish originating from Thailand are green, while fish from Java are pink.

FACT FILE	
Length:	30cm (12in)
Distribution:	Thailand to Indonesia
Diet:	Algae
Reproduction:	1000 eggs laid on floating leaves
Status (IUCN Red List):	Not evaluated

Groupers

The Serranidae form a family of perch-like fish. The family contains about 450 species, most of which live in the sea and have large mouths. The family includes the sea basses, a popular medium-sized food fish, and the groupers, large reef fish that are characterized by their wide heads and thick lips.

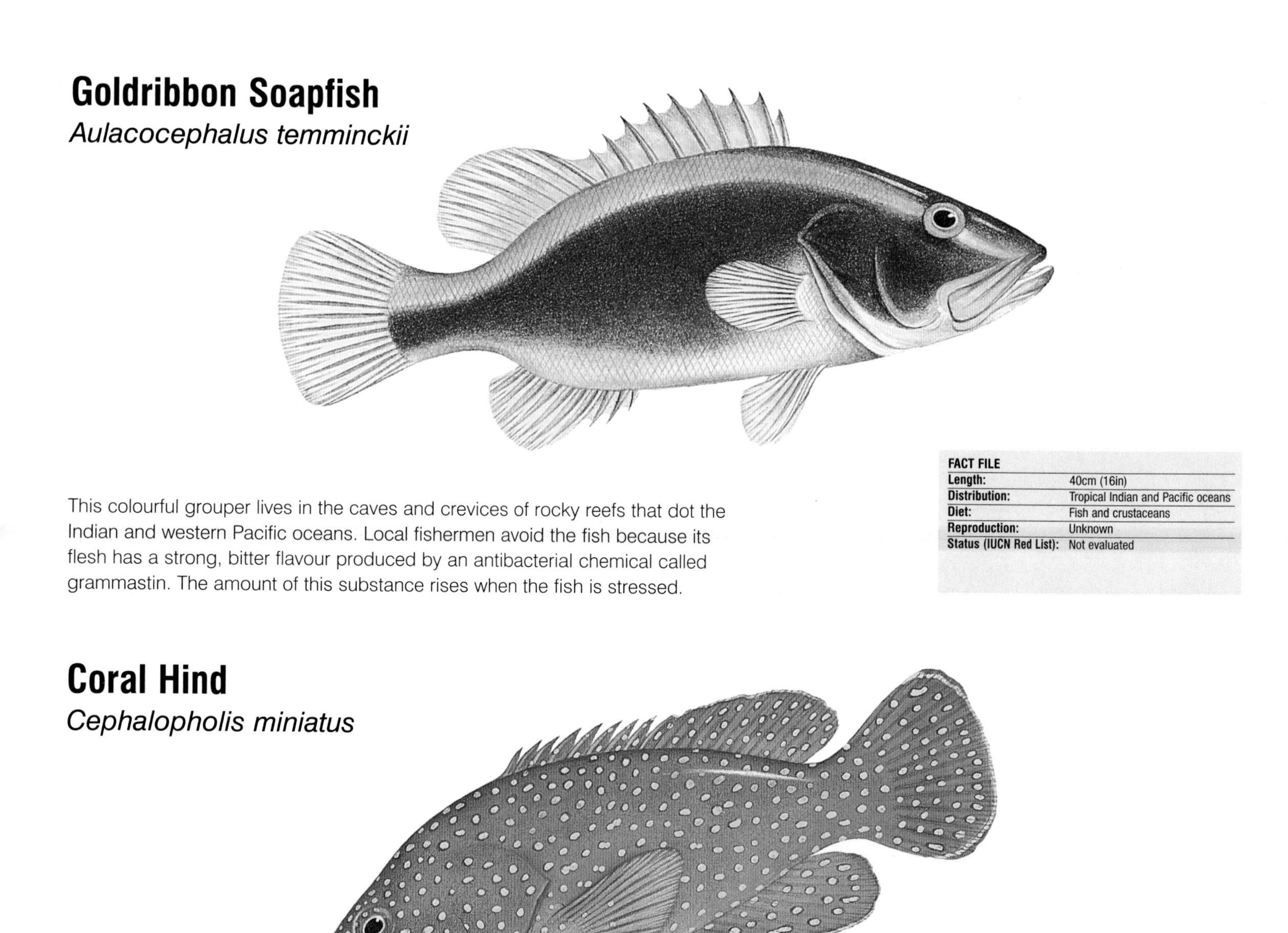

Goldribbon Soapfish

Aulacocephalus temminckii

FACT FILE	
Length:	40cm (16in)
Distribution:	Tropical Indian and Pacific oceans
Diet:	Fish and crustaceans
Reproduction:	Unknown
Status (IUCN Red List):	Not evaluated

This colourful grouper lives in the caves and crevices of rocky reefs that dot the Indian and western Pacific oceans. Local fishermen avoid the fish because its flesh has a strong, bitter flavour produced by an antibacterial chemical called grammastin. The amount of this substance rises when the fish is stressed.

Coral Hind

Cephalopholis miniatus

FACT FILE	
Length:	45cm (17¾in)
Distribution:	Tropical Indian and Pacific oceans
Diet:	Fish and crustaceans
Reproduction:	Males guard harems
Status (IUCN Red List):	Least concern

Although it looks bright in the light of a diver's torch or full sunlight, this species is a dark presence in the half-light along the edge of a deep reef. It hunts in the clear waters near the reef, with a single male dominating a harem of five or six females. When the male dies, the largest female changes sex to take his place.

Nassau Grouper

Epinephelus striatus

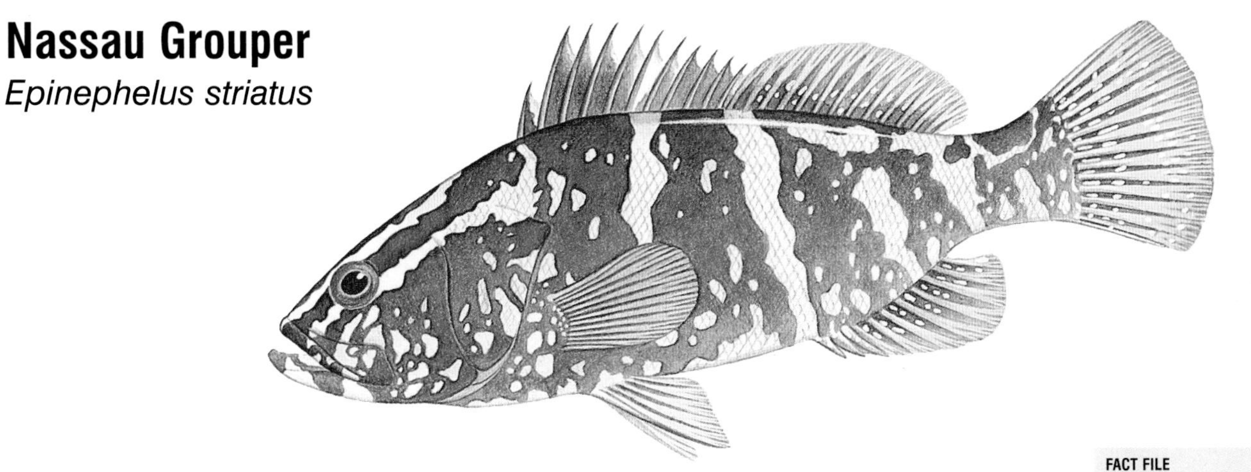

FACT FILE	
Length:	32cm (12½in)
Distribution:	Warm western Atlantic waters
Diet:	Fish and crustaceans
Reproduction:	Spawns at full moon
Status (IUCN Red List):	Endangered

The Nassua grouper is a bit of a loner. It feeds during the day around reefs in the Caribbean and along the South American coast. The fish spawn in December and January, always around the time of a full moon. They gather in traditional locations to breed, making them an easy target for fishing boats.

Yellow-edged Lyretail

Variola louti

FACT FILE	
Length:	80cm (32in)
Distribution:	Indo-Pacific
Diet:	Fish and crabs
Reproduction:	Unknown
Status (IUCN Red List):	Least concern

A very widespread species of grouper, this fish can be found as far afield as the reefs of the Red Sea, the southern Japanese islands, and the remote outpost of Pitcairn in the central Pacific. This big fish can be eaten, although in some regions they produce high levels of the toxin ciguatera.

Yellowfin Grouper

Mycteroperca venenosa

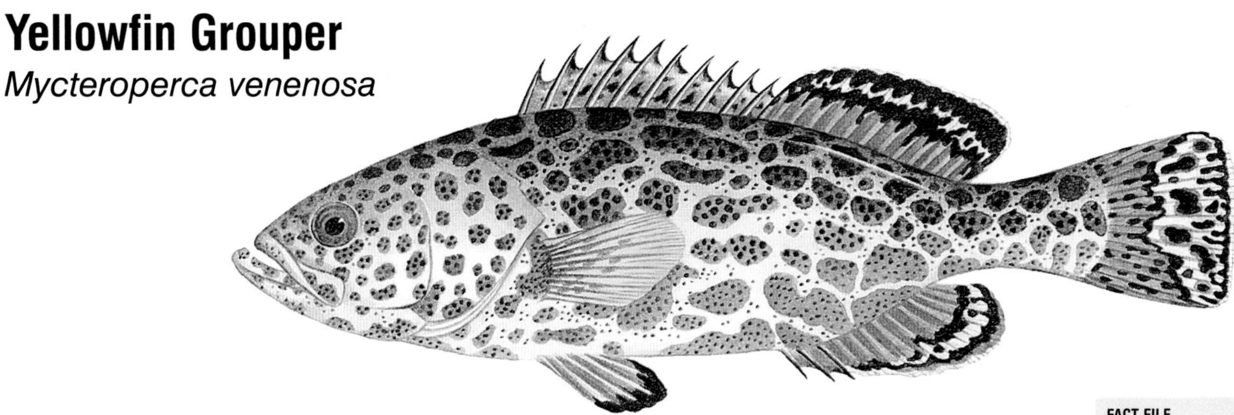

FACT FILE	
Length:	1m (3ft 3in)
Distribution:	Western Atlantic Ocean
Diet:	Fish and crabs
Reproduction:	Young gather in grass beds
Status (IUCN Red List):	Near threatened

This massive species lives in the gloom around deep reefs and only rarely ventures above 60m (200ft), generally during late winter when the waters near the surface have cooled down. A build-up of microorganisms in its flesh can mean it is unsafe to eat this otherwise tasty fish.

Queen Parrotfish

Scarus vetula

The parrotfish is named after its beak-like mouth, which is formed by its teeth fusing into a curved scraper. Parrotfish are grazers, scouring mats of algae from rocks. The fish also swallow chunks of dead coral, which are ground up with the algae, helping to release more nutrients – converting the coral into fine sand in the process.

FACT FILE	
Length:	60cm (23½in)
Distribution:	Western Atlantic Ocean
Diet:	Algae on rocks and dead coral
Reproduction:	Eggs scattered; large females may change into males
Status (IUCN Red List):	Least concern

Until they realized that male and female parrotfish look very different, scientists used to think there were many more than the 52 species now recognized. Parrotfish sleep inside a bubble of slimy mucus. This cocoon is invisible to predators, which blunder into it as they approach the sleeping fish, waking it up in time to escape.

TEETH
The teeth do not bite into food; they scrape food off rocks. The food – and the coral mixed into it – is then crushed by bony plates in the pharynx.

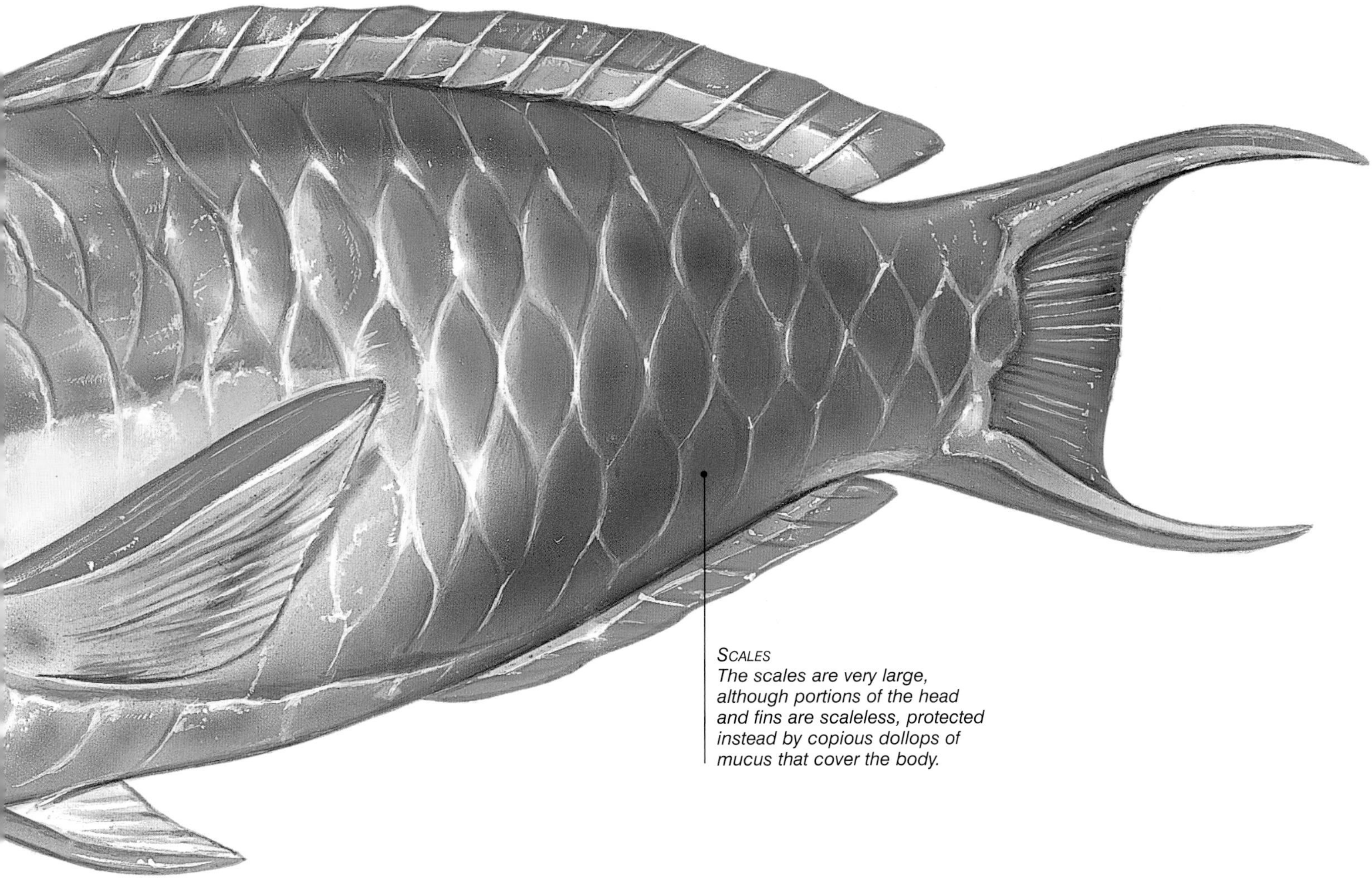

FEMALE
Females are smaller than the males, and look very different. Older females may continue to grow and transform into a male. This sex-change process, known as sequential hermaphroditism, is not unusual in fish.

SCALES
The scales are very large, although portions of the head and fins are scaleless, protected instead by copious dollops of mucus that cover the body.

Butterflyfish and Angelfish

The butterflyfish belong to the Chaetodontidae family. These are small reef fish, some of which go by the name of bannerfish due to a long trailing dorsal fin. Butterflyfish look like small versions of angelfish, which belong to the closely related Pomacanthidae family. Both groups belong to the Perciformes order.

Copperband Butterflyfish

Chelmon rostratus

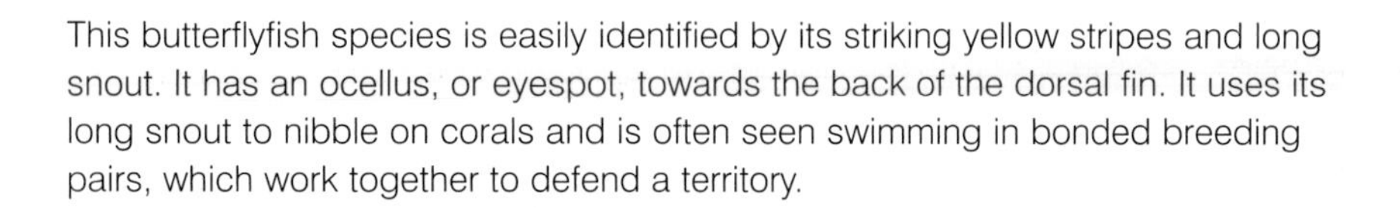

This butterflyfish species is easily identified by its striking yellow stripes and long snout. It has an ocellus, or eyespot, towards the back of the dorsal fin. It uses its long snout to nibble on corals and is often seen swimming in bonded breeding pairs, which work together to defend a territory.

FACT FILE	
Length:	20cm (8in)
Distribution:	Western Pacific Ocean
Diet:	Corals, worms, clams and shrimp
Reproduction:	Forms pairs and lays eggs
Status (IUCN Red List):	Least concern

Longnose Butterflyfish

Forcipiger longirostris

Named after its exceptionally long – even for a butterflyfish – and probing mouthparts, this species lives below 60m (200ft) on the seaward edges of rocky reefs. It pecks the coral for small crustaceans and other tiny invertebrates. This species is monogamous and pairs mate for life.

FACT FILE	
Length:	22cm (8½in)
Distribution:	Indian Ocean to Hawaii
Diet:	Crustaceans
Reproduction:	Forms pairs and lays eggs
Status (IUCN Red List):	Least concern

Pennant Coralfish

Heniochus acuminatus

This fish is named after the long dorsal fin that streams behind it, resembling the pennant of a medieval knight. The coralfish lives at the top of the reef, normally about 20m (65ft) down. It is most common in lagoons. Any fish swimming on their own are probably unbreeding juveniles, as adults live in breeding pairs.

FACT FILE	
Length:	25cm (10in)
Distribution:	Indian and western Pacific oceans
Diet:	Plankton
Reproduction:	Forms pairs and lays eggs
Status (IUCN Red List):	Least concern

Royal Angelfish

Pygoplites diacanthus

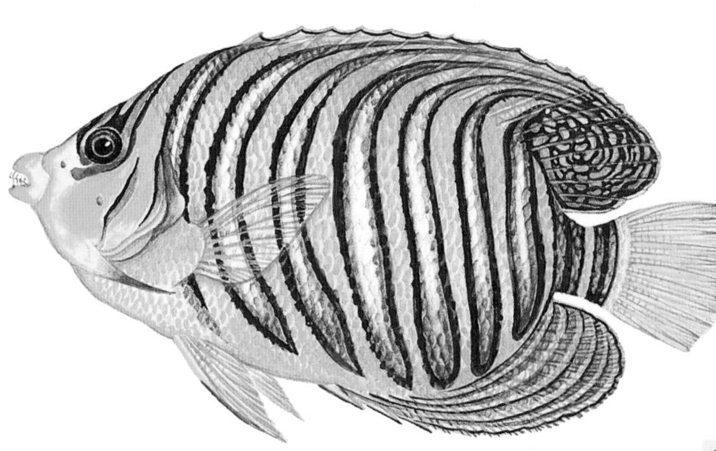

Larger and more rounded than its cousins the butterflyfish, this species lives on the seaward edges of reefs. Here currents bring in cooler, mineral-rich waters, ideal for the fish's main prey, sponges and tunicates, which filter food particles from the water.

FACT FILE	
Length:	25cm (10in)
Distribution:	Red Sea to Micronesia
Diet:	Sponges and tunicates
Reproduction:	Eggs float freely
Status (IUCN Red List):	Least concern

Emperor Angelfish

Pomacanthus imperator

Young emperor angelfish are dark blue with electric blue and white rings. When they reach four years old, adults have yellow and blue stripes, with black around the eyes. They are territorial and hard to keep in aquaria with other fish because they need a lot of space and hiding places.

FACT FILE	
Length:	40cm (16in)
Distribution:	Red Sea to Hawaii
Diet:	Sponges and tunicates
Reproduction:	Eggs float freely
Status (IUCN Red List):	Least concern

Cichlids

The cichlids are freshwater perch-like fish living worldwide. Biologists have identified more than 1600 cichlids in Africa alone, and it is estimated that the whole Cichlidae family contains about 3000 species. Some habitats, such as Africa's great lakes, are dominated by cichlids, with each species adapted to a unique microhabitat.

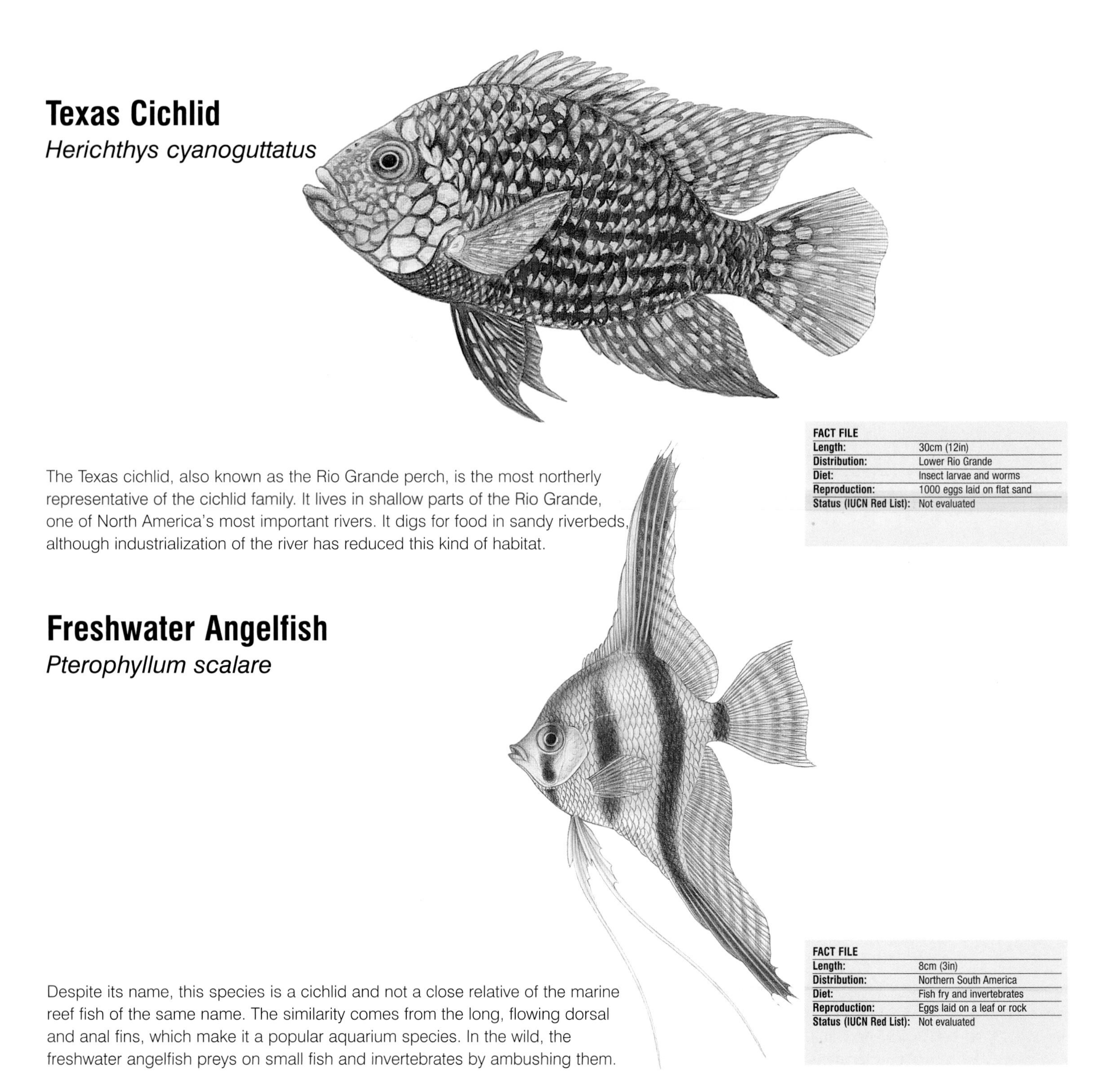

Texas Cichlid

Herichthys cyanoguttatus

The Texas cichlid, also known as the Rio Grande perch, is the most northerly representative of the cichlid family. It lives in shallow parts of the Rio Grande, one of North America's most important rivers. It digs for food in sandy riverbeds, although industrialization of the river has reduced this kind of habitat.

FACT FILE	
Length:	30cm (12in)
Distribution:	Lower Rio Grande
Diet:	Insect larvae and worms
Reproduction:	1000 eggs laid on flat sand
Status (IUCN Red List):	Not evaluated

Freshwater Angelfish

Pterophyllum scalare

Despite its name, this species is a cichlid and not a close relative of the marine reef fish of the same name. The similarity comes from the long, flowing dorsal and anal fins, which make it a popular aquarium species. In the wild, the freshwater angelfish preys on small fish and invertebrates by ambushing them.

FACT FILE	
Length:	8cm (3in)
Distribution:	Northern South America
Diet:	Fish fry and invertebrates
Reproduction:	Eggs laid on a leaf or rock
Status (IUCN Red List):	Not evaluated

Discus

Symphysodon aequifasciatus

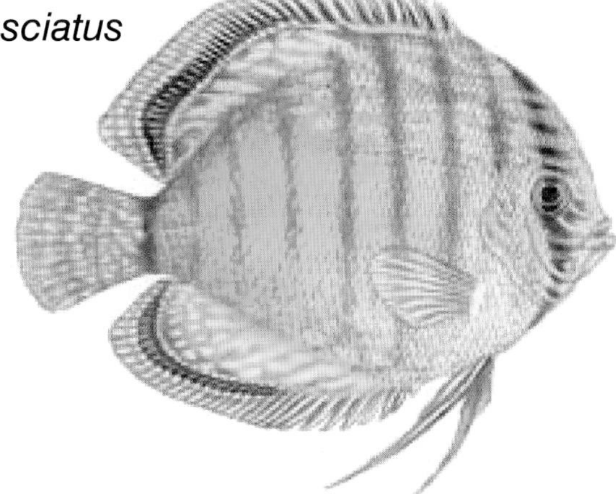

The discus cichlid has a laterally compressed, round body, hence the name. The species is known for the way both parents care of their young. The adults produce a secretion from their skin on which the larvae feed. The fish forage on gravel riverbeds, out of sight among water plants.

FACT FILE	
Length:	25cm (10in)
Distribution:	Brazil, Colombia and Peru
Diet:	Invertebrates
Reproduction:	200 eggs laid on a leaf or rock
Status (IUCN Red List):	Not evaluated

Lifalili Jewel Cichlid

Hemichromis lifalili

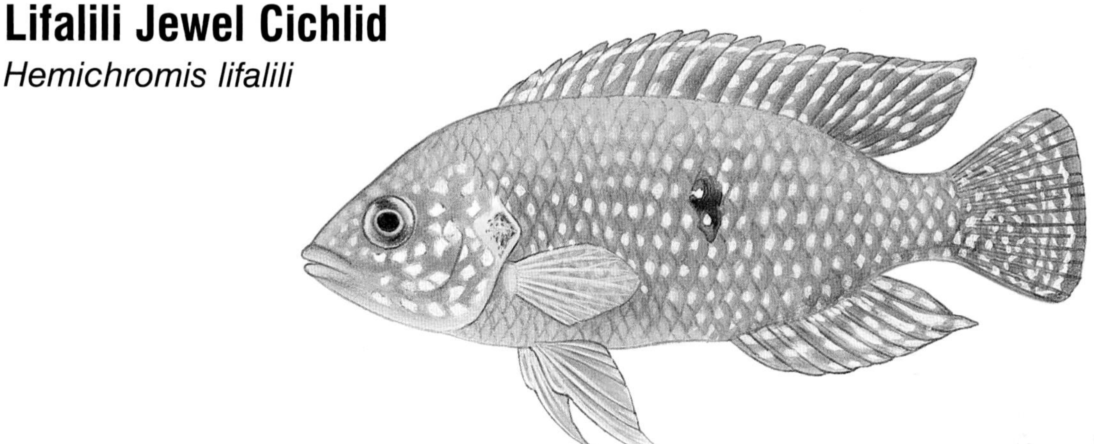

When spawning, this cichlid is blood red, with iridescent spots of yellow to turquoise. At other times, the fish is less vibrant. An aggressive and territorial fish, the jewel cichlid is not well suited to life in captivity. In the wild, mates pair up and work together to defend a territory and then guard their egg masses.

FACT FILE	
Length:	13cm (5in)
Distribution:	Congo Basin
Diet:	Invertebrates
Reproduction:	Up to 400 eggs laid on a rock
Status (IUCN Red List):	Least concern

Kribensis

Pelvicachromis pulcher

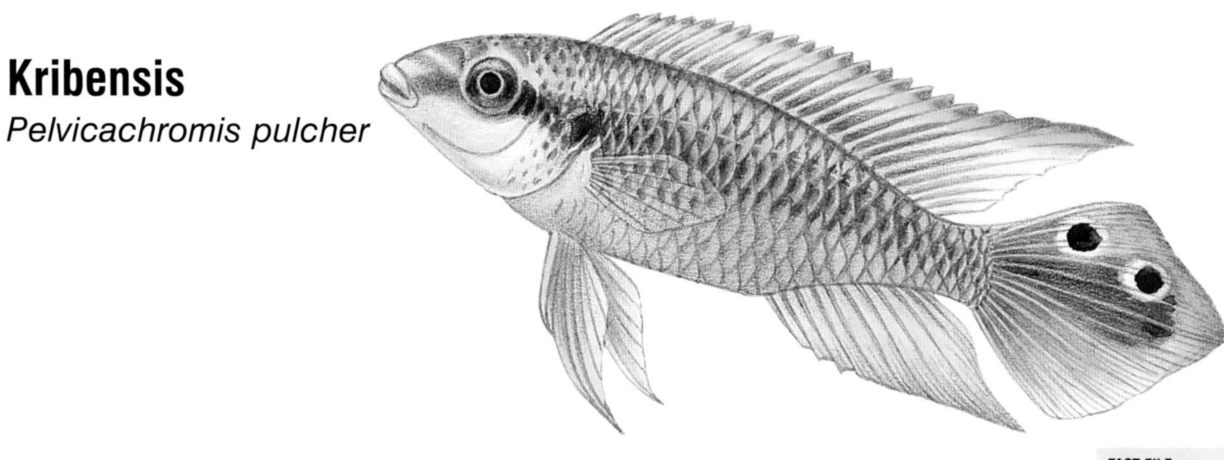

Also known as the rainbow cichlid or common krib, this colourful fish lives in the rivers of west Africa, especially the Niger Delta in Nigeria and the coastal areas of Cameroon. Males have a diamond-shaped tail fin and often pair up with a female in tanks, but generally form complex harem systems in the wild.

FACT FILE	
Length:	13cm (5in)
Distribution:	West Africa
Diet:	Microscopic algae
Reproduction:	Eggs laid in pit under water plants
Status (IUCN Red List):	Least concern

Damselfish

Looking for a damselfish? You are not alone. The famous animated film character Nemo is a member of this family, the Pomacentridae. Members are also called clownfish, anemonefish and chromises. Most are marine species, although a few live in brackish and freshwater habitats.

False Clownfish

Amphiprion ocellaris

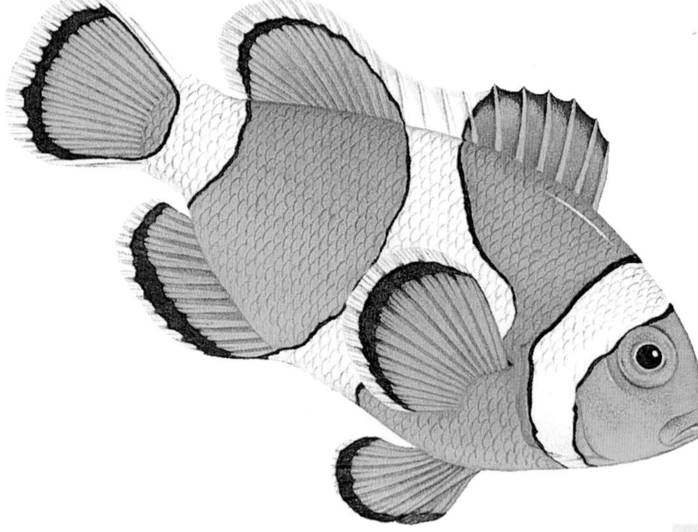

Perhaps surprisingly, this is Nemo's species. It gets its name due to its close resemblance to the similar, albeit more vibrantly coloured, true clownfish species. The fish seeks protection from predators among stinging sea anemones. A layer of mucus protects the fish from its host's stings.

FACT FILE	
Length:	9cm (3½in)
Distribution:	E. Indian and W. Pacific oceans
Diet:	Algae, crustaceans and molluscs
Reproduction:	1000 eggs laid on a rock
Status (IUCN Red List):	Not evaluated

Four Stripe Damselfish

Dascyllus melanurus

Also known as the blacktail humbug, this damselfish generally has four black bars (including on the tail) and three white bars. The fish is territorial; a breeding pair chases away rivals before preparing a nest for their eggs by cleaning the algae from a crevice in the rock. The male then guards the eggs.

FACT FILE	
Length:	8cm (3in)
Distribution:	E. Indian and W. Pacific oceans
Diet:	Algae, crustaceans and molluscs
Reproduction:	600 eggs laid on dead coral
Status (IUCN Red List):	Not evaluated

Cinnamon Clownfish

Amphiprion melanopus

Also known as the fire clownfish, this species is widespread. As is common among the Perchiformes, clownfish change sex as they get older and larger. Unusually, clownfish start as males and then become females. The dominant females are very territorial and frequently attack other fish.

FACT FILE	
Length:	12cm (4¾in)
Distribution:	Indonesia to western Pacific
Diet:	Algae, crustaceans and molluscs
Reproduction:	Eggs laid on flat rock
Status (IUCN Red List):	Not evaluated

Domino Damsel

Dascyllus trimaculatus

Sometimes named the threespot dascyllus – one on the head, two on the flanks – this species is found around reefs from the East Africa coast to the islands of the South Pacific. It does not reach as far north as Hawaii. Young domino damsels hide from predators among sea anemones.

FACT FILE	
Length:	11cm (4¼in)
Distribution:	Red Sea to Pitcairn
Diet:	Algae and copepods
Reproduction:	Eggs laid on rocks and coral
Status (IUCN Red List):	Not evaluated

Sulphur Damsel

Pomacentrus sulfureus

As its name suggests, the sulphur damsel is bright yellow, with only faint vertical bars. These fish are popular in mixed-species reef aquaria because their grazing habits keep coral algae-free without harming it. They also eat the naturally occurring zooplankton.

FACT FILE	
Length:	11cm (4¼in)
Distribution:	Western Indian Ocean
Diet:	Algae, crustaceans and molluscs
Reproduction:	600 eggs laid on dead coral
Status (IUCN Red List):	Not evaluated

Wrasses

The name 'wrasse' comes from the Welsh word *gwrach*, which means 'old hag'. The German name is *Lippfische*, or 'lip-fish'; both names probably refer to the protrusible lips of this family (the Labridae). Despite this perhaps unsightly feature, the wrasses are known for the great variety of their vibrant colouring.

Wolf Fish

Anarhichas lupus

The wolf fish is a powerful predator with excellent vision. Its preferred prey are crustaceans, molluscs and starfish, and it makes short work of them in its powerful jaws. For many years, this monstrous fish was thought to be a close relative of the wrasses and blennies. It is now classified in a separate family.

FACT FILE	
Length:	1.3m (4ft 3in)
Distribution:	Northern Arctic Ocean
Diet:	Bottom-dwelling animals
Reproduction:	Born female, become male as they grow larger; males defend harems
Status (IUCN Red List):	Not evaluated

Clown Coris

Coris aygula

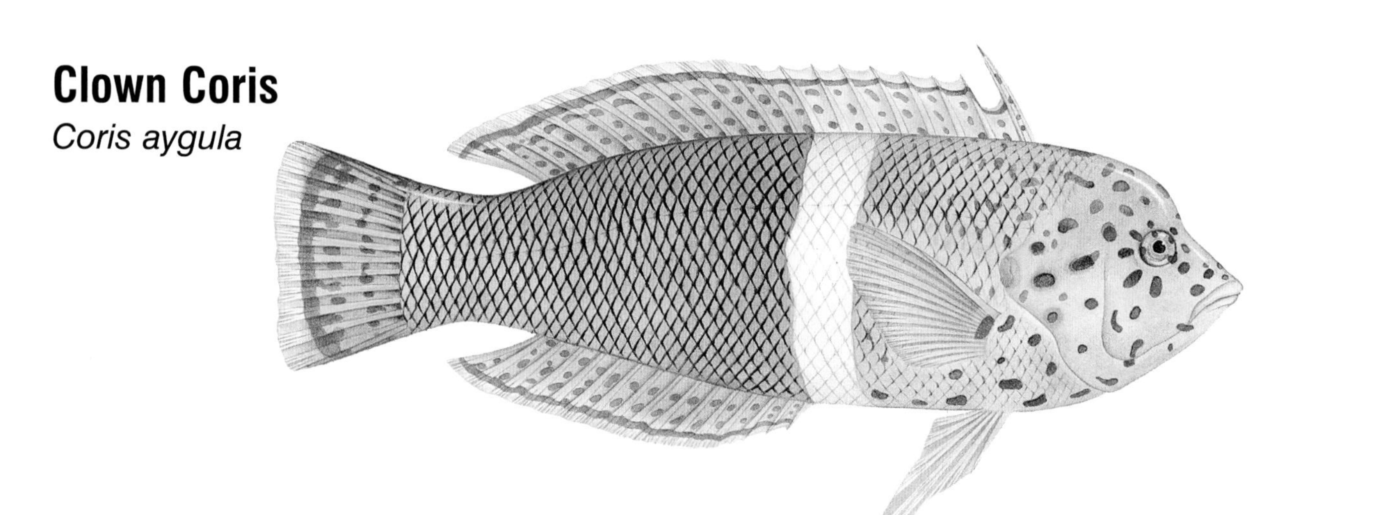

Also known as the clown wrasse, this solitary fish can grow very large. The fish looks very different in its juvenile and adult colours. The juvenile is white and orange with eyespots on its dorsal fin. The adult, which develops a bulging forehead, is dark green with a paler band around its midsection.

FACT FILE	
Length:	1.2m (4ft)
Distribution:	Indian and western Pacific oceans
Diet:	Shellfish
Reproduction:	Hatch as female; become male as they grow larger
Status (IUCN Red List):	Least concern

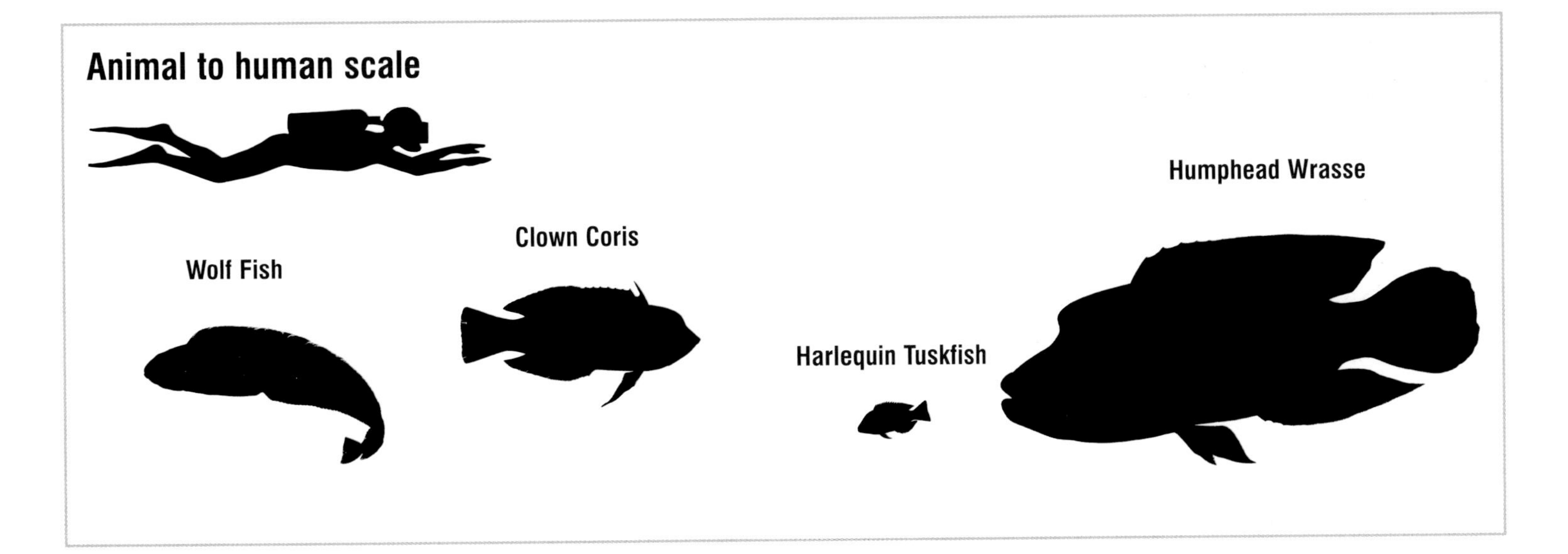

Harlequin Tuskfish

Lienardella fasciata

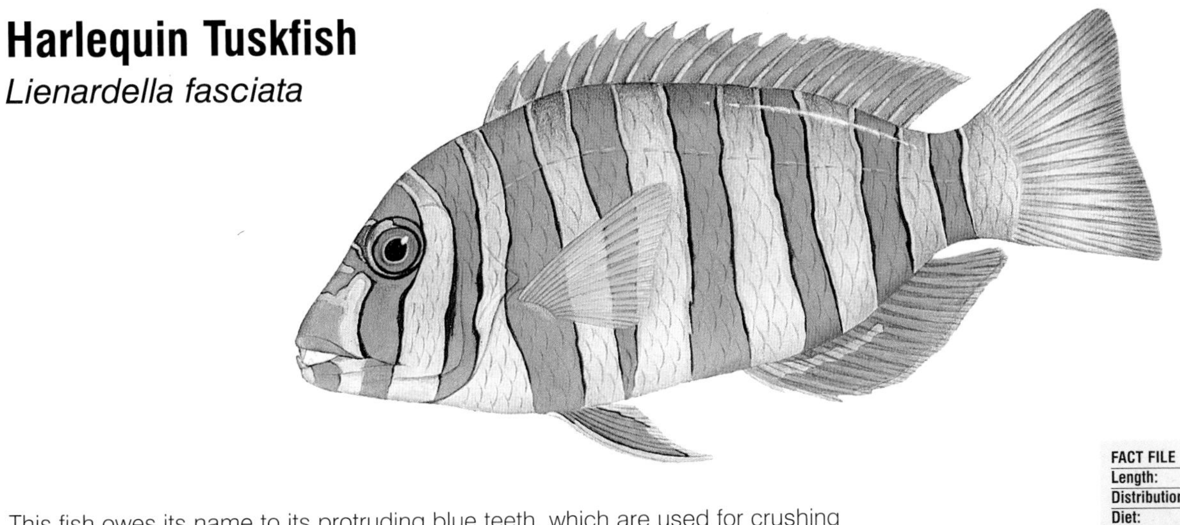

FACT FILE	
Length:	23cm (9in)
Distribution:	Indian and western Pacific oceans
Diet:	Small fish, crustaceans, shellfish
Reproduction:	Born female, become male as they grow larger; males defend harems
Status (IUCN Red List):	Least concern

This fish owes its name to its protruding blue teeth, which are used for crushing crustaceans. The harlequin displays wide vertical orange and white bands over its head and most of its body. The wrasses are one of the few fish that bury themselves in the sand when sleeping or threatened.

Humphead Wrasse

Cheilinus undulatus

FACT FILE	
Length:	2.3m (7ft 6in)
Distribution:	Red Sea to New Caledonia
Diet:	Shellfish
Reproduction:	Born female, become male as they grow larger; males defend harems
Status (IUCN Red List):	Endangered

This immense fish is the largest reef fish in the world. Apart from its unusual size, the fish's other striking feature is its bulbous forehead, which develops upon reaching adulthood. As with other wrasse, the species is protogynous – female first, with a few specimens then becoming male after about ten years.

Cleaner Wrasse

Labroides phthirophagous

There are several species of cleaner wrasse living in the reefs of the Indo-Pacific. This fish lives on the western fringes, around Hawaii. The fish is a symbiotic cleaner. A range of reef fish visit it for a spruce-up from time to time. The wrasse nips off the parasites from its clients' gills and cleans out scraps of food from their teeth.

FACT FILE	
Length:	12cm (4¾in)
Distribution:	Hawaiian Islands
Diet:	Parasitic crustaceans
Reproduction:	Born female, become male later; males control a harem
Status (IUCN Red List):	Not evaluated

The cleaner wrasse live in a harem, with a single large male lording it over several smaller – and younger – females. When the male dies, something rather unusual happens. The biggest female changes her sex and becomes male, and then takes over the running of the harem.

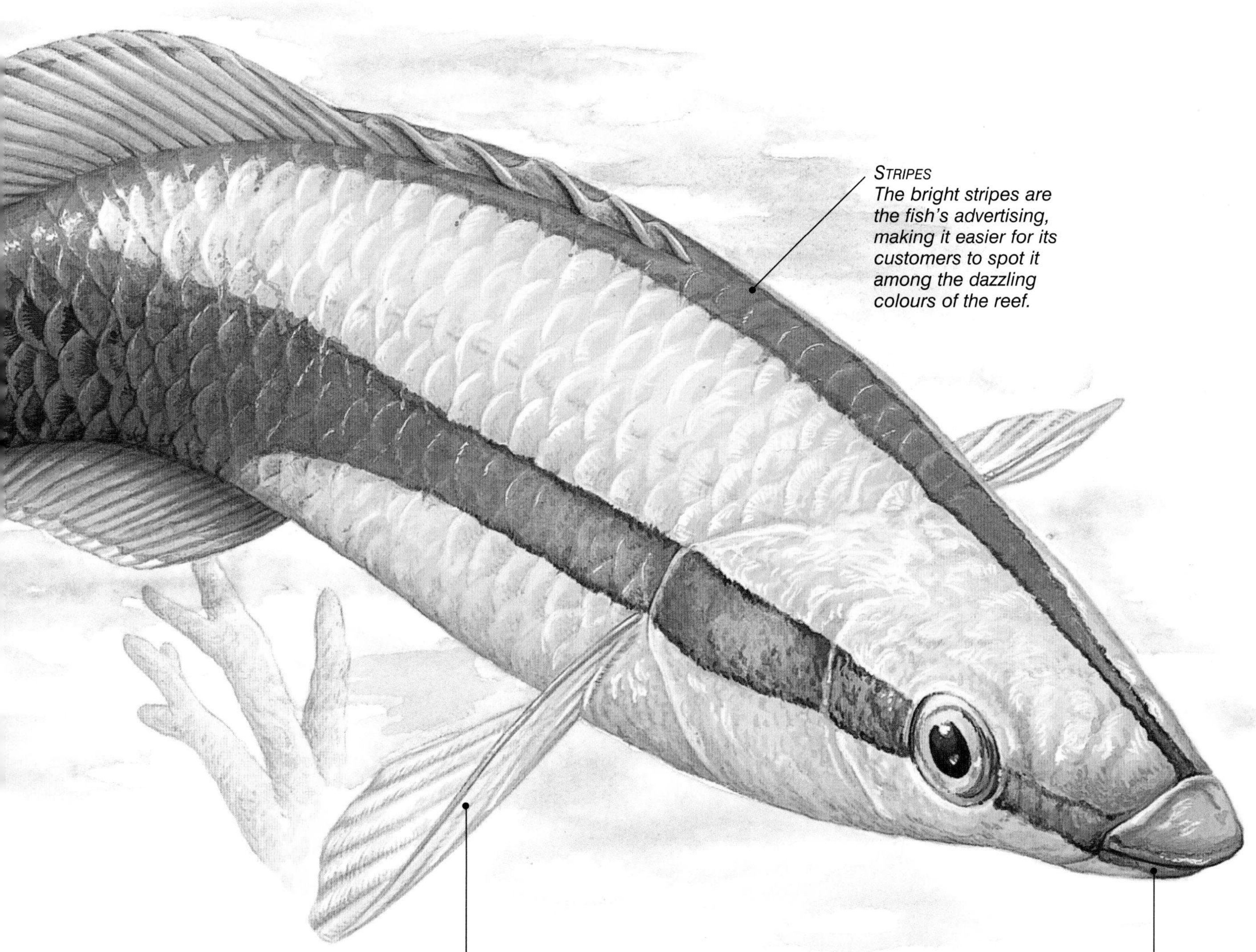

MUCUS
Like the related parrotfish, the cleaner wrasse sleeps in a protective bubble of mucus.

STRIPES
The bright stripes are the fish's advertising, making it easier for its customers to spot it among the dazzling colours of the reef.

STIFF FINS
The pectoral fins are stiffened, so only small movements are needed to steer the slender fish in and around its clients' gills and potentially deadly teeth.

MOUTH
The cleaner wrasse has smaller teeth than other wrasse species, making it easier to perform delicate cleaning. The fish can also protrude its lips to help it grab food.

Aquarium Fish

There are thousands of species and domestic breeds, many of them perch-like fish, available for aquaria of any size and habitat. Keeping fish makes a very rewarding hobby, but fish should be chosen carefully to ensure they are suited to the salinity and temperature of the tank – and will get on with the other occupants.

Yellowhead Jawfish

Opistognathus aurifrons

Jawfishes often jump out of the tank if startled, so a cover is essential, especially at night. The tank should contain plenty of rocks and must have a deep sandy substrate, as this species is a compulsive burrower. The pearly jawfish spends most of its time burrowing in its den or hovering vertically outside.

FACT FILE	
Length:	10cm (4in)
Distribution:	Tropical western Atlantic Ocean
Diet:	Plankton
Reproduction:	100 eggs incubated in the male's mouth
Status (IUCN Red List):	Not evaluated

Mandarinfish

Pterosynchiropus splendidus

The gorgeous mandarin dragonet gets its name from its vivid colorations, said to resemble the robes of a Chinese official, or mandarin. The mandarin belongs to the dragonet, or 'little dragon', family, characterized by long and scaleless bodies, with elongated and showy fins.

FACT FILE	
Length:	6cm (2¼in)
Distribution:	Western Pacific Ocean
Diet:	Copepods and small crustaceans
Reproduction:	Eggs float in open water
Status (IUCN Red List):	Not evaluated

Sohal Surgeonfish

Acanthurus sohal

FACT FILE	
Length:	40cm (16in)
Distribution:	Red Sea
Diet:	Algae and crustaceans
Reproduction:	Unknown
Status (IUCN Red List):	Not evaluated

The sohal surgeonfish sports a scalpel-like spine along the base of its tail on both sides. When threatened, it flicks the spines at its aggressor, sometimes causing severe injuries. This is one of the most aggressive of a group of fish called the tangs. Generally, an aquarium should have just one tang species.

Achilles Tang

Acanthurus achilles

FACT FILE	
Length:	25cm (10in)
Distribution:	Tropical Pacific Ocean
Diet:	Algae and crustaceans
Reproduction:	Unknown
Status (IUCN Red List):	Not evaluated

The Achilles tang is black with orange and white colorations along its fins and tail. As the fish matures, an orange teardrop shape develops on the back portion of the body, terminating in a sharp spine. These spines earned the Acanthuridae family its name, which translates as 'thorn tail'.

Royal Pleco

Panaque nigrolineatus

FACT FILE	
Length:	44cm (17in)
Distribution:	Amazon and Orinoco rivers
Diet:	Algae and wood pulp
Reproduction:	Lays eggs
Status (IUCN Red List):	Not evaluated

The royal pleco is a type of freshwater catfish. It is one of the few fish that can eat wood. It has a sucker-like mouth that it uses to hold onto wood and rocks in fast-flowing rivers in the wild. Its aquarium should include bogwood, which it needs to chew on to stay healthy.

Triggerfish and Relatives

The Tetraodontiformes is an order of unusual, sometimes downright bizarre, fish. The 360 species include the triggerfish, named after spines that raise to lock the fish in a crevice at the slightest hint of danger; the cowfish, which have horn-like spines and a box-shaped skeleton; and the sunfish, which looks like a mouth with fins.

Clown Triggerfish

Balistoides conspicillum

FACT FILE	
Length:	51cm (20in)
Distribution:	Indian and Pacific oceans
Diet:	Crustaceans and molluscs
Reproduction:	Eggs stick to corals
Status (IUCN Red List):	Not evaluated

It may not seem it, but this fish's fantastically varied colorations makes ideal camouflage. From below, the white spots resemble the light-dappled surface. From above, the fish blends in with the corals among which it lives. From the side, the fish's silhouette is broken up, making it harder to spot.

Crowned Puffer

Canthigaster coronata

FACT FILE	
Length:	11cm (4¼in)
Distribution:	Indian Ocean to Tonga
Diet:	Bottom-dwelling animals
Reproduction:	Spawns at surface
Status (IUCN Red List):	Not evaluated

Puffers inflate their bodies to scare away predators, and make it harder for them to be swallowed. They lack the spines of the related porcupinefish, but they have a much deadlier weapon – poison. The poisons in some puffers, such as the fugu, are strong enough to kill a human with a single mouthful.

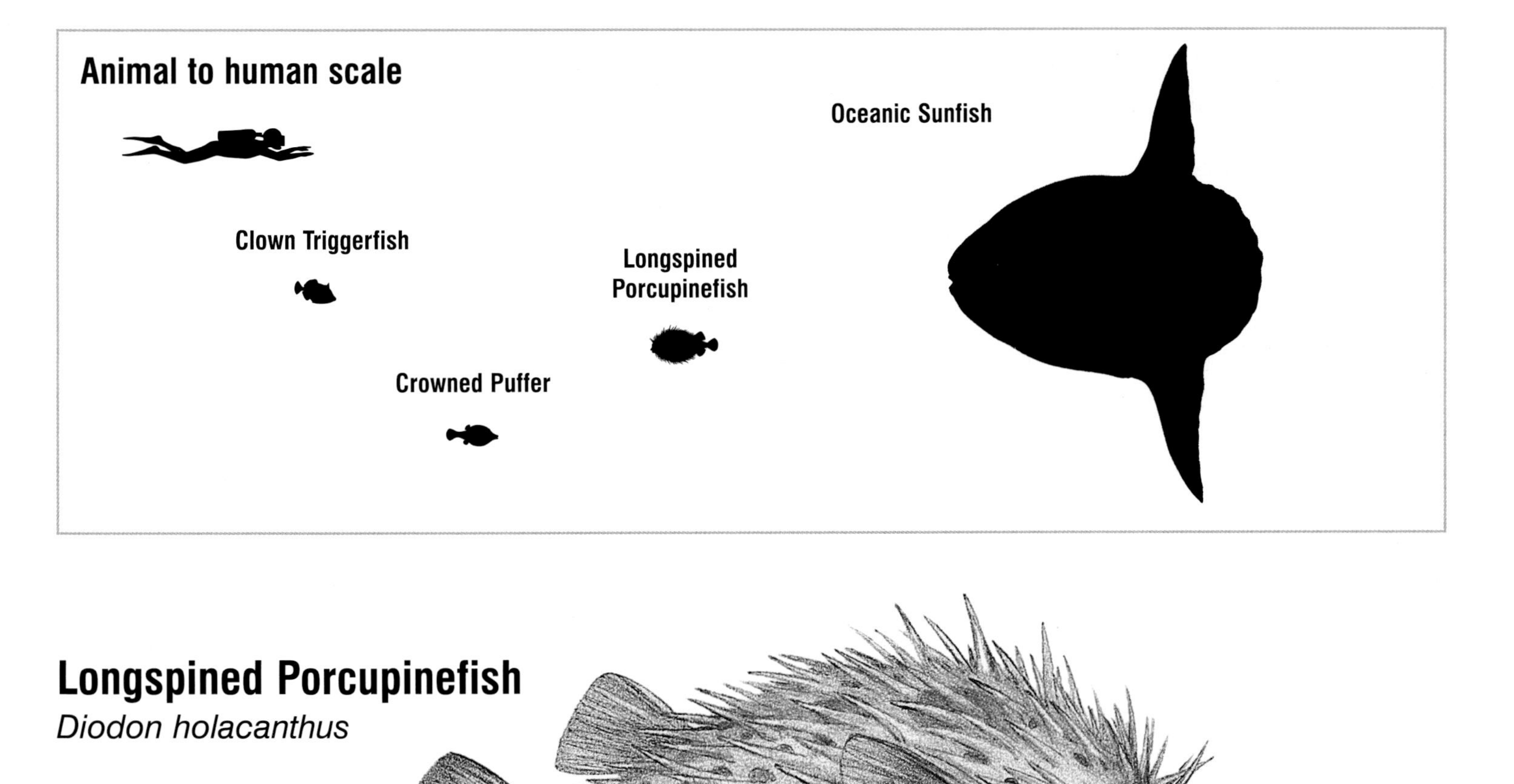

Longspined Porcupinefish

Diodon holacanthus

When threatened, this porcupinefish sucks water into its stomach and puffs itself up like a ball. Few predators are big or brave enough to swallow such a large, spiny object. This species, sometimes described as a blowfish, is not toxic, unlike many of its relatives.

FACT FILE	
Length:	50cm (19½in)
Distribution:	Tropical and subtropical waters
Diet:	Shellfish
Reproduction:	Spawns on bottom, in nest
Status (IUCN Red List):	Not evaluated

Oceanic Sunfish

Mola mola

This is the heaviest bony fish on earth, weighing 2 tonnes (2¼ tons). Only the biggest sharks are larger. The fish appears to be missing the rear part of its body; it has virtually no tail. Despite its size and ungainly appearance, it can swim at a good speed. It also drifts at the surface on warm days.

FACT FILE	
Length:	3.3m (11ft)
Distribution:	Worldwide in warm waters
Diet:	Small invertebrates
Reproduction:	Female may produce more than 300 million floating eggs
Status (IUCN Red List):	Not evaluated

Mudskipper

Periophthalmus koelreuteri

Despite their looks, mudskippers are not ancestors of land vertebrates. However, they are a good example of how our distant ancestors began the transition as creatures that divided their time between land and water. To do this, they had to solve the same problem as the mudskipper: how to breathe both air and water.

PELVIC FINS
The rear fins are much further up the body than is usual. They form sucker-like grippers that anchor the fish to the ground while in the surf and also help it to climb mangrove trees and rocks.

FACT FILE	
Length:	Up to 20cm (8in), depending on species
Distribution:	Tropical and subtropical Africa; Asia and Australia
Diet:	Small crustaceans, insects, fish
Reproduction:	Eggs laid in a burrow
Status (IUCN Red List):	Least concern

Mudskippers are a type of goby, a small group in a huge family of around 2000 purely aquatic species. There are about 35 species of mudskipper, which haul themselves onto flat muddy coastlines around the Indian Ocean and the western Pacific. These curious fish actually spend more time out of the water than in it.

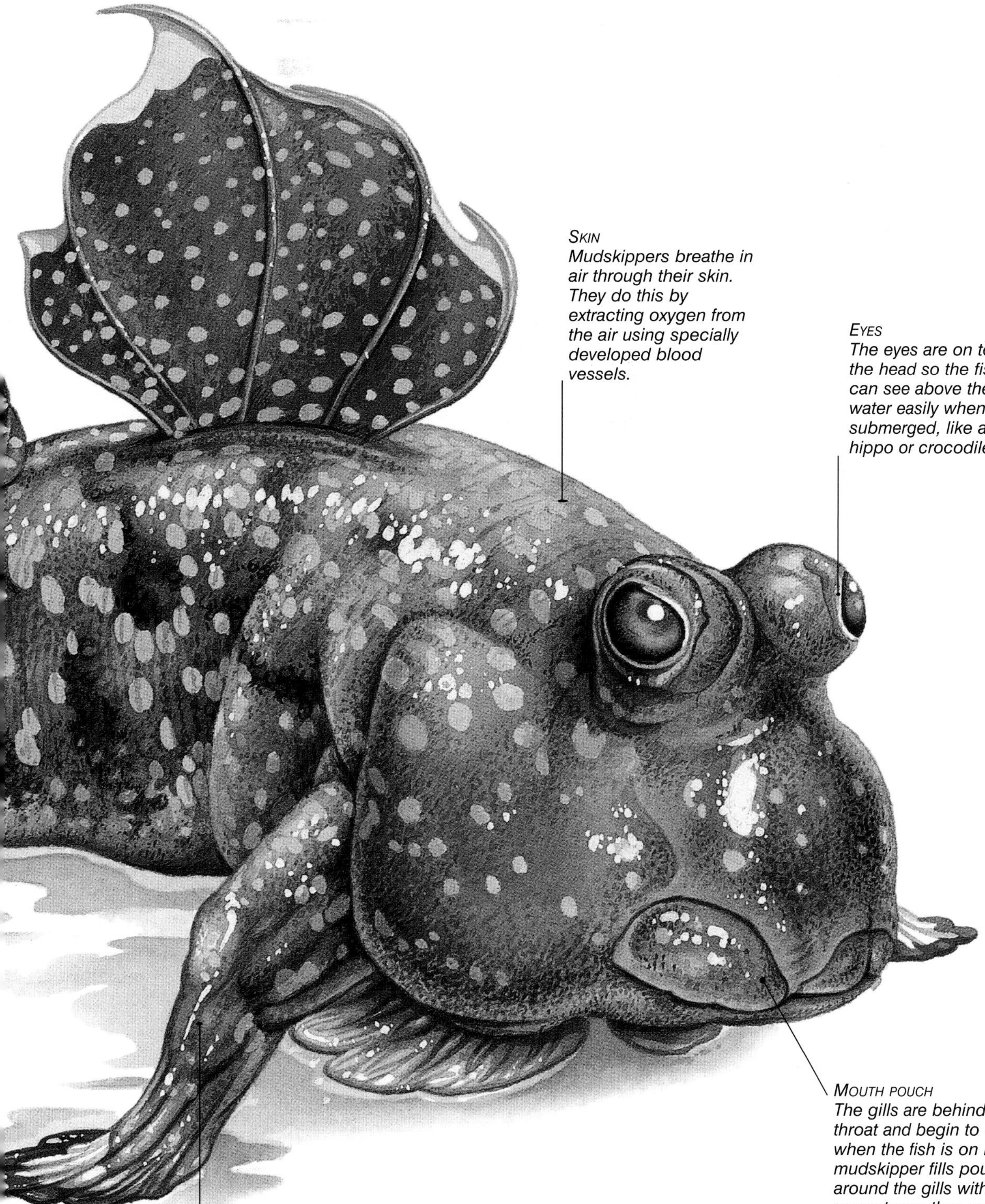

DISPLAY TACTICS
Once out of the water, mudskippers are highly territorial and use their dorsal fins in displays.

SKIN
Mudskippers breathe in air through their skin. They do this by extracting oxygen from the air using specially developed blood vessels.

EYES
The eyes are on top of the head so the fish can see above the water easily when submerged, like a frog, hippo or crocodile.

MOUTH POUCH
The gills are behind the throat and begin to dry out when the fish is on land. The mudskipper fills pouches around the gills with seawater so they continue to function in air.

PECTORAL FINS
The fish 'walk' on their pectoral fins, largely pushed forward by their powerful tail in a series of slow, jerky motions, on the muddy surface.

Flatfish

The flatfish form the Pleuronectiformes order, the name of which translates as 'side-swimmer'. Adult flatfish spend their days lying on their sides on the seabed. Young ones swim normally in open water, but as they develop into adults one of their eyes migrates around the brain, until both are looking out from one side of the head.

Brill

Scophthalmus rhombus

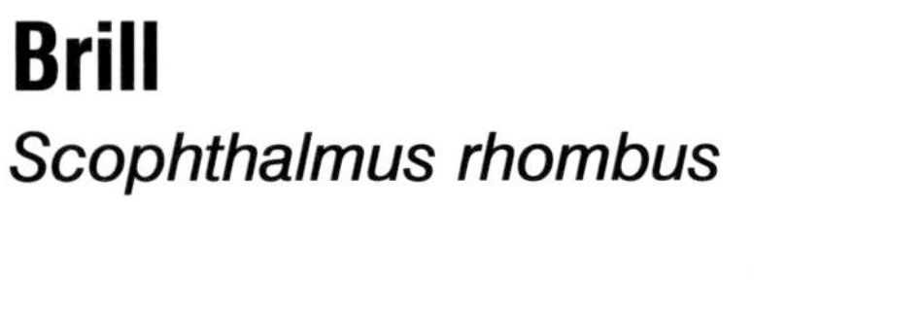

FACT FILE	
Length:	76cm (30in)
Distribution:	Eastern Atlantic, Mediterranean and Black Sea
Diet:	Fish and crustaceans
Reproduction:	Eggs and larvae float on water
Status (IUCN Red List):	Not evaluated

The brill is a master of disguise. Its flat body helps to keep it hidden when on the seabed, but it can also alter its colour to match the surrounding substrate. It is most commonly a spotted grey-green and prefers to hunt on the sandy seabed, covered in patches of algae.

Turbot

Scophthalmus maximus

FACT FILE	
Length:	1m (3ft 3in)
Distribution:	Eastern Atlantic Mediterranean and Black Sea
Diet:	Bottom-living fish
Reproduction:	Spawns in spring and summer
Status (IUCN Red List):	Not evaluated

Despite its relatively small size, the turbot is probably the most prized of all the flatfishes for its fine flavour and texture. It is almost circular in outline, and most are left-sided. The brown upper (left) side is scaleless, but has large bony tubercles. The lower side is pale and has no tubercles.

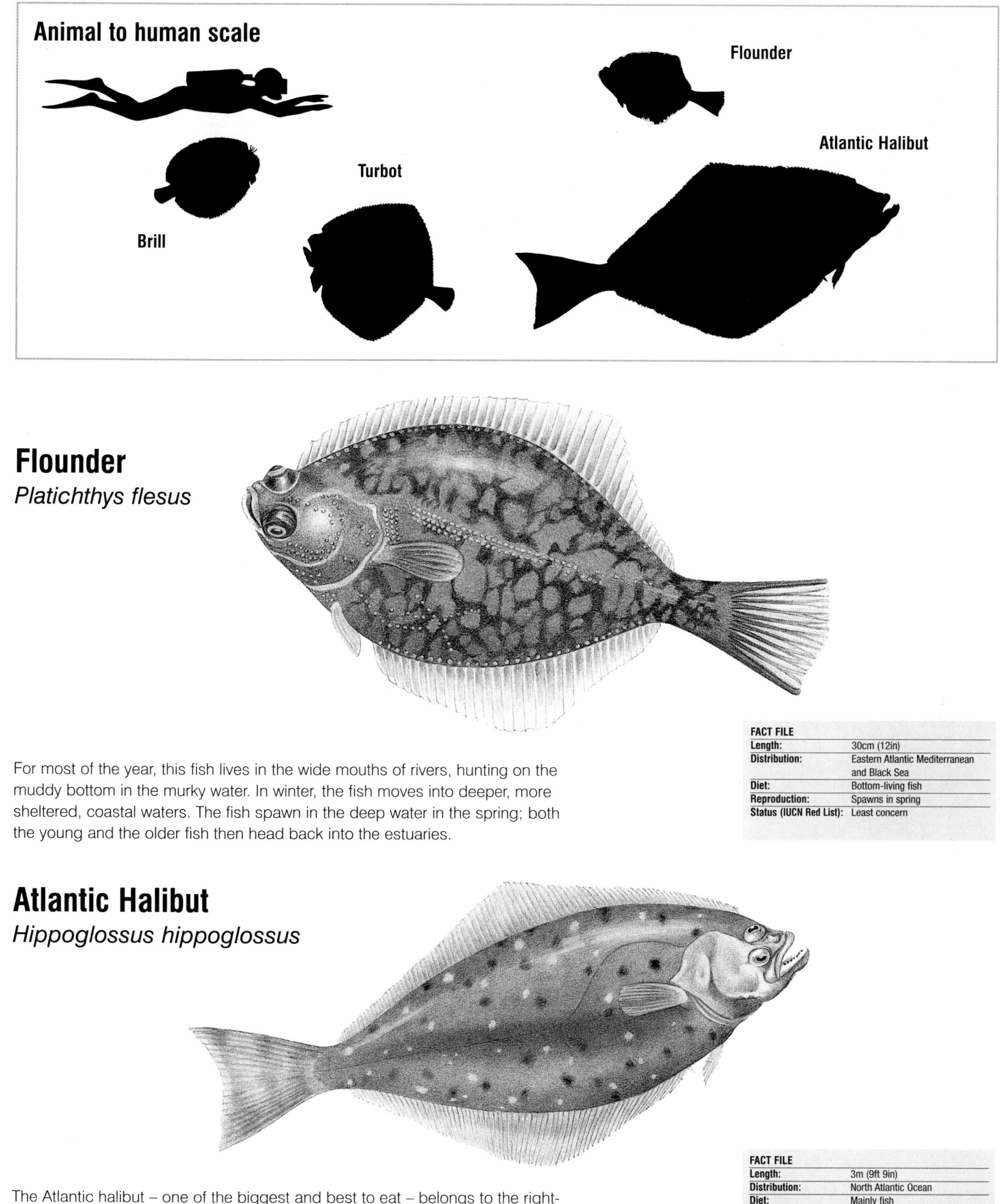

Flounder

Platichthys flesus

FACT FILE	
Length:	30cm (12in)
Distribution:	Eastern Atlantic Mediterranean and Black Sea
Diet:	Bottom-living fish
Reproduction:	Spawns in spring
Status (IUCN Red List):	Least concern

For most of the year, this fish lives in the wide mouths of rivers, hunting on the muddy bottom in the murky water. In winter, the fish moves into deeper, more sheltered, coastal waters. The fish spawn in the deep water in the spring; both the young and the older fish then head back into the estuaries.

Atlantic Halibut

Hippoglossus hippoglossus

FACT FILE	
Length:	3m (9ft 9in)
Distribution:	North Atlantic Ocean
Diet:	Mainly fish
Reproduction:	Spawns in winter and spring
Status (IUCN Red List):	Endangered

The Atlantic halibut – one of the biggest and best to eat – belongs to the right-eyed flounder family. It has a relatively elongated body. Females live longer and grow larger than males. They shed up to two million eggs each year. The fish start to breed only at ten years old, and so are very vulnerable to overfishing.

INVERTEBRATES

The vertebrates – animals with backbones, such as humans, fish and snakes – are contained within a single phylum, the Chordata. By contrast the invertebrates are grouped into at least 30.

The vertebrates make up just 3 per cent of the known animals on Earth. The rest are invertebrates. The main invertebrate phyla are the Mollusca, which includes the snails, clams and squids, and the Arthropoda, animals that includes all the insects, spiders and crustaceans. There are also thousands of soft-bodied creatures, such as jellies and sponges and microscopic worms and water bears.

Left: The octopus is the most intelligent of invertebrates. Its flexible body has just one hard section – the sharp beak at the base of its tentacles.

Worms

There are worms living just about everywhere: in soil, on the seashore, and even inside the bodies of larger animals. There are three basic types of worm: the round worms, or nematodes; the segmented worms, or annelids; and the flatworms and flukes, which make up the platyhelminths group.

Turbellarian

Pseudoceros ferrugineus

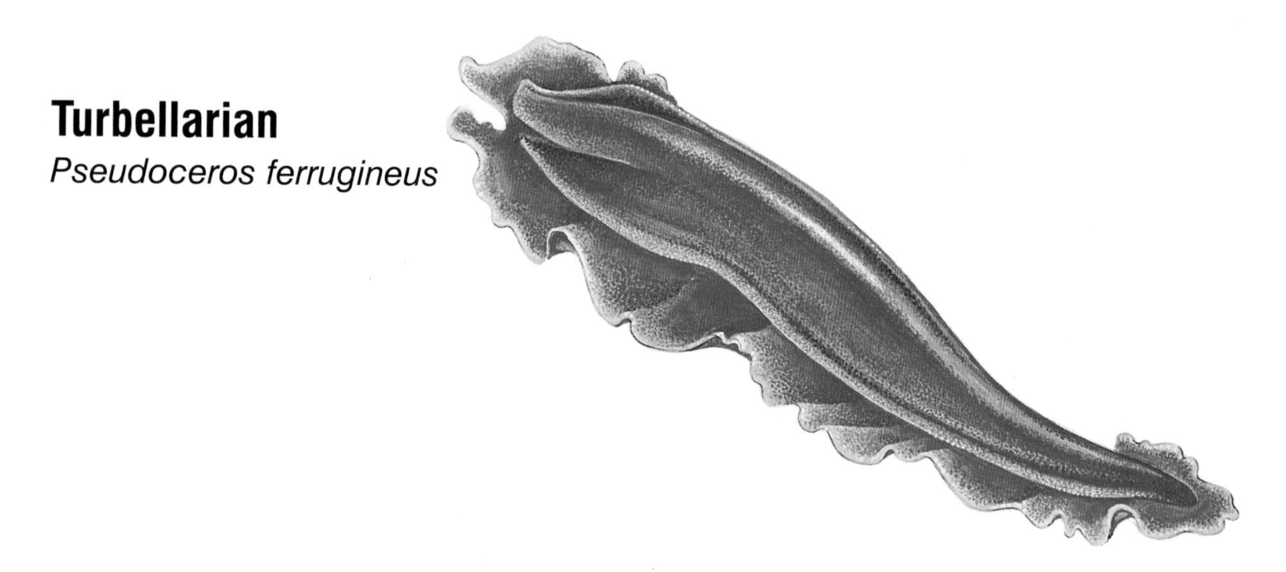

Flatworms are a simple type of worm with thin, solid bodies and a gut running down their centres. They have no blood and no lungs – instead they absorb oxygen directly from the waters around them through their paper-thin bodies. Some flatworms are parasitic, but turbellarians are free-swimming.

FACT FILE	
Distribution:	Tropical water
Habitat:	Coral reefs
Diet:	Shell fish
Reproduction:	Asexual and sexual
Status (IUCN Red List):	Not evaluated

Earthworm

Lumbricus terrestris

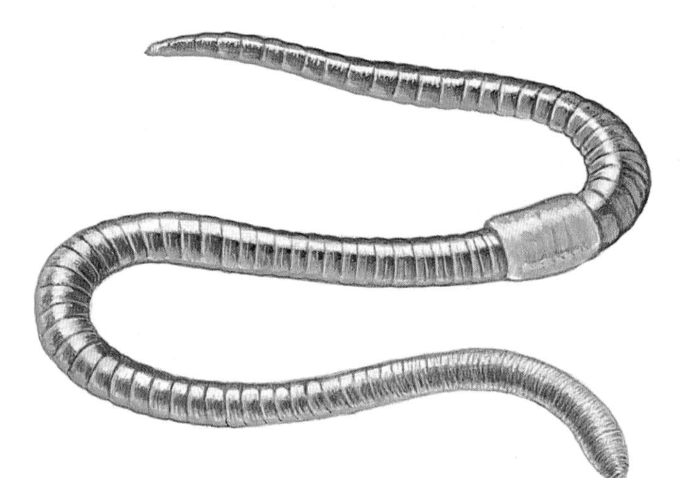

The humble earthworm is the most familiar type of annelid worm. Its elongated body is built for life wiggling under the ground, literally eating its way through the soil, extracting fragments of nutritional material as it goes. The worms are air-breathers and head for the surface when heavy rain waterlogs the soil.

FACT FILE	
Distribution:	Worldwide
Habitat:	Soil
Diet:	Organic waste material
Reproduction:	Hermaphrodite
Status (IUCN Red List):	Not evaluated

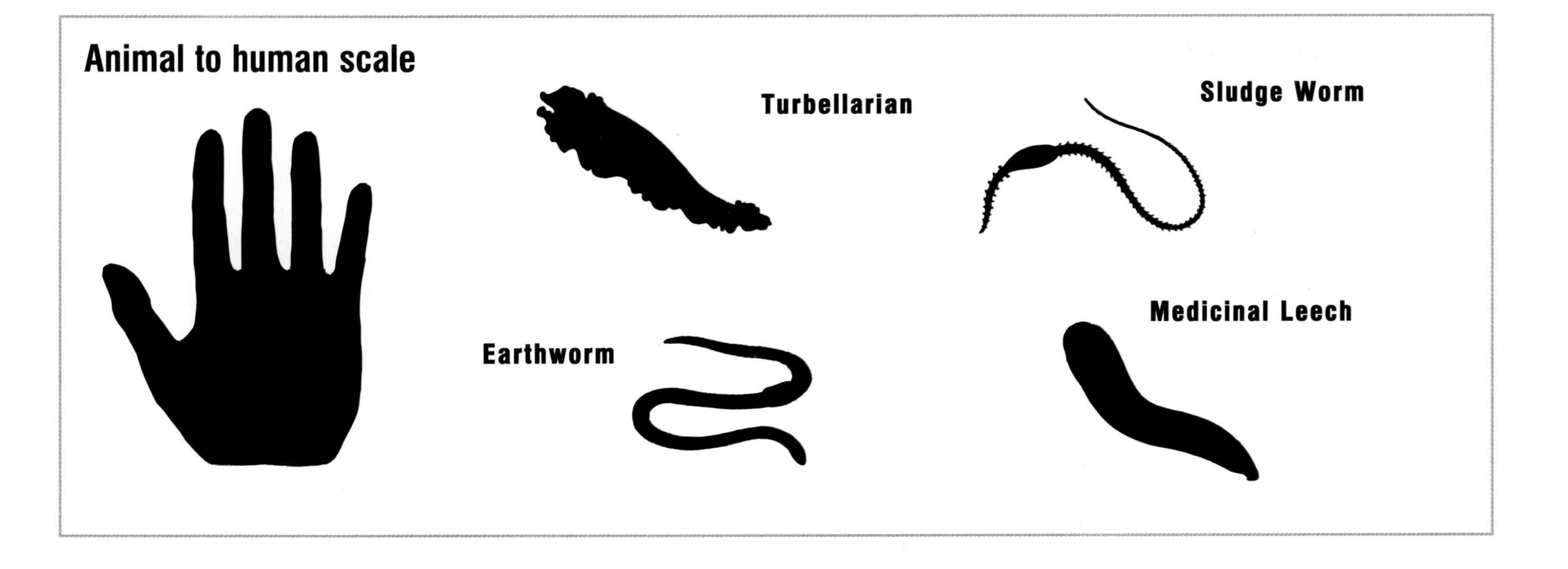

Sludge Worm

Tubifex tubifex

The sludge lives in the mud of riverbeds and sewers. Like their cousins, the earthworms, these worms eat the sediments around them, digesting any bacteria mixed into it. There is very little oxygen down among the mud, and the worm pokes its blood-rich tail out of the sludge to absorb oxygen from the water.

FACT FILE	
Distribution:	Worldwide
Habitat:	Muddy seabed
Diet:	Organic matter
Reproduction:	Hermaphrodite
Status (IUCN Red List):	Not evaluated

Medicinal Leech

Hirudo medicinalis

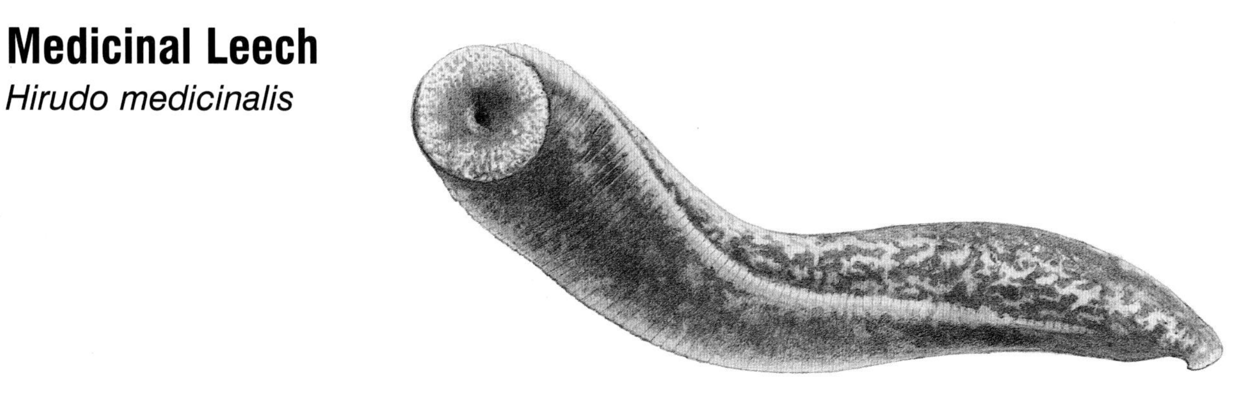

This is the largest leech living in Europe, growing to about 20cm (8in). It is a bloodsucker that lurks in still waters, using suckers at both ends of its pulsating body to latch onto fish, snails and mammals that come near enough. The leech was used by medieval doctors to draw blood, and it is sometimes used in modern medicine to draw blood through wounded extremities to aid healing.

FACT FILE	
Distribution:	Europe
Habitat:	Swamps and pools
Diet:	Blood
Reproduction:	Hermaphrodite
Status (IUCN Red List):	Near threatened

Portuguese Man o' War

Physalia physalis

Often thought to be a jellyfish, the man o' war is actually a distant relative. It looks like one individual, but is really a colony of separate, interdependent life forms, or polyps. The multicoloured gas canopy floating above the waves is the colony 'founder' and produces the other colony members.

FACT FILE	
Distribution:	Worldwide
Habitat:	Tropical and temperate waters
Diet:	Fish and shrimps
Reproduction:	Sexual with external fertilization
Status (IUCN Red List):	Not evaluated

The Portuguese man o' war has a fearsome reputation as one of the most deadly creatures in the sea, although its stings are rarely fatal to humans. The stingers are located on the long tentacles that can trail several metres through the water, stinging small fish that stray too close.

Cold Water Coral

Lophelia Perstusa

The Portuguese man o'war is a cnidarian, meaning it belongs to the same phylum of animals as the jellyfish, sea anemones and corals. Corals, such as this cold-water species from the North Alantic, form colonies in a similar way to the man o'war. Each piece of coral is covered in millions of tiny polyps, which are sifting food from the water. Reef-forming corals grow a hard exoskeleton, which is left behind when the polyp dies, and new polyps grow on top of it. Over millions of years, the skeletons of many billions of corals grow into the rocky coral reefs that bless shallow tropical waters.

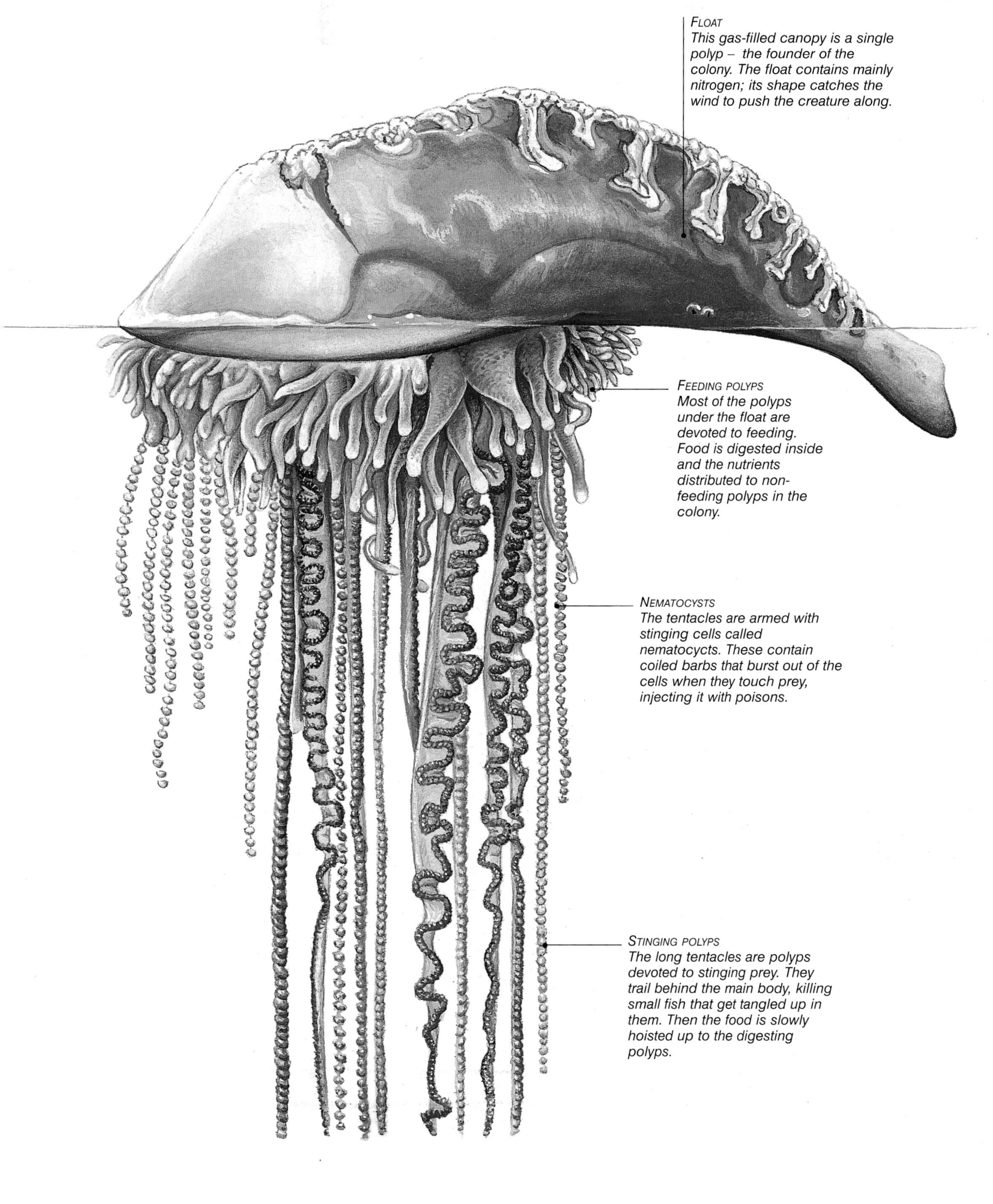

FLOAT
This gas-filled canopy is a single polyp – the founder of the colony. The float contains mainly nitrogen; its shape catches the wind to push the creature along.

FEEDING POLYPS
Most of the polyps under the float are devoted to feeding. Food is digested inside and the nutrients distributed to non-feeding polyps in the colony.

NEMATOCYSTS
The tentacles are armed with stinging cells called nematocycts. These contain coiled barbs that burst out of the cells when they touch prey, injecting it with poisons.

STINGING POLYPS
The long tentacles are polyps devoted to stinging prey. They trail behind the main body, killing small fish that get tangled up in them. Then the food is slowly hoisted up to the digesting polyps.

Sea Snails

Snails make up the largest order of molluscs, known as the gastropods ('stomach foot'). The gastropods generally have one shell, although some have none at all. Gastropods that live in the sea and other aquatic areas breathe with gills. They are most easy to find in coastal waters, where their shells wash up on the shore.

Common Limpet

Patella vulgata

The limpet is a ubiquitous form of wildlife on any rocky shoreline. When the tide is out, it hunkers down close to the rock to avoid losing water. Once the sea has returned, the limpet goes foraging, but must return to the exact spot as the tide turns again – its shell has grown to fit the shape of the rocks exactly.

FACT FILE	
Distribution:	Eastern coasts of North Atlantic
Habitat:	Rocky seabed
Diet:	Algae
Reproduction:	Sexual, external fertilization
Status (IUCN Red List):	Not evaluated

Queen Conch

Lobatus gigas

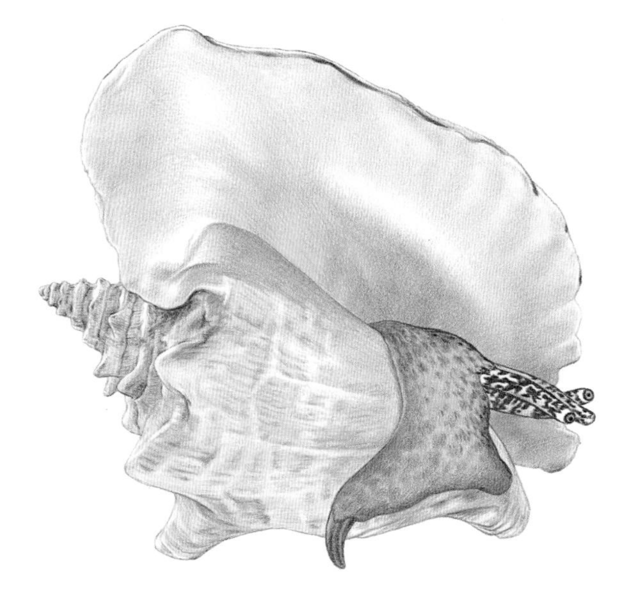

Conches (pronounced 'konks') have some of the most attractive shells found in nature, and have been prized for many centuries. Unfortunately, this means they are overfished and are already a protected species in U.S. waters. The name 'conch' comes from the Greek word for shell.

FACT FILE	
Distribution:	Western Atlantic coasts
Habitat:	Tropical waters
Diet:	Seaweeds and algae
Reproduction:	Sexual, external fertilization
Status (IUCN Red List):	Not evaluated

Common Egg Cowrie

Ovula ovum

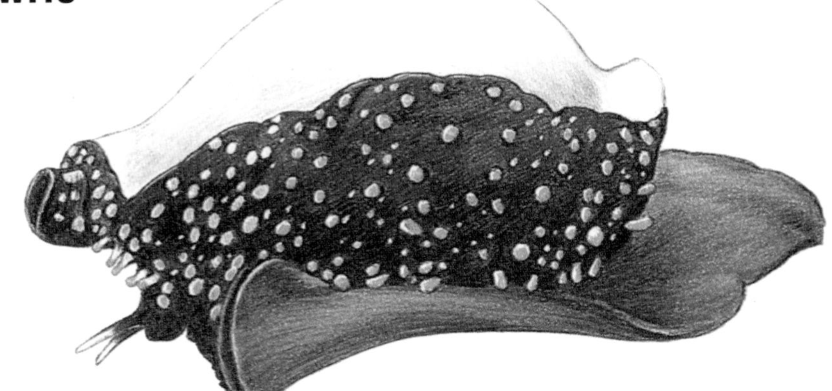

FACT FILE	
Distribution:	Indian and Pacific oceans
Habitat:	Coral reefs
Diet:	Coral
Reproduction:	Sexual, internal fertilization
Status (IUCN Red List):	Not evaluated

This species of egg cowry inhabits coral reefs in the Indian Ocean and West Pacific, where it wanders over the surfaces of mushroom leather corals, feeding on polyps. Its spotted mantle blends perfectly with the coral; as an additional defence, this cowry tastes extremely unpleasant to predators.

Purple Dye Murex

Bolinus brandarius

FACT FILE	
Distribution:	Central and W. Mediterranean
Habitat:	Beaches
Diet:	Molluscs
Reproduction:	Sexual, internal fertilization
Status (IUCN Red List):	Not evaluated

The murexes are a highly evolved type of marine snail. They are voracious predators with a unique method of feeding, drilling holes into the shells of bivalves with its toothed tongue, the radula. This species was used in ancient times to make an expensive red dye called Tyrian purple.

Sea Slug

Phyllidia ocellata

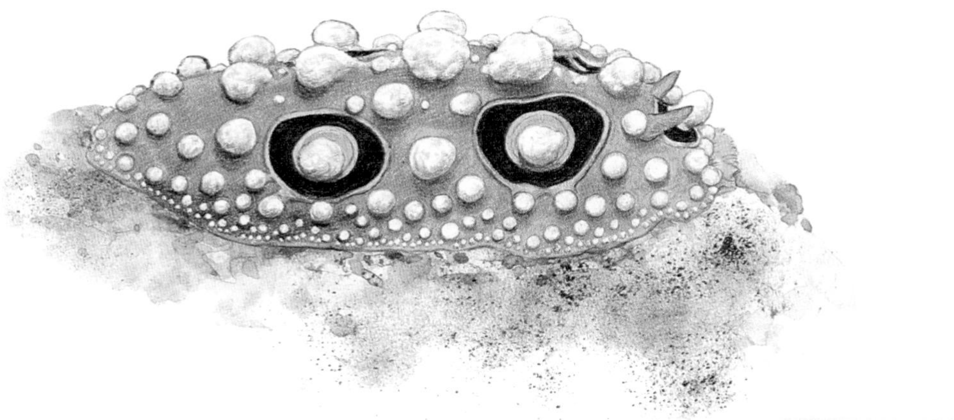

FACT FILE	
Distribution:	Indian and Pacific oceans
Habitat:	Seabed
Diet:	Sponges
Reproduction:	Hermaphrodite
Status (IUCN Red List):	Not evaluated

Despite their pedestrian common name, most of these soft-bodied molluscs are brightly coloured. These voracious hunters are shell-less, but often have horn-like lumps called cerata protruding from their backs. Sea slugs have the unusual ability of being able to eat stinging creatures such as sea anemones.

Land Snails

Some gastropod molluscs live on land and breathe air. The shells of land snails tend to be smooth and round compared to those of sea snails. The snail moves by rippling its single foot. The foot secretes mucus to help with motion. The shell is used as defensive armour and as a refuge during dry periods.

Edible Snail

Helix pomatia

This is a very close relative of the common snail, although it has a paler shell. Snails have been eaten since prehistoric times, and they are a popular delicacy in many European cuisines. Wild-caught snails cannot be cooked immediately; they must first be purged of toxins by being fed a diet of clean vegetables.

FACT FILE	
Distribution:	Europe
Habitat:	Forests and gardens
Diet:	Algae
Reproduction:	Internal fertilization
Status (IUCN Red List):	Not evaluated

Emerald Green Snail

Papustyla pulcherrima

This large land snail lives only in a small island province of Papua New Guinea. Its exquisite pearly green shell has meant that the snail has traditionally been collected for use in jewellery; international demand for the shells has now driven the species' decline. It is uncertain whether the species can avoid extinction.

FACT FILE	
Distribution:	Manus Island, New Guinea
Habitat:	Trees
Diet:	Algae
Reproduction:	Internal fertilization
Status (IUCN Red List):	Data deficient

White-lipped Snail

Cepaea hortensis

FACT FILE	
Distribution:	Western and central Europe
Habitat:	Woods and grassland
Diet:	Algae
Reproduction:	Internal fertilization
Status (IUCN Red List):	Not evaluated

The common name of this snail refers to the pale band that circles the rim of the shell. This is the only identifying feature on the shell, since the striped pattern varies immensely. On the forest floor, the light and dark swirls provide good camouflage, although darker snails heat up faster and lose water more quickly.

Carpathian Blue Slug

Bielzia coerulans

FACT FILE	
Distribution:	Carpathian Mountains
Habitat:	Forests
Diet:	Algae
Reproduction:	80 eggs laid under logs
Status (IUCN Red List):	Not evaluated

This large slug from the mountains of Eastern Europe becomes blue only when it is fully grown – about 12cm (4¾in) long. The juveniles are yellow-brown, more like common slugs. The slug is a member of the keel back group, owing to a small swirling shell that grows hidden away inside the mantle.

Garden Slug

Arion hortensis

FACT FILE	
Distribution:	Europe
Habitat:	Gardens, fields and pastures
Diet:	Leaves
Reproduction:	Internal fertilization
Status (IUCN Red List):	Not evaluated

This species, also known as the black field slug, is a representative of the roundback slugs. They have no internal shell, like a few other slug groups. This species and its close relatives are the curse of gardeners, because they eat leaves rather than grazing on microscopic algae like many land gastropods.

Bivalves

The bivalves are the second main group of shelled molluscs. While gastropods have a single shell, or valve, members of this group have two, which are hinged on one side. Bivalves are largely sedentary creatures, staying in one place for much of their lives, and slamming the shells shut when danger is near.

Atlantic Thorny Oyster

Spondylus americanus

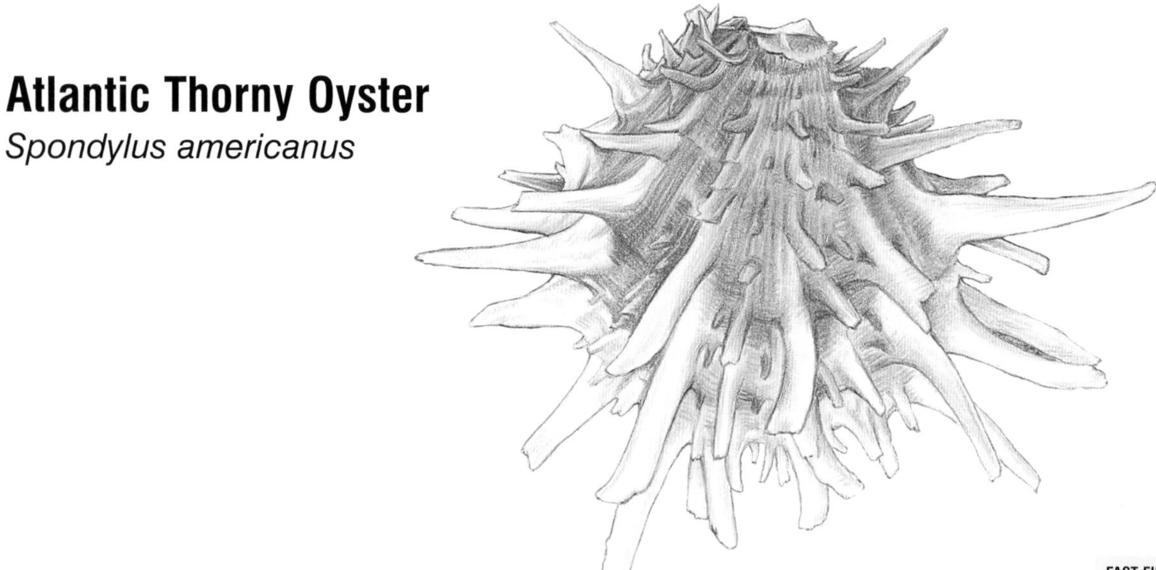

Despite their common name, thorny oysters are not oysters at all – they are a type of scallop. While oysters (and most bivalves) have a simple toothed hinge held together by muscle, the thorny oysters have a more complex ball-and-socket arrangement. Thorny oysters seem to have developed their thorns for camouflage – they encourage the growth of other marine creatures on them.

FACT FILE	
Distribution:	Indo-Pacific
Habitat:	Coral reefs
Diet:	Algae and organic debris
Reproduction:	Sexual, with external fertilization
Status (IUCN Red List):	Not evaluated

Noble Pen Shell

Pinna nobilis

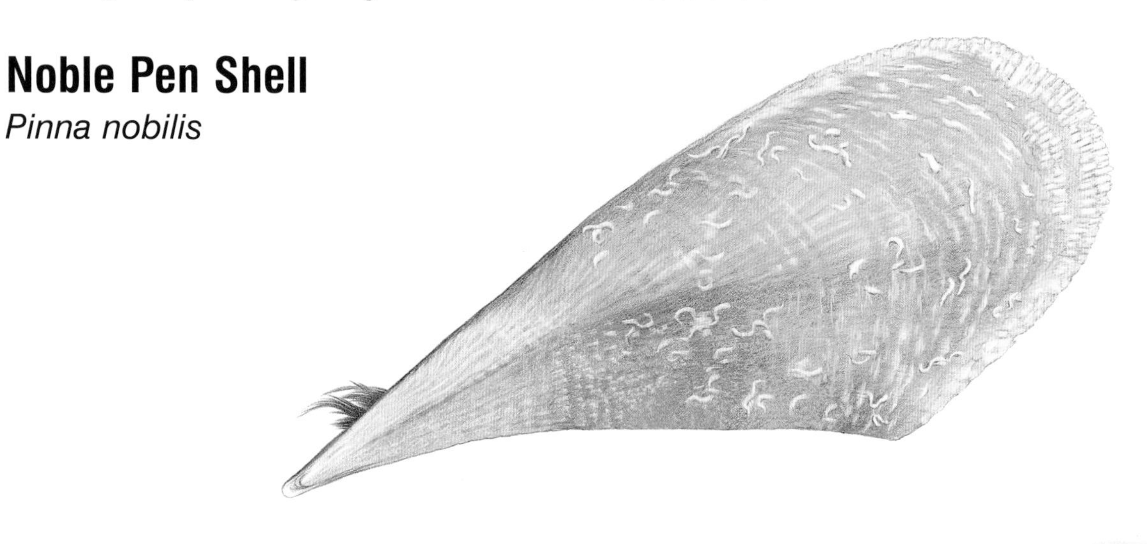

One of the largest bivalves in the world, this species lives across the Mediterranean region. Most grow to around 50cm (19½in), but they may reach 1.2m (4ft) if left to grow for many years. One-third of the shell's body is buried beneath the sand in coastal waters overgrown with plants.

FACT FILE	
Distribution:	Mediterranean
Habitat:	Coastal waters with plant life
Diet:	Algae and organic debris
Reproduction:	Hermaphrodites, switching sexes
Status (IUCN Red List):	Not evaluated

Blue Mussel

Mytilus edulis

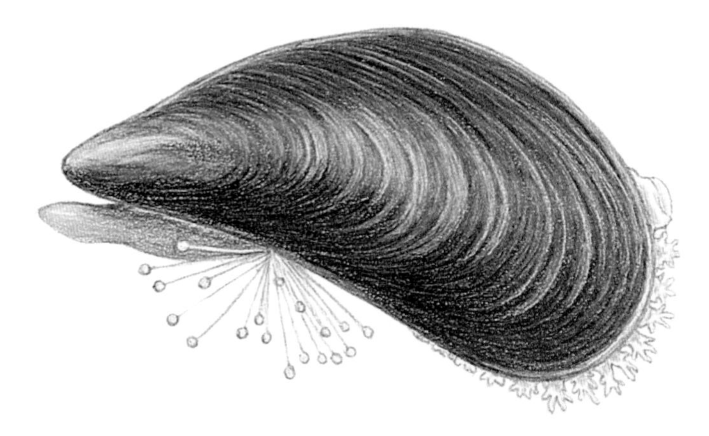

FACT FILE	
Distribution:	Atlantic Ocean
Habitat:	Coastal waters
Diet:	Plankton and detritus
Reproduction:	Sexual, with external fertilization
Status (IUCN Red List):	Not evaluated

The blue mussel lives in the tidal zone, mostly between the middle shore and the low-water mark – where they are underwater more often than not. When exposed to the air, the mussels clamp their valves shut to conserve water. When submerged, they filter bacteria, plankton and detritus from seawater.

Zebra Mussel

Dreissensa polymorpha

FACT FILE	
Distribution:	S.E. Russia, introduced worldwide
Habitat:	Lakes
Diet:	Plankton and detritus
Reproduction:	Sexual, with external fertilization
Status (IUCN Red List):	Not evaluated

This hardy freshwater mussel originates in the lakes and waterways of southern Russia, including the Volga Basin. However, in the last 30 years, the species has spread rapidly around the world, travelling on the hulls of lakers – ocean-going ships that are designed to travel to inland ports.

Giant Clam

Tridacna gigas

FACT FILE	
Distribution:	Indo-Pacific
Habitat:	Coral reefs
Diet:	Nutrients from algae
Reproduction:	Sexual, with external fertilization
Status (IUCN Red List):	Vulnerable

Giant clams are the largest of all bivalves, growing to more than 1m (3ft 3in) across, and weighing up to 270kg (595lb). They feed off nutrients produced by the algae that grows on the fleshy body, or mantle. The mollusc extends its mantle out over the lips of its shell to absorb sunlight that fuels the algae.

Cephalopods

It is sometimes hard to remember that squids and octopuses, as molluscs, are related to oysters and snails, in the same way that frogs are related to mammals. The term cephalopod means 'head foot'. The foot of a cephalopod is divided into several tentacles, armed with suckers and hooks.

Nautilus

Nautilus pompilius

The bizarre, prehistoric-looking nautilus is the most primitive member of the class still surviving, and the only one with an outer shell. Nautiluses grow up to 20cm (8in) in diameter and have 90 tentacles on their heads. The shells consist of a number of chambers; the animal sits in the outermost one.

FACT FILE	
Distribution:	Western Pacific
Habitat:	Surface to 500m (1600ft)
Diet:	Crustaceans and small fish
Reproduction:	Sexual, through copulation
Status (IUCN Red List):	Not evaluated

Cuttlefish

Sepia officinalis

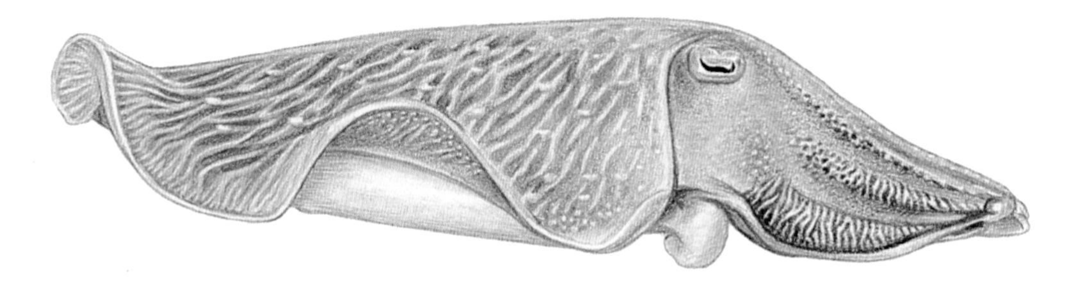

Cuttlefish are built around a curved internal 'bone' (actually the remnant of their ancestors' shells). They grow up to 40cm (16in). Their most impressive feature is their ability to rapidly alter their skin pigmentation – for courtship, camouflage, help in hunting, or even, it seems, depending on their mood.

FACT FILE	
Distribution:	E. North Atlantic, Mediterranean
Habitat:	Shallow offshore waters
Diet:	Small fish, molluscs, crustaceans
Reproduction:	Sexual, through transfer of sperm
Status (IUCN Red List):	Not evaluated

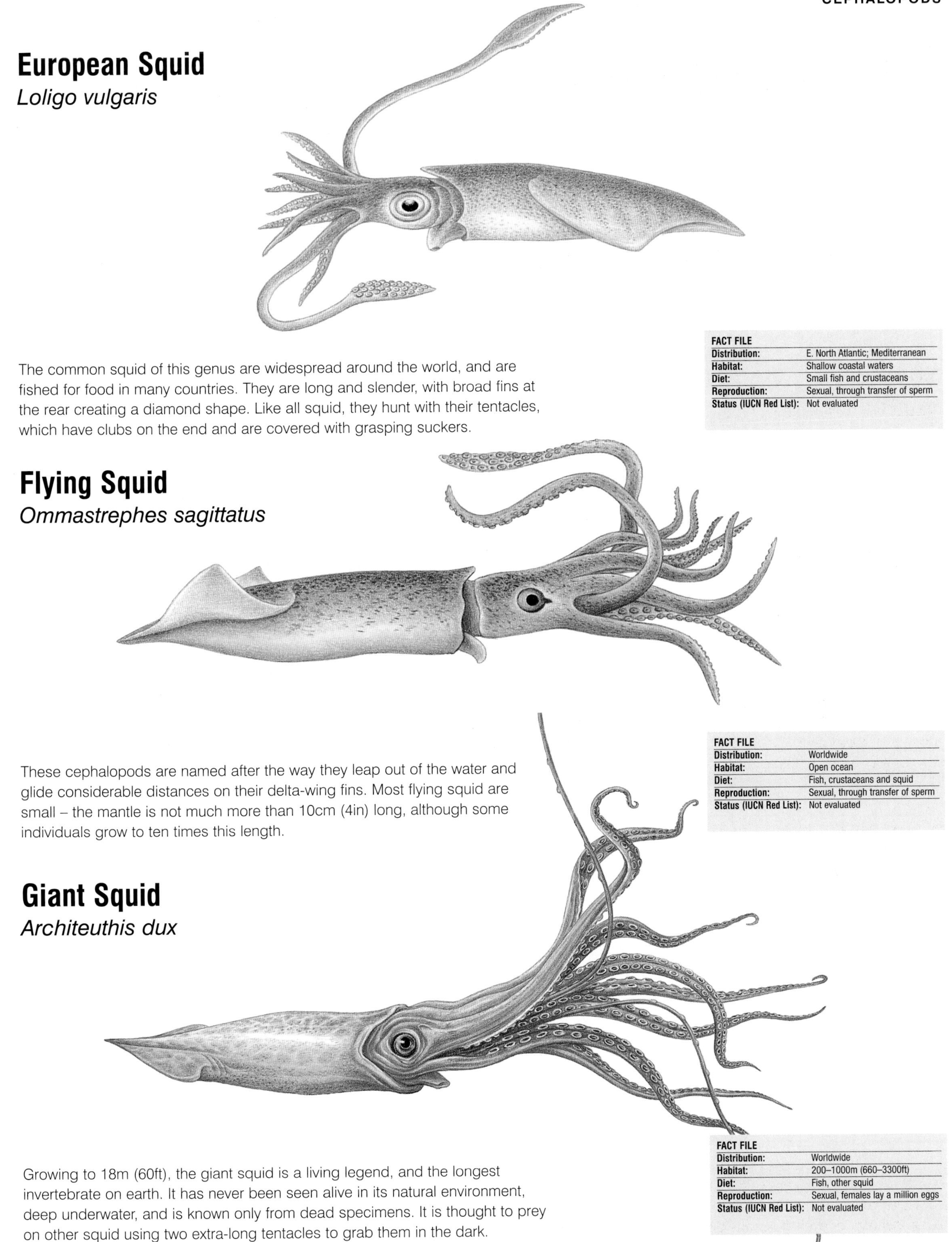

European Squid

Loligo vulgaris

The common squid of this genus are widespread around the world, and are fished for food in many countries. They are long and slender, with broad fins at the rear creating a diamond shape. Like all squid, they hunt with their tentacles, which have clubs on the end and are covered with grasping suckers.

FACT FILE	
Distribution:	E. North Atlantic; Mediterranean
Habitat:	Shallow coastal waters
Diet:	Small fish and crustaceans
Reproduction:	Sexual, through transfer of sperm
Status (IUCN Red List):	Not evaluated

Flying Squid

Ommastrephes sagittatus

These cephalopods are named after the way they leap out of the water and glide considerable distances on their delta-wing fins. Most flying squid are small – the mantle is not much more than 10cm (4in) long, although some individuals grow to ten times this length.

FACT FILE	
Distribution:	Worldwide
Habitat:	Open ocean
Diet:	Fish, crustaceans and squid
Reproduction:	Sexual, through transfer of sperm
Status (IUCN Red List):	Not evaluated

Giant Squid

Architeuthis dux

Growing to 18m (60ft), the giant squid is a living legend, and the longest invertebrate on earth. It has never been seen alive in its natural environment, deep underwater, and is known only from dead specimens. It is thought to prey on other squid using two extra-long tentacles to grab them in the dark.

FACT FILE	
Distribution:	Worldwide
Habitat:	200–1000m (660–3300ft)
Diet:	Fish, other squid
Reproduction:	Sexual, females lay a million eggs
Status (IUCN Red List):	Not evaluated

Common Octopus

Octopus vulgaris

The common octopus is a remarkable and highly successful creature. It is found all around the world, favouring sandy seabeds where it can dig itself a burrow and disguise itself when not feeding or breeding. Octopuses feed on a variety of creatures, including crustaceans and molluscs, and they stockpile food supplies.

FACT FILE	
Distribution:	Worldwide
Habitat:	Shallow coastal waters
Diet:	Molluscs, crustaceans and fish
Reproduction:	Sexual, females lay 250,000 eggs
Status (IUCN Red List):	Not evaluated

This octopus grows to around 90cm (35in) long. When threatened, it can rapidly change its body shape and colour, and squirts ink to cover a rapid, jet-propelled escape. Octopuses are highly intelligent – laboratory experiments have shown that they are skilled problem-solvers and have long memories.

SUCKERS
Each of the octopus's eight tentacles has a double row of suckers. These are sensitive feelers as well as powerful tools for grasping prey.

MANTLE
The mantle is a muscular sac holding the main organs. It is the back of the body – the octopus normally moves tentacles first. Like other cephalopods, the octopus can alter the colour of its mantle to camouflage itself or display its mood.

BEAK
The only hard part of an octopus is the beak, which is made from keratin (the material found in hair and fingernails). The beak bites prey with a rough tongue and is use to grind through shellfish.

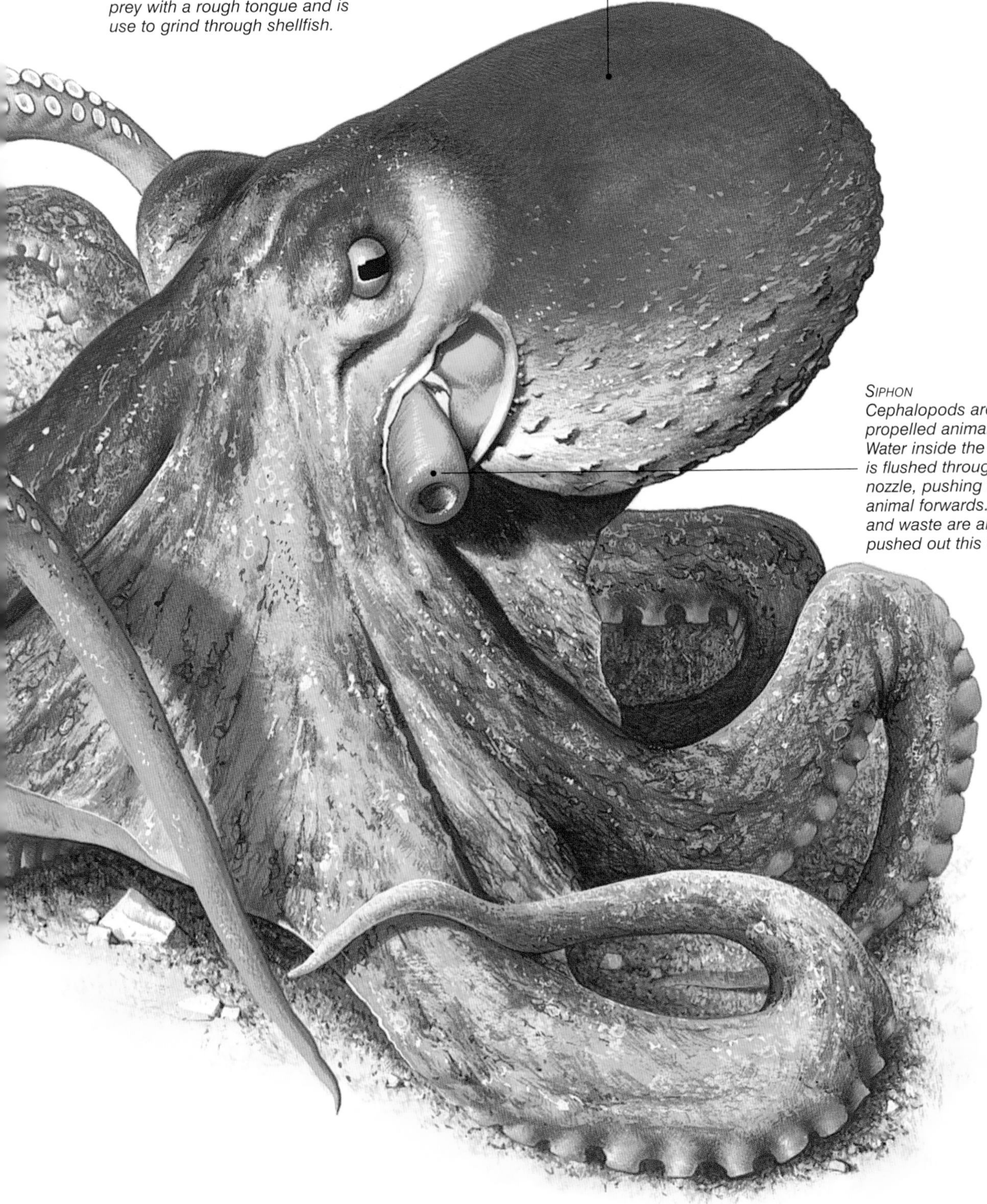

SIPHON
Cephalopods are jet-propelled animals. Water inside the mantle is flushed through this nozzle, pushing the animal forwards. Ink and waste are also pushed out this way.

Starfish and Urchins

The starfish and sea urchins belong to a phylum of animals called the echinoderms. Their bodies are arranged radially, with up to 50 arms or tentacles. Their bodies do not have bones; they are given shape by the fluids inside. The skin is covered in hard plates, often pointed – hence the phylum's name, meaning 'spine skin'.

Common Starfish

Asterias rubens

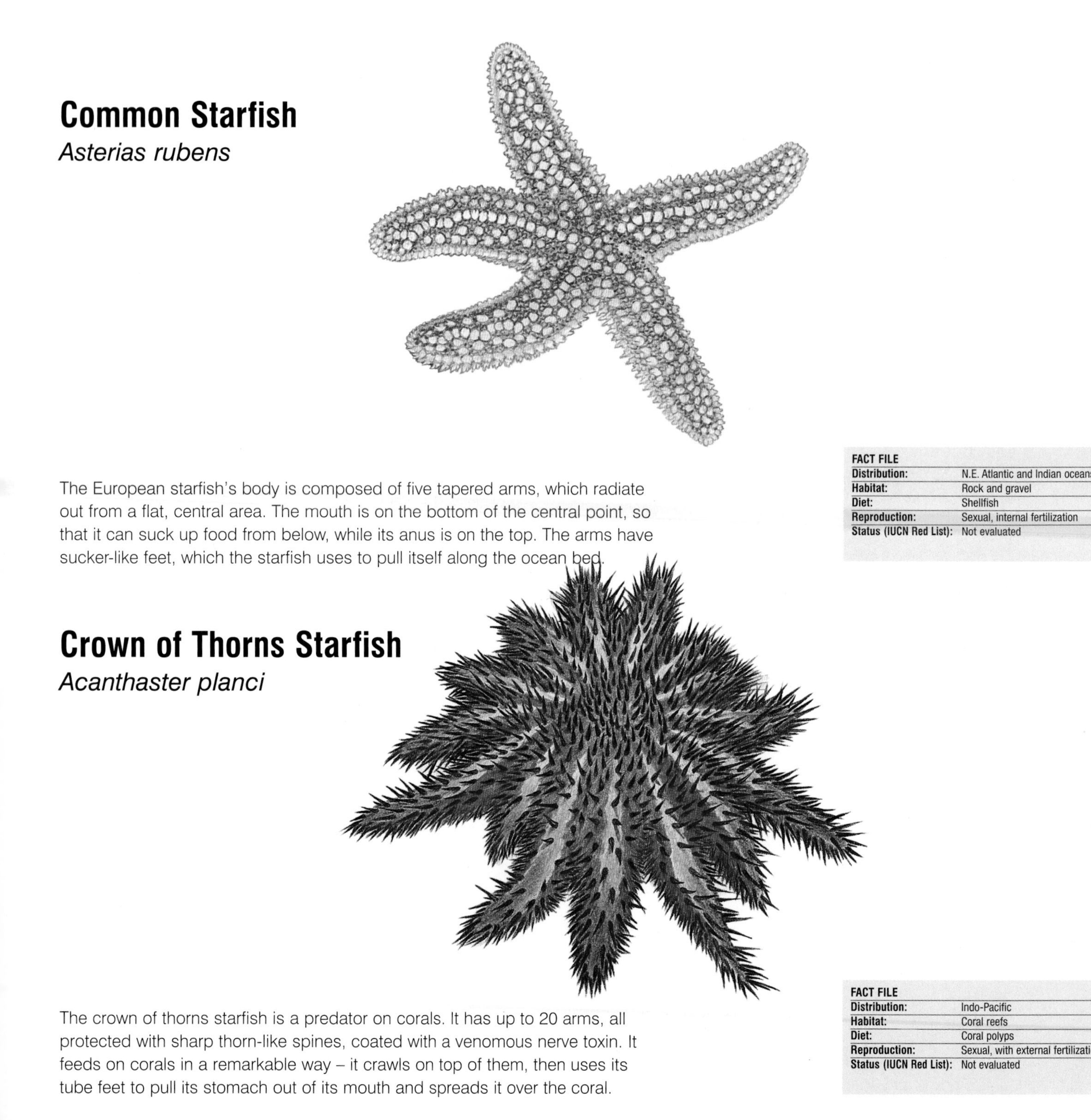

FACT FILE	
Distribution:	N.E. Atlantic and Indian oceans
Habitat:	Rock and gravel
Diet:	Shellfish
Reproduction:	Sexual, internal fertilization
Status (IUCN Red List):	Not evaluated

The European starfish's body is composed of five tapered arms, which radiate out from a flat, central area. The mouth is on the bottom of the central point, so that it can suck up food from below, while its anus is on the top. The arms have sucker-like feet, which the starfish uses to pull itself along the ocean bed.

Crown of Thorns Starfish

Acanthaster planci

FACT FILE	
Distribution:	Indo-Pacific
Habitat:	Coral reefs
Diet:	Coral polyps
Reproduction:	Sexual, with external fertilization
Status (IUCN Red List):	Not evaluated

The crown of thorns starfish is a predator on corals. It has up to 20 arms, all protected with sharp thorn-like spines, coated with a venomous nerve toxin. It feeds on corals in a remarkable way – it crawls on top of them, then uses its tube feet to pull its stomach out of its mouth and spreads it over the coral.

Brittle Star

Ophiocomina nigra

FACT FILE	
Distribution:	Eastern Atlantic Ocean
Habitat:	Coastlines and offshore sea floor
Diet:	Plankton, organic detritus, carrion
Reproduction:	Sexual, with external fertilization
Status (IUCN Red List):	Not evaluated

The brittle star is relatively large. Its central disc reaches around 20mm (⅘in) across, but its arms grow to 10cm (4in) long. It comes in a variety of colours, is covered in untidy spines, and, as the name suggests, is very fragile – though it can regenerate lost limbs, and new individuals even grow from severed limbs.

Edible Sea Urchin

Paracentrotus lividus

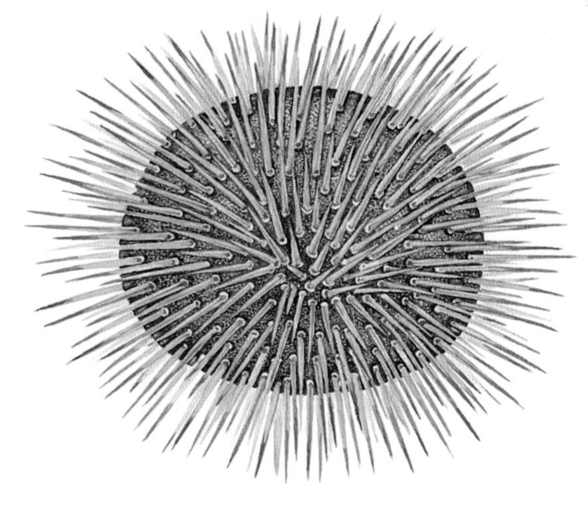

FACT FILE	
Distribution:	Mediterranean
Habitat:	Shallow seas
Diet:	Algae
Reproduction:	Eggs float freely
Status (IUCN Red List):	Not evaluated

Sea urchins have globe-shaped bodies covered with long, movable spines. Beneath this prickly outer coating is a 'shell' made up of hard, close-fitting chalky plates, called a 'test'. The urchin's mouth is located on the flat underside of the test and is used to scrape up algae and plant matter from rocks.

Sand Dollar

Clypeaster humilis

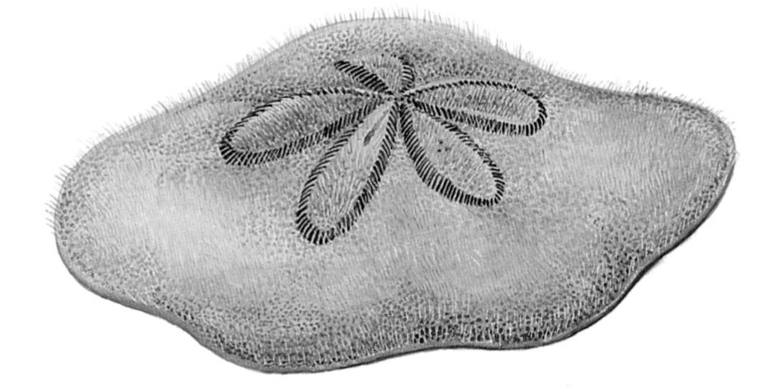

FACT FILE	
Distribution:	E. and W. coasts of North America
Habitat:	Sandy seabeds
Diet:	Algae and organic debris
Reproduction:	Sexual, with external fertilization
Status (IUCN Red List):	Not evaluated

The flattened sand dollars are close relatives of sea urchins that have evolved specifically for burrowing in sandy and muddy seabeds. Their spines are shortened into a bristly coat of 'fur'; they collect food, which hair-like cilia on the underside of the body transfer to the mouth.

Spiders

Spiders are familiar members of the arthropod ('jointed feet') phylum. There are 40,000 species forming the Araneae order, one of the largest within the arachnid class. Spiders have eight legs and two body sections – a cephalothorax (head and midbody), and an abdomen. They breathe air using organs called book lungs.

Baboon Spider

Pterinochilus murinus

This large, rusty red arachnid is an African relative of American tarantulas, and has similarly hairy legs. When threatened or annoyed, it will rear up on its back legs to display its large, hooked fangs. The spider also constructs extensive burrows, which can be as much as 60cm (23½in) long.

FACT FILE	
Distribution:	Central, Eastern and South Africa
Habitat:	All habitats
Diet:	Insects, mice and lizards
Reproduction:	Eggs held in sac
Status (IUCN Red List):	Not evaluated

European Garden Spider

Araneus diadematus

This spider is not only one of the most commonly seen spiders, it also weaves some of the most intricate webs in the world. The best time to see them is in the autumn, when the females are swollen with eggs and set up larger and larger webs in sunny spots between shrubs.

FACT FILE	
Distribution:	Europe and North America
Habitat:	Shrubs
Diet:	Insects
Reproduction:	Eggs laid in silken sac
Status (IUCN Red List):	Not evaluated

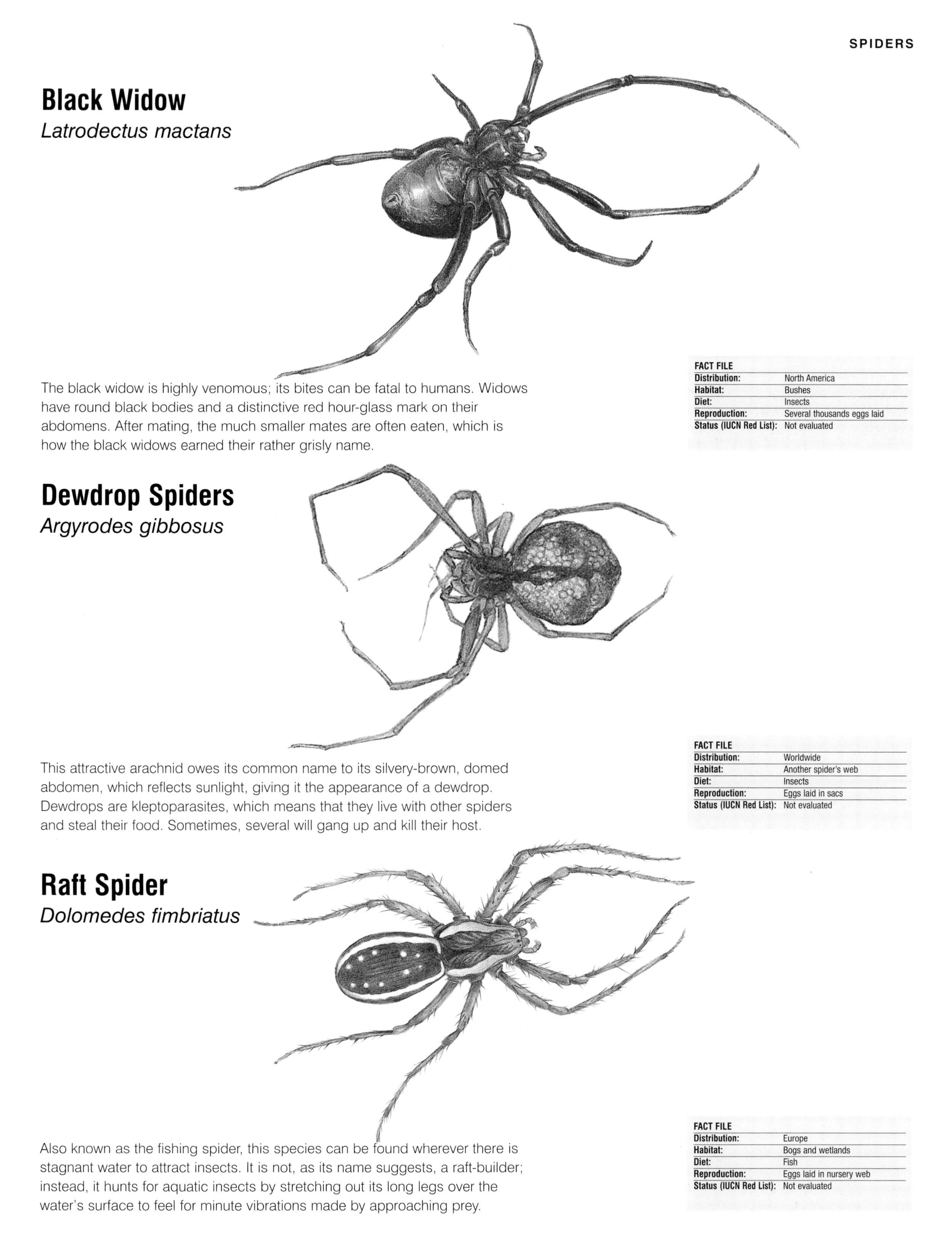

Black Widow

Latrodectus mactans

The black widow is highly venomous; its bites can be fatal to humans. Widows have round black bodies and a distinctive red hour-glass mark on their abdomens. After mating, the much smaller mates are often eaten, which is how the black widows earned their rather grisly name.

FACT FILE	
Distribution:	North America
Habitat:	Bushes
Diet:	Insects
Reproduction:	Several thousands eggs laid
Status (IUCN Red List):	Not evaluated

Dewdrop Spiders

Argyrodes gibbosus

This attractive arachnid owes its common name to its silvery-brown, domed abdomen, which reflects sunlight, giving it the appearance of a dewdrop. Dewdrops are kleptoparasites, which means that they live with other spiders and steal their food. Sometimes, several will gang up and kill their host.

FACT FILE	
Distribution:	Worldwide
Habitat:	Another spider's web
Diet:	Insects
Reproduction:	Eggs laid in sacs
Status (IUCN Red List):	Not evaluated

Raft Spider

Dolomedes fimbriatus

Also known as the fishing spider, this species can be found wherever there is stagnant water to attract insects. It is not, as its name suggests, a raft-builder; instead, it hunts for aquatic insects by stretching out its long legs over the water's surface to feel for minute vibrations made by approaching prey.

FACT FILE	
Distribution:	Europe
Habitat:	Bogs and wetlands
Diet:	Fish
Reproduction:	Eggs laid in nursery web
Status (IUCN Red List):	Not evaluated

Fat-tailed Scorpion

Androctonus australis

Scorpion venom is held in two glands positioned just below the stinger – the barbed point at the tip of the tail. Their especially large venom glands make this species of scorpion's tail look 'fat'. Fat-tailed scorpion venom is most toxic to vertebrates and is primarily used for defence rather than killing prey.

FACT FILE	
Distribution:	North Africa and Arabia
Habitat:	Desert
Diet:	Insects and spiders
Reproduction:	Sexual, internal fertilization
Status (IUCN Red List):	Not evaluated

The fat-tailed scorpion grows to 10cm (4in) and weighs 28g (1oz). Insects, such as locusts or beetles, are its usual diet, but its toxin is so powerful that the scorpion can also tackle mice and small lizards. Once its prey has been incapacitated, the scorpion dismembers the body using its razor-sharp pincers.

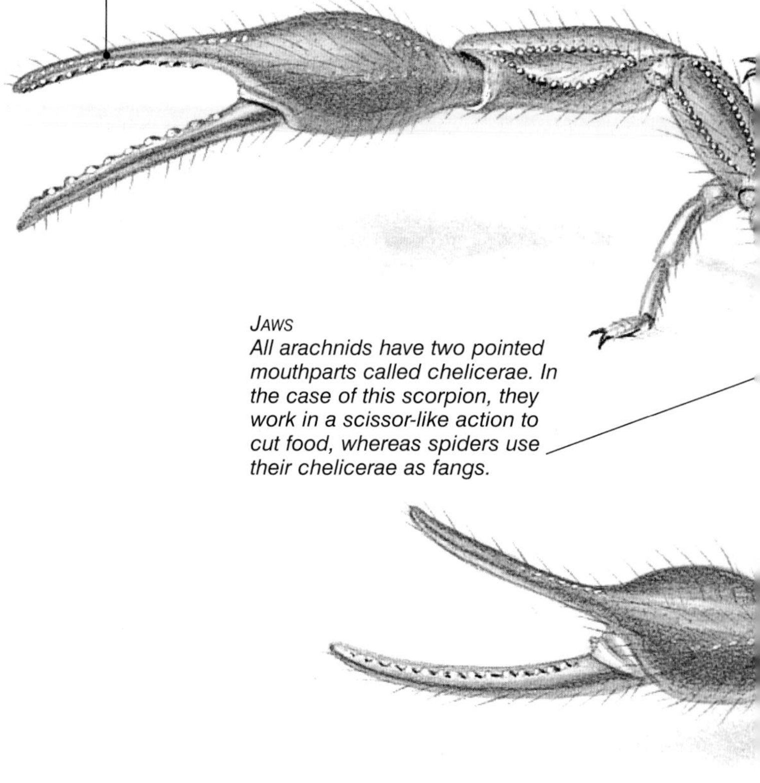

PEDIPALPS
The first pair of limbs, called the pedipalps (meaning 'foot feelers'), are equipped with pincers. Despite the stinger at the rear, these toothed grippers are the chief weapon for killing prey.

JAWS
All arachnids have two pointed mouthparts called chelicerae. In the case of this scorpion, they work in a scissor-like action to cut food, whereas spiders use their chelicerae as fangs.

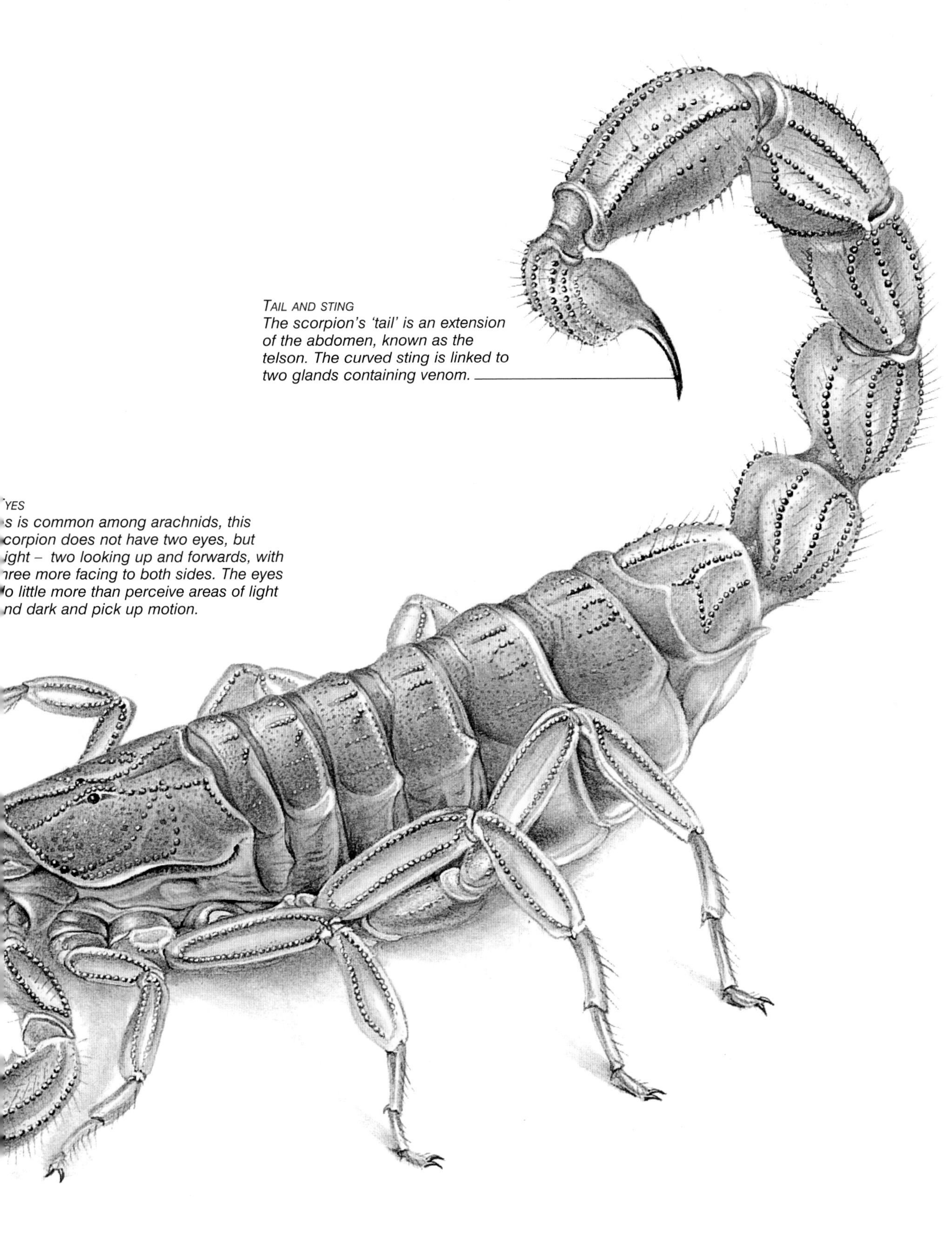
TAIL AND STING
The scorpion's 'tail' is an extension of the abdomen, known as the telson. The curved sting is linked to two glands containing venom.
YES
s is common among arachnids, this
corpion does not have two eyes, but
ight – two looking up and forwards, with
ree more facing to both sides. The eyes
o little more than perceive areas of light
nd dark and pick up motion.

Other Arachnids

Spiders are not the only arachnids. The class also includes stinging scorpions, long-legged harvestmen and blood-sucking ticks, all of which share the eight-legged body plan. The most common arachnids are the microscopic mites, which live in all habitats: in soil, at the bottom of the ocean, and even on people's eyelashes.

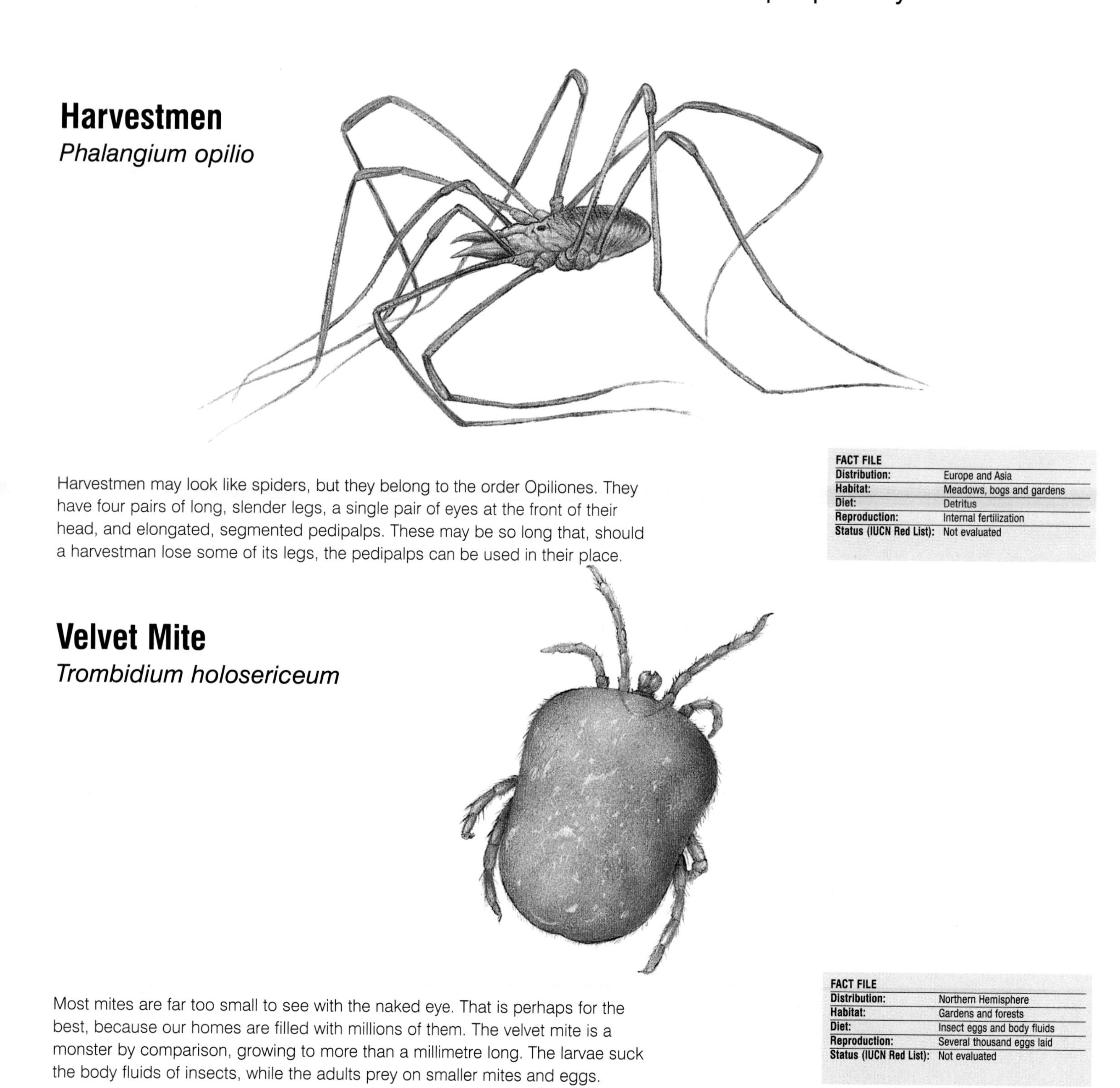

Harvestmen

Phalangium opilio

Harvestmen may look like spiders, but they belong to the order Opiliones. They have four pairs of long, slender legs, a single pair of eyes at the front of their head, and elongated, segmented pedipalps. These may be so long that, should a harvestman lose some of its legs, the pedipalps can be used in their place.

FACT FILE	
Distribution:	Europe and Asia
Habitat:	Meadows, bogs and gardens
Diet:	Detritus
Reproduction:	Internal fertilization
Status (IUCN Red List):	Not evaluated

Velvet Mite

Trombidium holosericeum

Most mites are far too small to see with the naked eye. That is perhaps for the best, because our homes are filled with millions of them. The velvet mite is a monster by comparison, growing to more than a millimetre long. The larvae suck the body fluids of insects, while the adults prey on smaller mites and eggs.

FACT FILE	
Distribution:	Northern Hemisphere
Habitat:	Gardens and forests
Diet:	Insect eggs and body fluids
Reproduction:	Several thousand eggs laid
Status (IUCN Red List):	Not evaluated

Castor Bean Tick
Ixodes ricinus

FACT FILE	
Distribution:	Europe
Habitat:	Woodlands, heaths and forests
Diet:	Mammal blood
Reproduction:	Females die after laying eggs
Status (IUCN Red List):	Not evaluated

These flat, round-bodied arachnids have a flexible abdomen that stretches to a hundred times its previous size when the tick becomes engorged with fresh blood, on which it feeds. Juvenile ticks have six legs and must feed and moult again before they adopt their final adult form.

Wind Spider
Eremochelis bilobatus

FACT FILE	
Distribution:	North America
Habitat:	Dry areas
Diet:	Insects, small rodents and lizards
Reproduction:	External fertilization
Status (IUCN Red List):	Not evaluated

This is not a true spider but a member of the separate order Solifugae. The wind spider runs on six legs. The remaining two front legs have become adapted as feelers to detect prey. Their pedipalp mouth parts are longer than their back legs, making them the largest jaws compared to body size of any animal.

Whip Scorpion
Charinus milloti

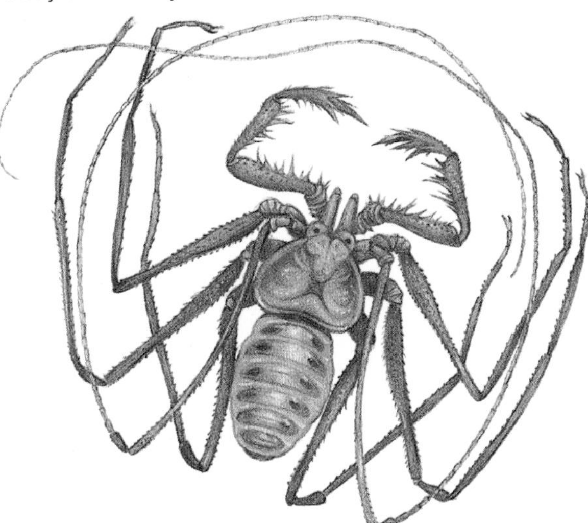

FACT FILE	
Distribution:	Southern Europe
Habitat:	Woodlands
Diet:	Insects and mites
Reproduction:	External fertilization
Status (IUCN Red List):	Not evaluated

Also known as a whip spider, this species is neither a spider nor a scorpion. They walk on just six of their eight legs. The first pair of legs, which may be longer than the length of the creature's entire body, have been adapted for use as feelers. They use these whip-like sensors to detect prey.

Shrimps and Crabs

The decapods are ten-legged animals belonging to the crustacean subphylum. Like spiders and insects, the crustaceans are arthropods. Most live in water, although some crabs survive in damp habitats on land. The decapod body is supported by an outer skeleton, which is strengthened by chalky calcium compounds.

Common Prawn

Palaemon serratus

The common prawn is harvested in large amounts for food. Its semi-transparent carapace, or shell, extends forward above the eyes to form a jagged head-shield. The prawn has extremely long antennae – up to one-and-a-half times its body length – which it uses to sense danger.

FACT FILE	
Distribution:	North Atlantic and Mediterranean
Habitat:	Open seas
Diet:	Plankton and organic debris
Reproduction:	Sexual, through copulation
Status (IUCN Red List):	Not evaluated

Common Spiny Lobster

Palinurus vulgaris

The spiny lobster grows to 60cm (23½in). It is a close relative of the common lobster, but with several differences – most noticeably, the front three pairs of legs all bear claws (albeit small ones), and most of the body is covered in sharp defensive spines. It hides in sand during the day, and emerges to hunt at night.

FACT FILE	
Distribution:	North Atlantic and Mediterranean
Habitat:	Rock-strewn, sandy seabeds
Diet:	Crustaceans, fish and molluscs
Reproduction:	Sexual; spawns once a year
Status (IUCN Red List):	Not evaluated

Common Lobster

Homarus gammarus

FACT FILE	
Distribution:	North Atlantic and Mediterranean
Habitat:	Rocky seabeds
Diet:	Crustaceans, fish and molluscs
Reproduction:	Sexual; spawns after moulting
Status (IUCN Red List):	Not evaluated

Lobsters are large crustaceans with huge claws on their first pair of legs. They are normally blue-black in colour (cooked lobster is pink because its pigments are destroyed by boiling), and can grow to around 1m (3ft 3in) long. As it grows, the lobster must shed its shell every year.

Robber Crab

Birgus latro

FACT FILE	
Distribution:	Indian and Pacific oceans
Habitat:	Islands and coasts
Diet:	Fruits
Reproduction:	External fertilization
Status (IUCN Red List):	Data deficient

Robber crabs are the world's largest land crab, growing to 60cm (23½in) long. They spend their entire adult lives on land, although females must lay their eggs in the sea, where the larvae hatch. Robber crabs still have gills, but they can absorb oxygen directly from the air as long as they keep them moist.

Edible Crab

Cancer pagurus

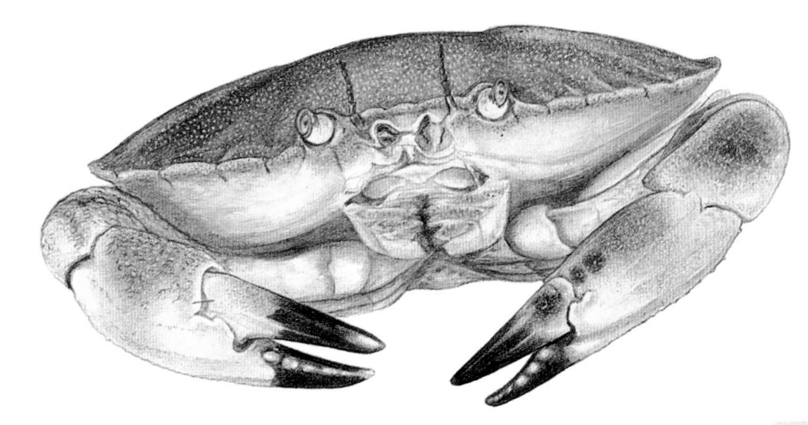

FACT FILE	
Distribution:	North Atlantic and Mediterranean
Habitat:	Muddy and sandy seabeds
Diet:	Shellfish
Reproduction:	Female carries a million eggs
Status (IUCN Red List):	Not evaluated

Also known as the brown crab, this tough-looking crab is easily identifiable by the 'pie crust' effect around the rim of its carapace, or upper shell. Large specimens with shell widths of 25cm (10in) take a decade or two to reach that size. The crab hides out by day, and hunts in the dark, mainly for smaller crabs.

Other Crustaceans

The crustaceans are a large group of animals, numbering more than 50,000 species. They range from microscopic copepods that float in the world's oceans in their billions, to the giant amphipods of deep ocean trenches, which grow to the size of a house cat. Many crustaceans have pincers on their front legs.

Mantis Shrimp

Squilla empusa

The mantis shrimp's name is doubly misleading – it is unrelated to preying mantises and is also not a shrimp. Mantis shrimps have super-strong forelimbs that move lightning-quick, lashing out faster than 10m/s (30ft/s) to spear or club passing prey, with the force of a 0.22-calibre bullet.

FACT FILE	
Distribution:	Gulf of Mexico
Habitat:	Seabeds down to 150m (500ft)
Diet:	Small fish and crustaceans
Reproduction:	Sexual, internal fertilization
Status (IUCN Red List):	Not evaluated

Pill Woodlouse

Armadillidium vulgare

Woodlice are one of the few species of crustaceans that have adapted to a life spent entirely on land. They have seven pairs of legs and a series of articulated armour plates that cover the body. Pill woodlice are able to curl themselves up into a tight ball when threatened by predators.

FACT FILE	
Distribution:	Europe
Habitat:	Damp woodland and gardens
Diet:	Plant matter
Reproduction:	Sexual, internal fertilization
Status (IUCN Red List):	Not evaluated

Water Flea

Holopedium gibberum

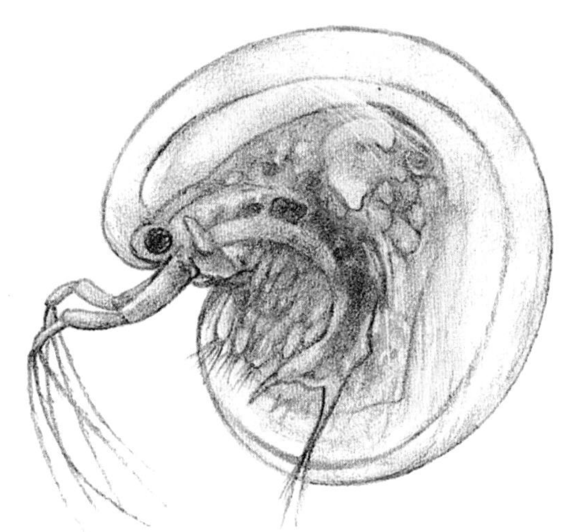

Water fleas are very different from the blood-sucking insects also called fleas; the only similarity is their small size. This species lives in freshwater. They live in the brightly lit water near the surface, often migrating up and down the water column as the light environment changes.

FACT FILE	
Distribution:	Northern Hemisphere
Habitat:	Surface water of lakes
Diet:	Plankton
Reproduction:	Eggs carried in pouch
Status (IUCN Red List):	Not evaluated

Goose Barnacle

Lepas anatifera

Goose barnacles spend all their adult lives in one place. They attach themselves to rocks by a stalk, or peduncle, that can grow up to 90cm (35in) long. Their main body has two plates that open to allow their six pairs of legs to emerge. These legs act as a net, filtering the waters for food particles.

FACT FILE	
Distribution:	Worldwide in warm waters
Habitat:	Intertidal zone
Diet:	Plankton
Reproduction:	Sexual, through copulation
Status (IUCN Red List):	Not evaluated

Antarctic Krill

Euphausia superba

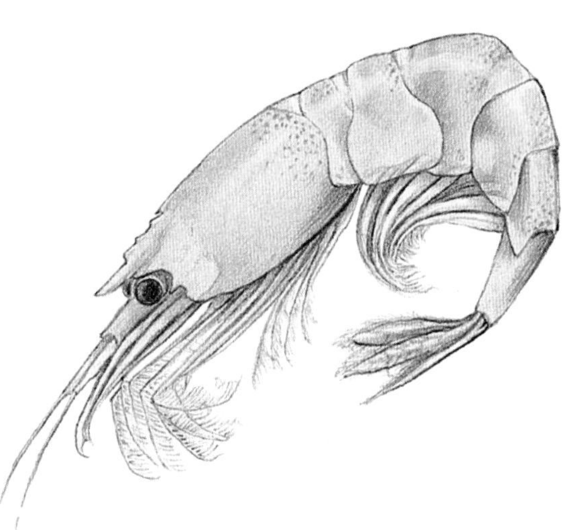

One of the most abundant animals on the planet, the shrimp-like krill forms the base of many food chains around the world. These small, transparent creatures form huge swarms. Antarctic krill are the main food supply for whales. The krill feed on phytoplankton floating on the water's surface.

FACT FILE	
Distribution:	Antarctic Ocean
Habitat:	Cold water
Diet:	Copepods
Reproduction:	Eggs laid at surface
Status (IUCN Red List):	Not evaluated

Cockroaches, Termites and Mantises

These animals are all insects, with a head, thorax (or midbody) and an abdomen. Six legs and perhaps one or two pairs of wings are attached to the thorax. The insects listed here are exopterygotes, which means that their young forms, or nymphs, are generally wingless versions of the adults.

German Cockroach

Blatella germanica

It is this German species that has given the other species of cockroach such a bad name. It invades human homes and cannot survive in areas without human food and waste. The German cockroach's life cycle is very fast; from egg to nymph to adult takes around 100 days.

FACT FILE	
Distribution:	Europe
Habitat:	Buildings
Diet:	Organic matter
Reproduction:	Sexual, eggs carried in sac
Status (IUCN Red List):	Not evaluated

Giant Cockroach

Blaberus giganteus

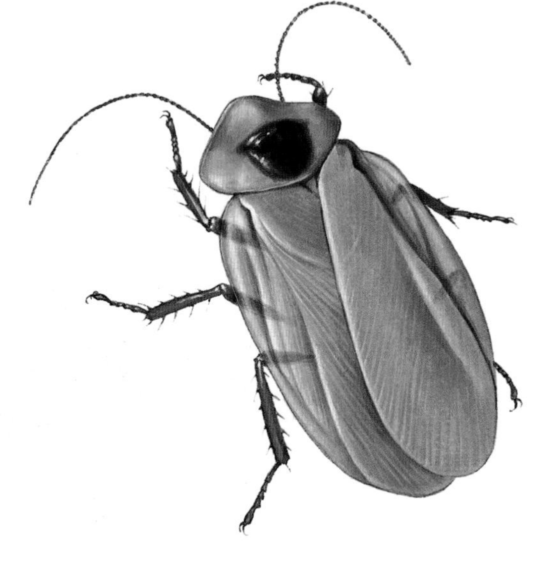

As its name suggests, this is one of the largest species of cockroach in the world, growing to 9cm (3½in) long. Only the distantly related hissing cockroach of Madagascar is appreciably bigger. The giant cockroach lives in humid caves in rainforests, feeding on rotting plant matter.

FACT FILE	
Distribution:	Central and South America
Habitat:	Caves and rainforest
Diet:	Organic matter
Reproduction:	Sexual, eggs carried in sac
Status (IUCN Red List):	Not evaluated

African Devil Flower Mantis

Idolum diabolicum

Praying mantises get their name from the way they hold their spiked forelegs when at rest, which makes them look as if they are praying. The folding arms are used to grab passing prey. The mantis sits motionless so as not to arouse suspicions from passing insects and avoid the attention of birds and bats.

FACT FILE	
Distribution:	Southern Africa
Habitat:	Bushes
Diet:	Insects
Reproduction:	Sexual, internal fertilization
Status (IUCN Red List):	Not evaluated

Magnetic Termite

Amitermes meridionalis

These curious insects get their names from the way they build their nests in the sun-baked outback. The tall, thin mounds are orientated north to south (like a magnetic compass), so the nest is warmed by the gentle morning and evening sun, but not baked in the midday heat when the sun is high in the sky.

FACT FILE	
Distribution:	Australia
Habitat:	Semi-desert
Diet:	Plant fibres
Reproduction:	Queen produces 100 million eggs
Status (IUCN Red List):	Not evaluated

Common Earwig

Forficula auricularia

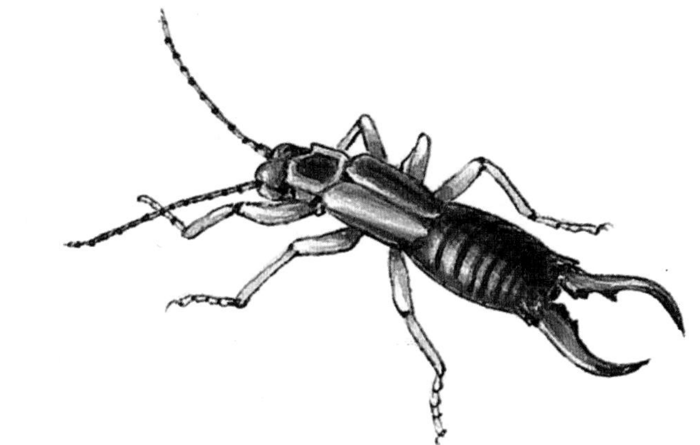

It used to be believed that these insects would crawl into the ear of a sleeping human at night and lay their eggs in their brain. It is more likely that the shape of the wings reminded early Britons of a human ear. Earwigs are totally harmless to people, although they may give a nasty nip if they are picked up.

FACT FILE	
Distribution:	Europe, North Africa and W. Asia
Habitat:	Cool, damp places
Diet:	Plants and insects
Reproduction:	Female nurtures litter of 50 young
Status (IUCN Red List):	Not evaluated

Bugs

The word 'bug' is often used to describe any insect or similar invertebrate. However, the bugs are a specific subgroup, forming the Hemiptera order. That name means 'half wing' and refers to how the hindwings tend to be longer than the leathery forewings. Bugs also have boat-shaped bodies and sucking mouthparts.

Water Measurer

Hydrometra stagnorum

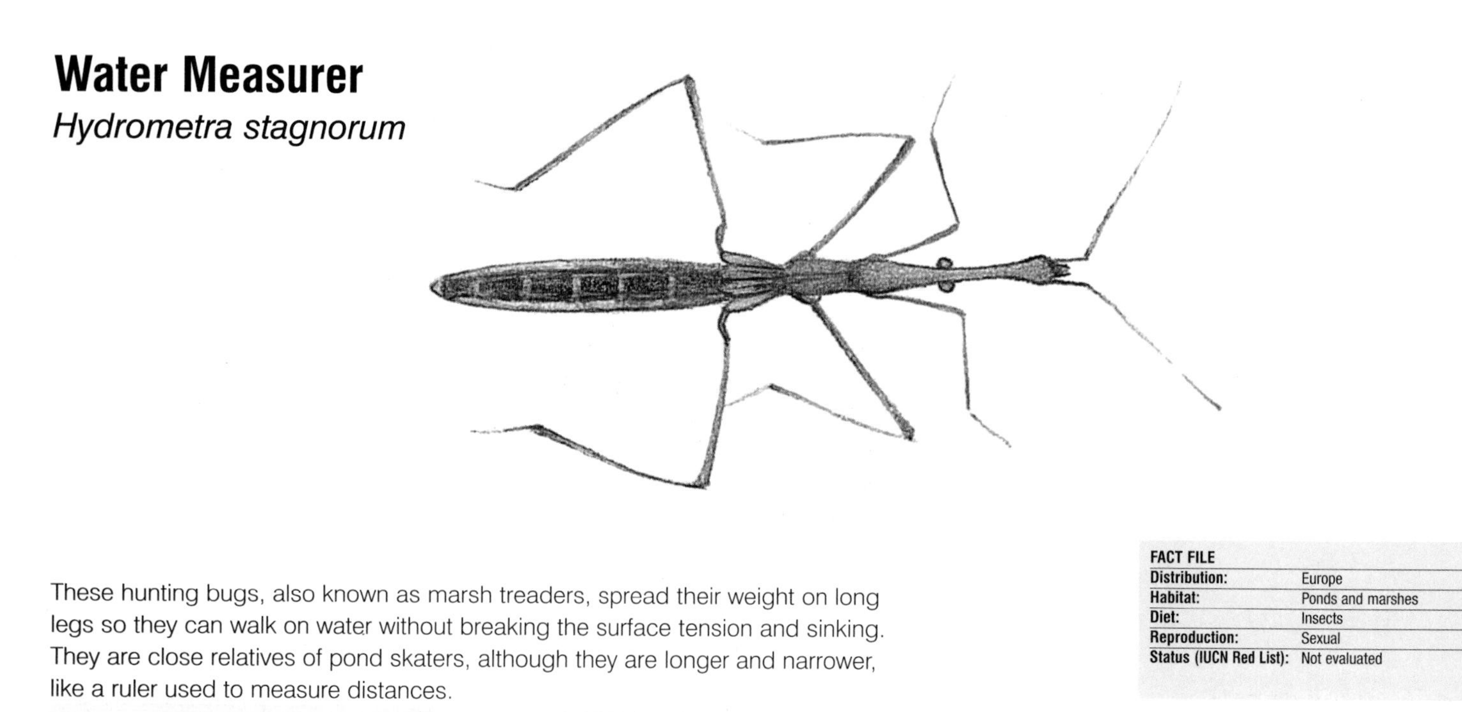

These hunting bugs, also known as marsh treaders, spread their weight on long legs so they can walk on water without breaking the surface tension and sinking. They are close relatives of pond skaters, although they are longer and narrower, like a ruler used to measure distances.

FACT FILE	
Distribution:	Europe
Habitat:	Ponds and marshes
Diet:	Insects
Reproduction:	Sexual
Status (IUCN Red List):	Not evaluated

Giant Water Bug

Lethocerus indicus

This big bug is a diving insect that preys on tadpoles and insect larvae with its clawed forelegs. It has powerful flight muscles to carry it between pools, and these masses of flesh give the insect a taste similar to shrimp. As a result, water bugs are a popular ingredient in Southeast Asian cuisine.

FACT FILE	
Distribution:	Southeast Asia
Habitat:	Freshwater
Diet:	Insects and tadpoles
Reproduction:	Sexual
Status (IUCN Red List):	Not evaluated

Firebug
Pyrrhocoris apterus

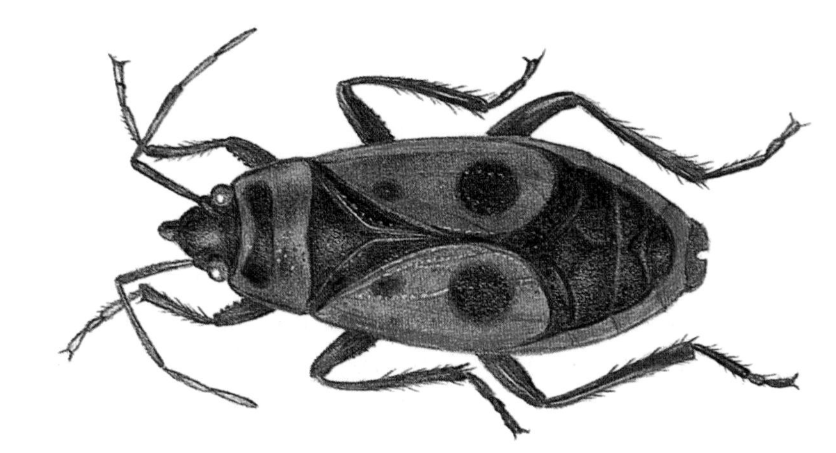

FACT FILE	
Distribution:	Europe to China
Habitat:	Woodland
Diet:	Lime seeds
Reproduction:	Copulation lasts a week
Status (IUCN Red List):	Not evaluated

Firebugs earn their name from the vibrant reds of the adults, which often gather in large crowds during the early summer. Mating takes place at this time, and male firebugs have a tactic for ensuring their sperm is successful. They ride on their chosen females for a week to ensure no other rivals mate with them.

Green Shield Bug
Palomena prasina

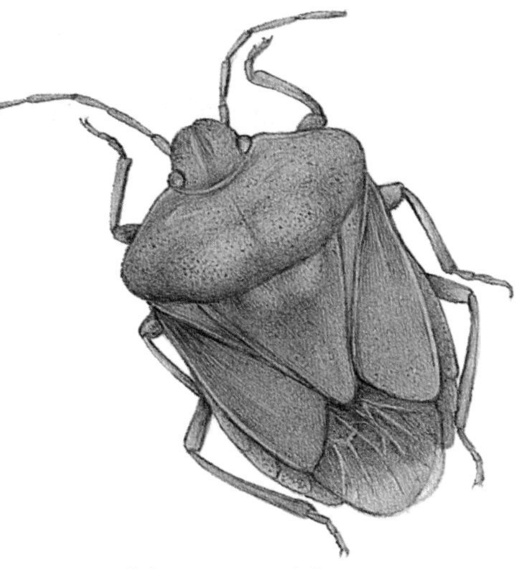

FACT FILE	
Distribution:	Europe and Asia
Habitat:	Garden and woodlands
Diet:	Sap
Reproduction:	Sexual
Status (IUCN Red List):	Not evaluated

These attractive insects are known as shield bugs because of the armour plate behind the head. They are also called stink bugs because of the foul-smelling liquid that squirts from their abdomens when threatened. The bugs are regarded as pests because they drain plants for sap.

Lantern Bug
Fulgora laternaria

FACT FILE	
Distribution:	Central and South America
Habitat:	Rainforest
Diet:	Sap
Reproduction:	Sexual
Status (IUCN Red List):	Not evaluated

The lantern bug is named after a bulbous appendage on its head. According to early observers, this bulbous 'snout' glowed. Although this has now been discounted, the name lantern bug has stuck. Instead, the appendage works with eyespots on its wings to create the look of a larger, more dangerous, creature.

Beetles

The insects are the largest group of animals, and the beetles (order Coleoptera) are the largest group of insects. There are at least 400,000 species of beetle, probably many more; one out of every four animals is a beetle. The forewings of a beetle are hardened into elytra, or covers, that protect the flimsy hindwings used for flying.

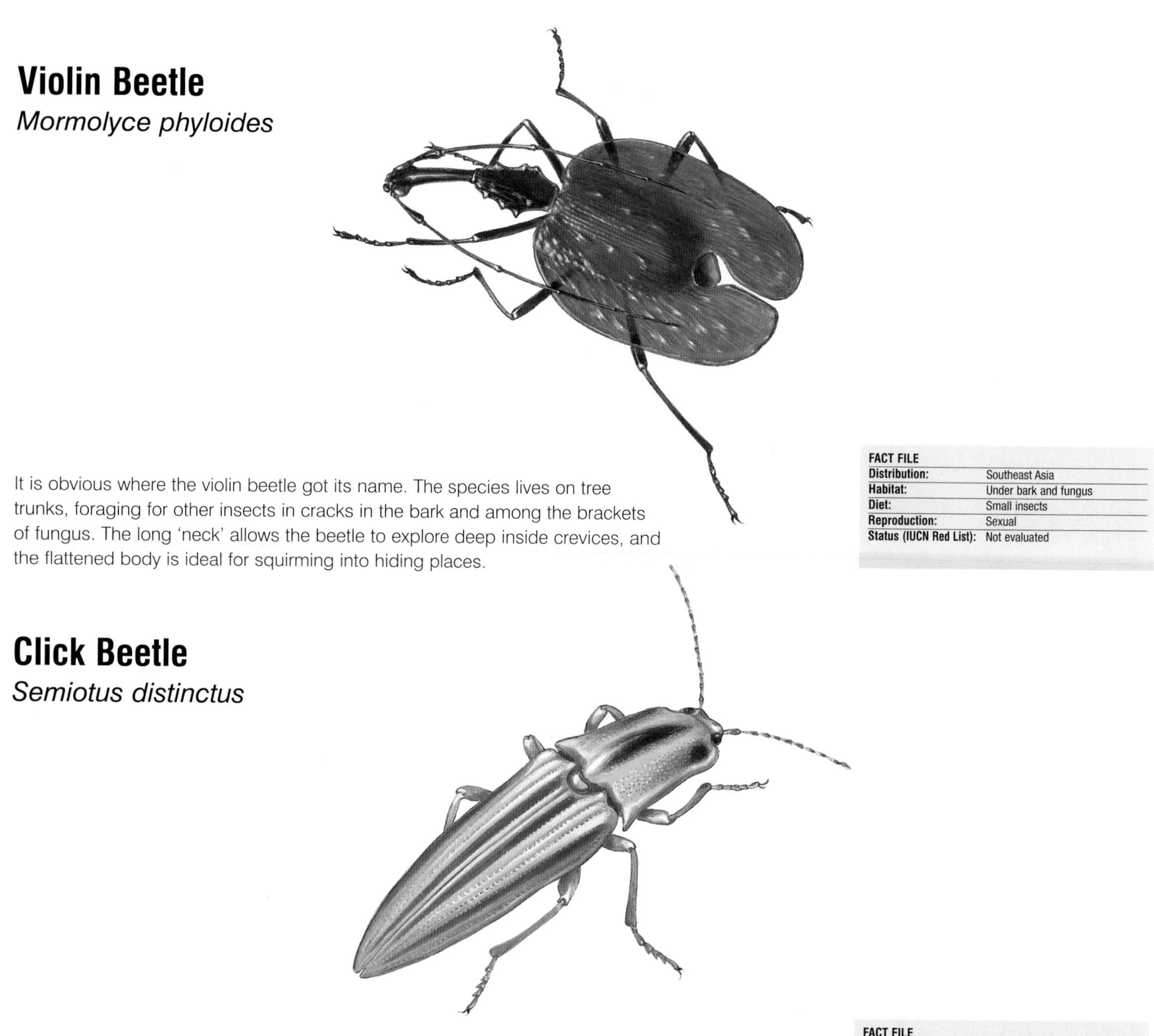

Violin Beetle

Mormolyce phyloides

It is obvious where the violin beetle got its name. The species lives on tree trunks, foraging for other insects in cracks in the bark and among the brackets of fungus. The long 'neck' allows the beetle to explore deep inside crevices, and the flattened body is ideal for squirming into hiding places.

FACT FILE	
Distribution:	Southeast Asia
Habitat:	Under bark and fungus
Diet:	Small insects
Reproduction:	Sexual
Status (IUCN Red List):	Not evaluated

Click Beetle

Semiotus distinctus

This is one of around 9000 species of click beetle. Their defining characteristic is their ability to catapult themselves in the air to escape predators. They do this using a hinge on the thorax. The beetle flexes its muscles to create tension until the hinge snaps shut, throwing the beetle into the air with an audible click.

FACT FILE	
Distribution:	Central and South America
Habitat:	Woodland and farms
Diet:	Plants
Reproduction:	Larvae live underground
Status (IUCN Red List):	Not evaluated

Hercules Beetle

Dynastes hercules

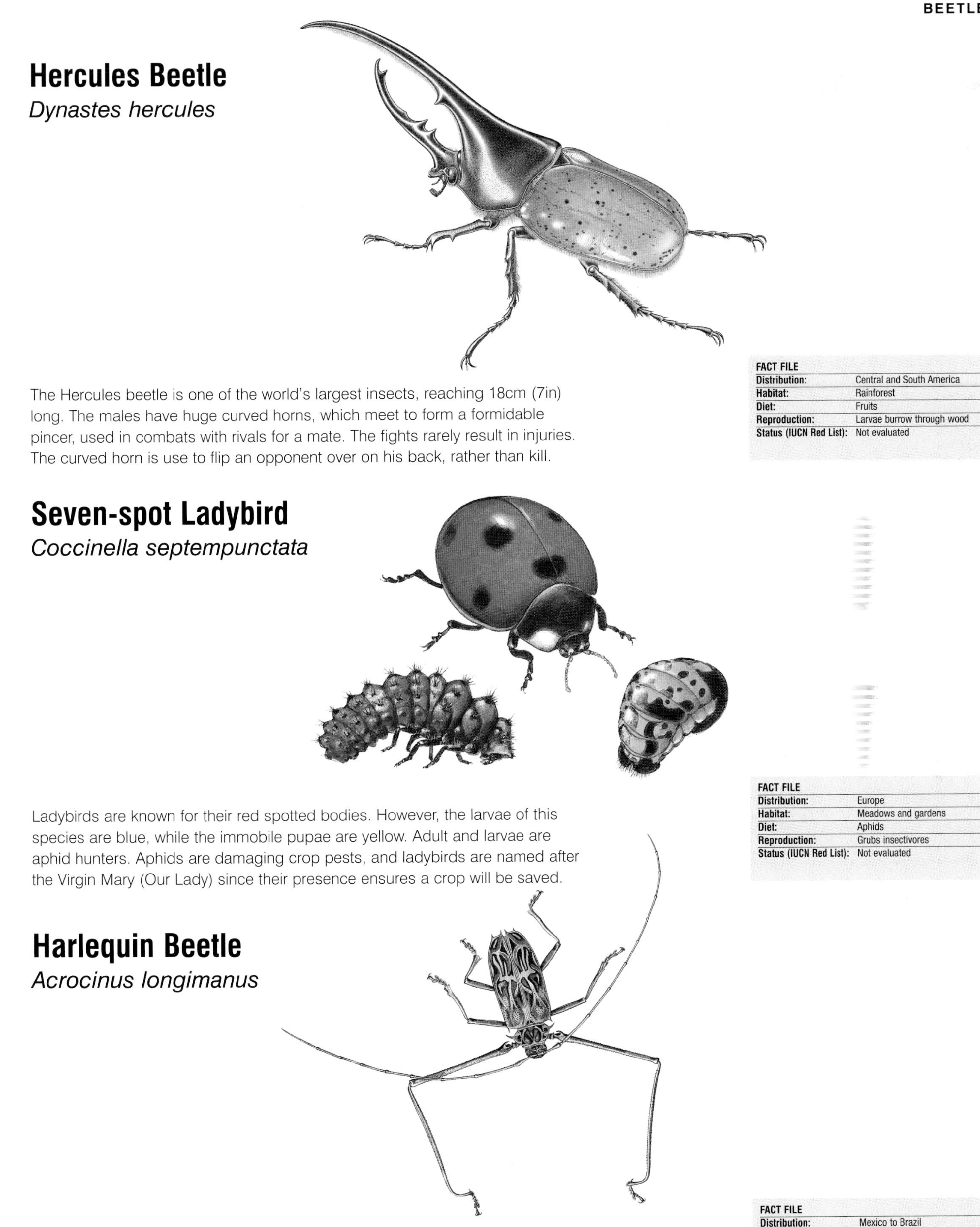

The Hercules beetle is one of the world's largest insects, reaching 18cm (7in) long. The males have huge curved horns, which meet to form a formidable pincer, used in combats with rivals for a mate. The fights rarely result in injuries. The curved horn is use to flip an opponent over on his back, rather than kill.

FACT FILE	
Distribution:	Central and South America
Habitat:	Rainforest
Diet:	Fruits
Reproduction:	Larvae burrow through wood
Status (IUCN Red List):	Not evaluated

Seven-spot Ladybird

Coccinella septempunctata

Ladybirds are known for their red spotted bodies. However, the larvae of this species are blue, while the immobile pupae are yellow. Adult and larvae are aphid hunters. Aphids are damaging crop pests, and ladybirds are named after the Virgin Mary (Our Lady) since their presence ensures a crop will be saved.

FACT FILE	
Distribution:	Europe
Habitat:	Meadows and gardens
Diet:	Aphids
Reproduction:	Grubs insectivores
Status (IUCN Red List):	Not evaluated

Harlequin Beetle

Acrocinus longimanus

The harlequin beetle makes its home in Latin America's tropical forests. They are also known as jak-tree borers, as their larvae are found mainly in jackfruit trees. The species belongs to a group called the long-horned beetles. The 'horns' in question are actually the antennae, which are longer than the body.

FACT FILE	
Distribution:	Mexico to Brazil
Habitat:	Forests
Diet:	Sap
Reproduction:	Larvae tunnel through wood
Status (IUCN Red List):	Not evaluated

Fogstand Beetle

Onymacris unguicularis

This beetle has developed an ingenious way of surviving the harsh, water-free environment among the sand dunes of the Namib Desert. The species is diurnal. However, on evenings when mist creeps across the desert from the ocean, the beetle climbs dunes to collect life-giving water from the foggy air.

FACT FILE	
Distribution:	Namib Desert
Habitat:	Coastal sand dunes
Diet:	Dead organic material
Reproduction:	Eggs laid all year
Status (IUCN Red List):	Not evaluated

Like the other 200 species of fog-basking beetles, this little beetle does a mini-handstand, raising its abdomen to allow the moisture contained in the fog to condense and trickle down its back into its mouth parts. Other species dig narrow trenches in the sand to collect the moisture that collects in hollows overnight.

Great Diving Beetle

Dytiscus marginalis

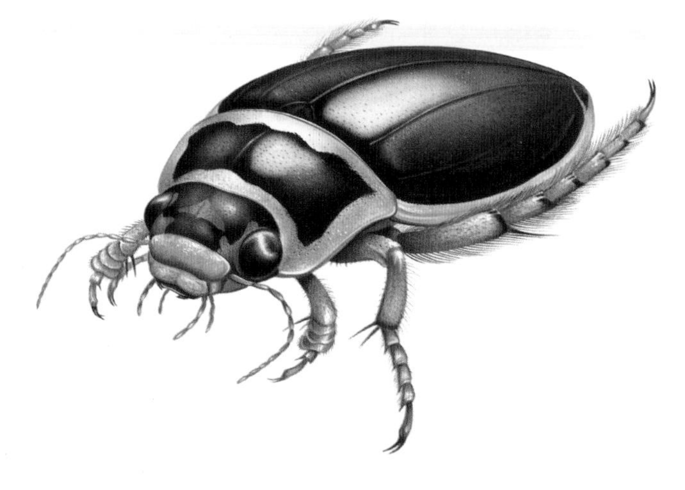

While this and other fog-basking beetles are well adapted to life in the dry, the great diving beetle lives in quite the opposite of habitats. This large hunting insect spends much of its time submerged in water. While the larval form has gills, the adults breathe through trachea, tubes that carry air inside the body. However, most insects drown in water. The diving beetle has developed a special underwater breathing system. It traps bubbles of air under its wing cases on each dive, which it uses to breathe while submerged.

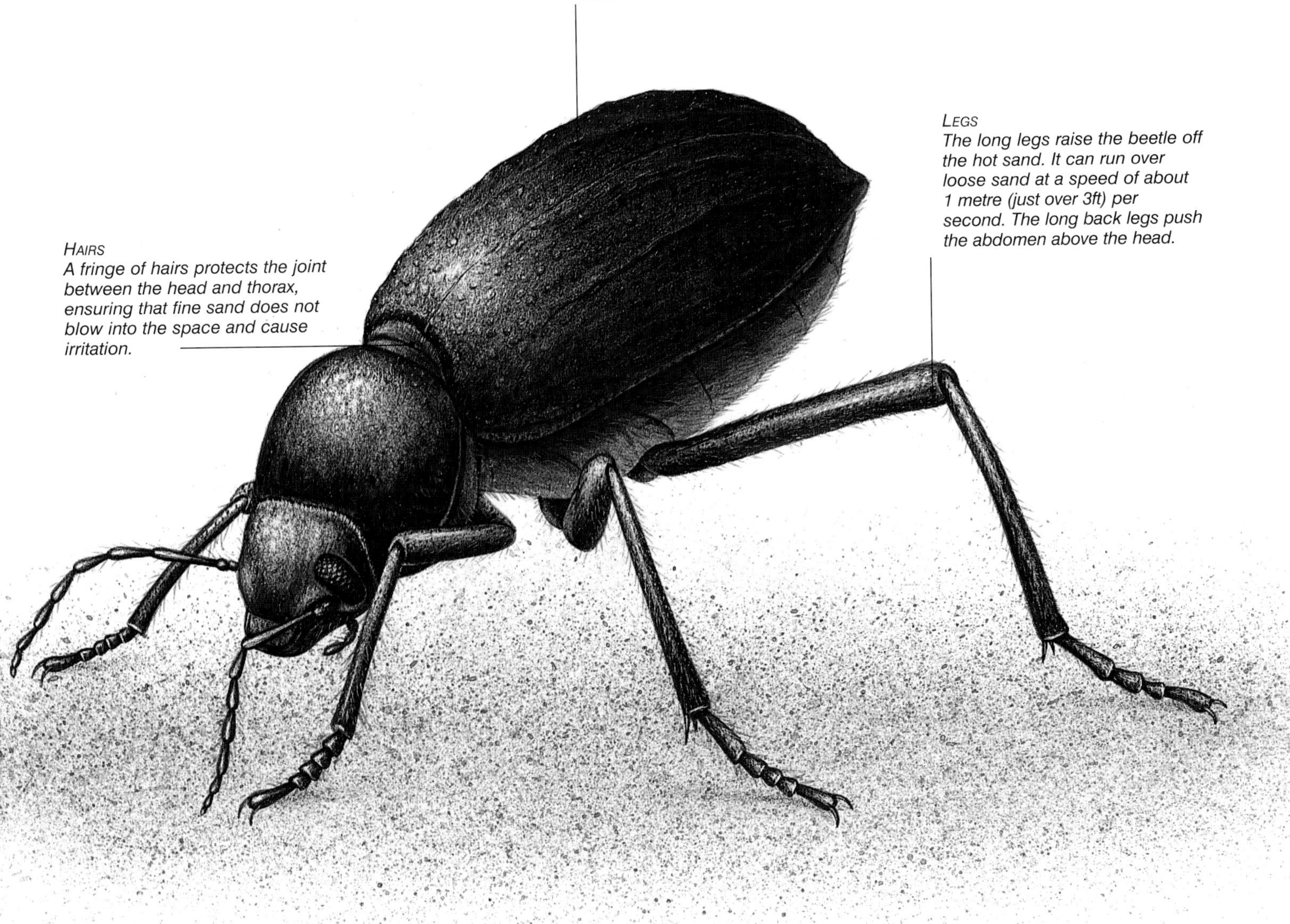

FEMALE
The females are larger than the males. The animals are known locally as tok tokkie beetles because of the noise they make when looking for a mate.

WING CASE
Fogstand beetles have lost the ability to fly. Their wing cases are fused shut, enclosing an air-filled space that reduces moisture loss.

LEGS
The long legs raise the beetle off the hot sand. It can run over loose sand at a speed of about 1 metre (just over 3ft) per second. The long back legs push the abdomen above the head.

HAIRS
A fringe of hairs protects the joint between the head and thorax, ensuring that fine sand does not blow into the space and cause irritation.

Flies

Many insects carry the name ‘flies’, and most belong to the order Diptera, a name that means ‘two wings’. The first flying insects are thought to have had four wings, but true flies use only two. The hind pair are just flexible stumps called halteres, which are used as a guidance system, helping flies perform their aerobatic feats.

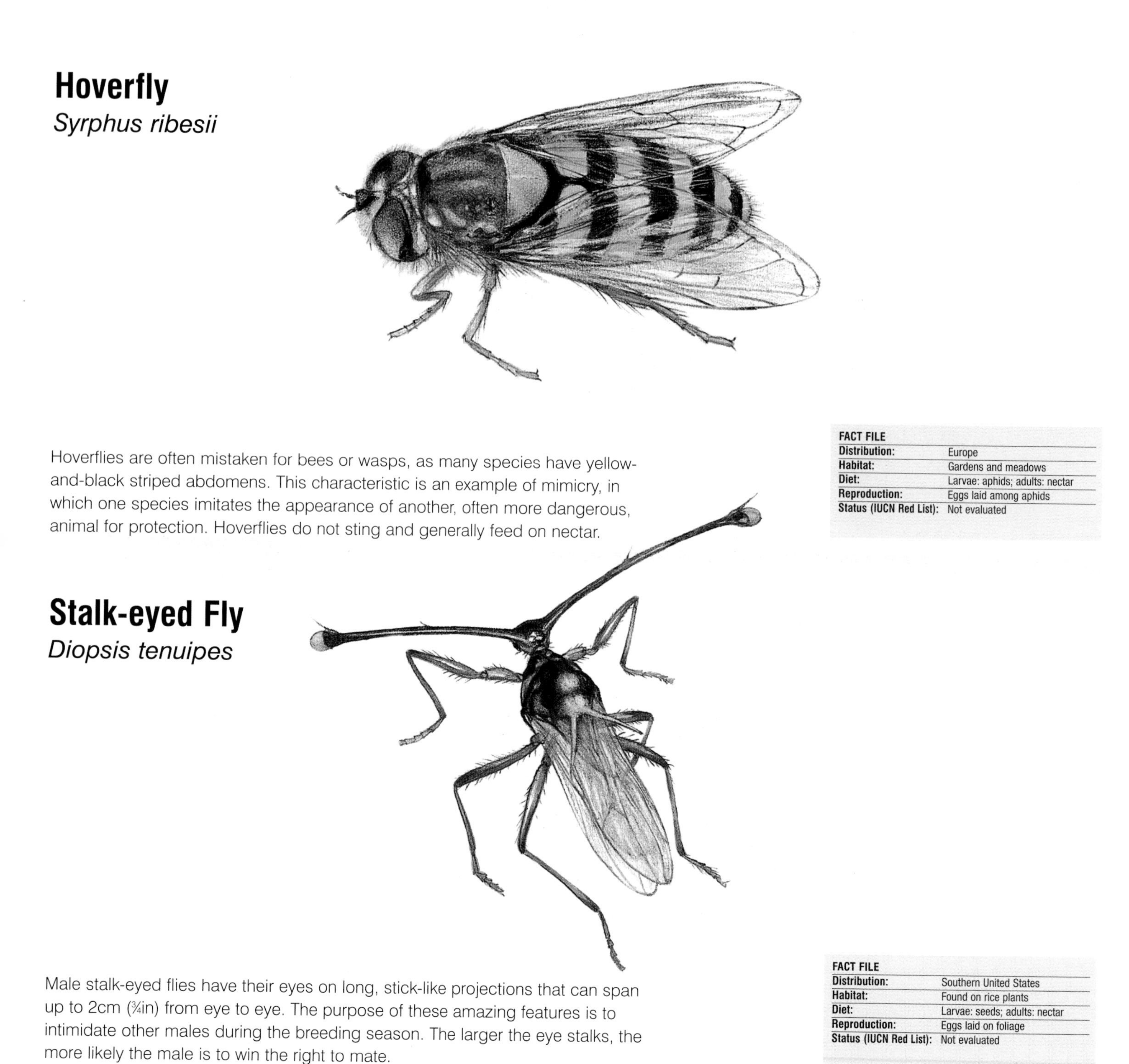

Hoverfly

Syrphus ribesii

Hoverflies are often mistaken for bees or wasps, as many species have yellow-and-black striped abdomens. This characteristic is an example of mimicry, in which one species imitates the appearance of another, often more dangerous, animal for protection. Hoverflies do not sting and generally feed on nectar.

FACT FILE	
Distribution:	Europe
Habitat:	Gardens and meadows
Diet:	Larvae: aphids; adults: nectar
Reproduction:	Eggs laid among aphids
Status (IUCN Red List):	Not evaluated

Stalk-eyed Fly

Diopsis tenuipes

Male stalk-eyed flies have their eyes on long, stick-like projections that can span up to 2cm (¾in) from eye to eye. The purpose of these amazing features is to intimidate other males during the breeding season. The larger the eye stalks, the more likely the male is to win the right to mate.

FACT FILE	
Distribution:	Southern United States
Habitat:	Found on rice plants
Diet:	Larvae: seeds; adults: nectar
Reproduction:	Eggs laid on foliage
Status (IUCN Red List):	Not evaluated

Housefly

Musca domestica

It is estimated that nine out of ten of the flies seen buzzing around our homes belong to this species. It feeds on waste food, spitting out a little stomach juice first to help soften up its meals. If it tucks into a plate of fresh food, the minute traces of its stomach contents might spread disease to a person.

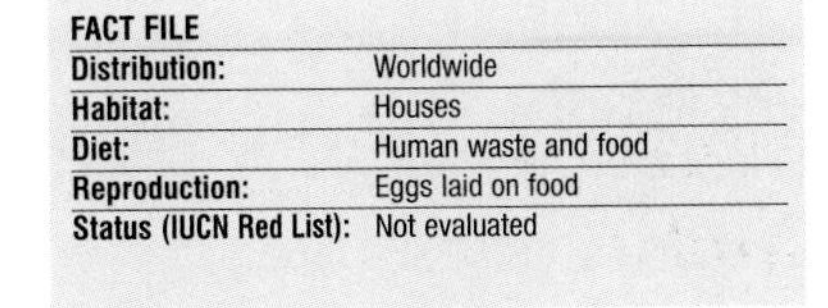

FACT FILE	
Distribution:	Worldwide
Habitat:	Houses
Diet:	Human waste and food
Reproduction:	Eggs laid on food
Status (IUCN Red List):	Not evaluated

Tsetse

Glossina palpalis

Tsetse flies are bloodsuckers that bite humans and large African mammals. The insects carry parasites called trypanosomes, which cause sleeping sickness in humans and a similar disease called nagana in cattle. Both male and female tsetse flies are blood drinkers, and both are capable of passing on infection.

FACT FILE	
Distribution:	Central Africa
Habitat:	Woodland and savannah
Diet:	Fresh blood
Reproduction:	Gives birth to a single maggot
Status (IUCN Red List):	Not evaluated

Green Bottle Fly

Lucilia sericata

This species of blow fly is named after the metallic green hues of its bristle-covered body. They are often seen near houses, but they are larger than the common house fly. Green bottle flies lay their eggs on rotten meat (including corpses) and excrement, which form the diet of the growing maggot larvae.

FACT FILE	
Distribution:	Worldwide, mainly S. Hemisphere
Habitat:	Gardens, woodland and houses
Diet:	Rotting material and nectar
Reproduction:	Eggs laid on rotting matter
Status (IUCN Red List):	Not evaluated

Butterflies

With their large, colourful wings and fluttering style of flight, the butterflies are perhaps the most easily discernible of any group of insects. They are the diurnal members of the insect order Lepidoptera, the 'scale wings'. They share this group with moths, which are most active in the dark.

Rajah Brooke's Birdwing

Trogonoptera brookiana

FACT FILE	
Distribution:	Southeast Asia
Habitat:	Sandbanks in rainforests
Diet:	Larvae: leaves; adults: nectar
Reproduction:	50 eggs laid on food plant
Status (IUCN Red List):	Not evaluated

Along with other birdwings, this species is one of the largest butterflies on earth, growing a wingspan of 17cm (6¾in). The butterflies hold their long wings in a V-shape when resting. The adults gather in gangs to sip salty water from muddy puddles. They squirt out excess water from their abdomens.

Swallowtail

Papilio machaon

FACT FILE	
Distribution:	Europe, Asia and North America
Habitat:	Fens and marshes
Diet:	Larvae eat milk parsley
Reproduction:	Eggs laid on food plant
Status (IUCN Red List):	Not evaluated

The swallowtail is named after the pointed tips that trail from both hind wings, and look a little like the forked tails of swallow birds. There are 550 similar species living on all continents. Another common feature of swallowtails is the fleshy horn, or osmeterium, used by the caterpillars to release foul smells.

Rhetenor Blue Morpho

Morpho rhetenor

When at rest, this large butterfly does not look remarkable, with its underwing pattern well suited to staying hidden in the forest. However, when the insect flies, the tops of its wings shimmer bright blue. This colour is not from a pigment, but is created by a trick of the light similar to the way oil on water emits colours.

FACT FILE	
Distribution:	South America
Habitat:	Rainforest
Diet:	Larvae: legumes; adults: fruit juice
Reproduction:	Eggs laid throughout the year
Status (IUCN Red List):	Not evaluated

European Peacock

Inachis io

This common species gets its name from the eyespots that dominate its wing pattern, which resemble similar features on the tail of a peacock. The difference is that the purpose of the butterfly's bright pattern is not to attract attention, but to spook predators into thinking the eyes belong to a bigger, meaner animal.

FACT FILE	
Distribution:	Northern Europe and Asia
Habitat:	Woodland and hedgerows
Diet:	Nettles
Reproduction:	Eggs laid in May
Status (IUCN Red List):	Not evaluated

Crowned Hairstreak

Thecla coronata

The common hairstreak is a member of the Lycaenidae family, which makes up about 40 per cent of all butterfly species. They are named after the hair-like markings on the underside of the wings. Male hairstreaks appear to have just four legs (the forelegs are tiny), while females still have six.

FACT FILE	
Distribution:	Southern Mexico and Ecuador
Habitat:	Rainforest
Diet:	Nectar and sap
Reproduction:	Eggs laid singly on leaves
Status (IUCN Red List):	Not evaluated

Moths

Moths make up about 90 per cent of the Lepidoptera order, with butterflies being a late offshoot from the main group. The main difference between the two groups is that moths lay their wings flat when resting, while butterflies hold them upright. Butterflies also tend to have clubbed antennae, while a moth's are feathery.

Broad-bordered Bee Hawkmoth

Hemaris fuciformis

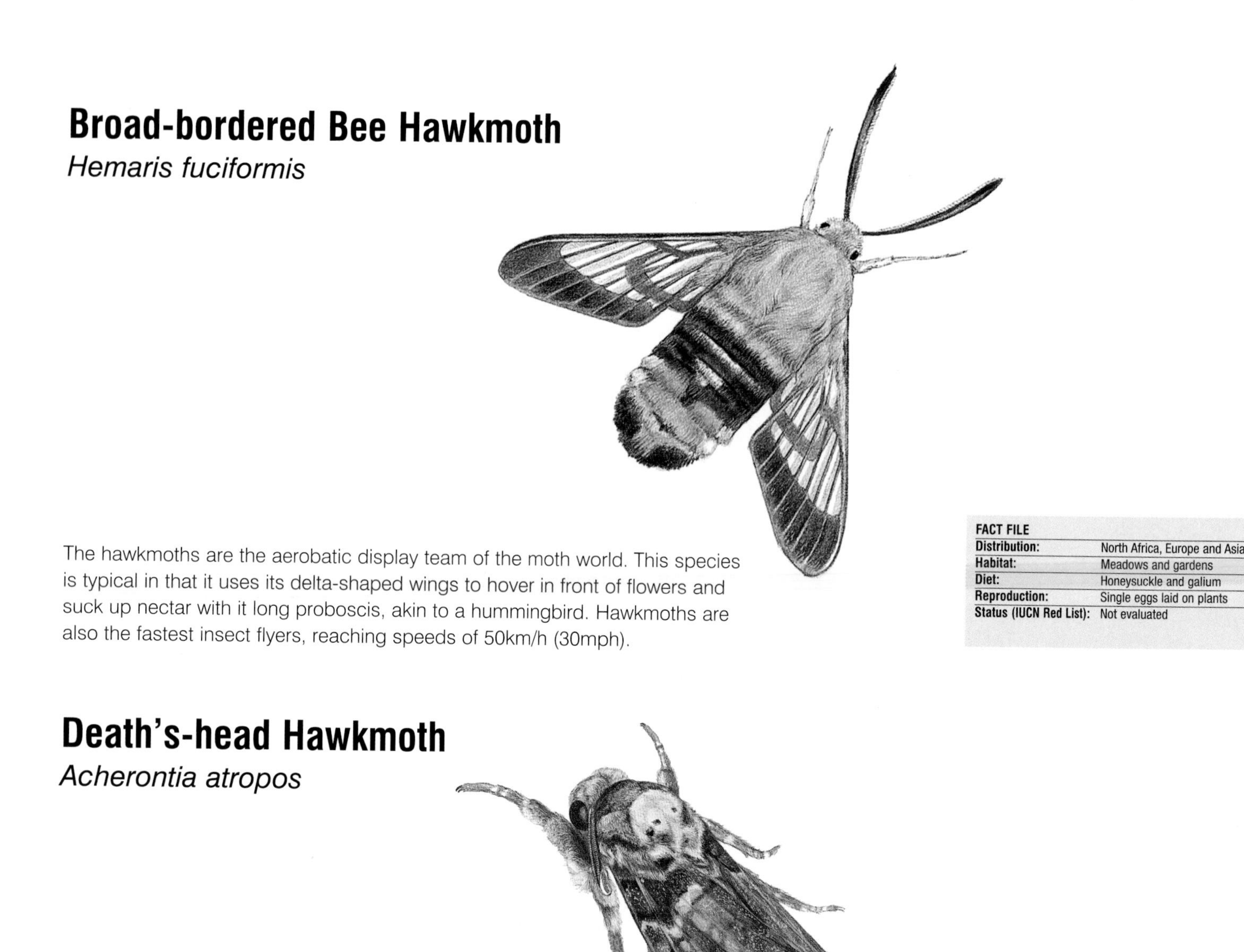

The hawkmoths are the aerobatic display team of the moth world. This species is typical in that it uses its delta-shaped wings to hover in front of flowers and suck up nectar with it long proboscis, akin to a hummingbird. Hawkmoths are also the fastest insect flyers, reaching speeds of 50km/h (30mph).

FACT FILE	
Distribution:	North Africa, Europe and Asia
Habitat:	Meadows and gardens
Diet:	Honeysuckle and galium
Reproduction:	Single eggs laid on plants
Status (IUCN Red List):	Not evaluated

Death's-head Hawkmoth

Acherontia atropos

The death's head hawkmoth is named after the skull-like pattern on its back. The forewings have a bark-like pattern, but its hind wings and abdomen mimic the colours of a queen bee. The moth's favourite food is honey; its disguise lets it stride in nests without the worker bees becoming suspicious.

FACT FILE	
Distribution:	North Africa and Southern Europe
Habitat:	Everywhere with enough water
Diet:	Larvae: leaves; adults: honey
Reproduction:	Lays up to 150 eggs
Status (IUCN Red List):	Not evaluated

Red Underwing Moth

Catocala nupta

This species spends its days motionless, hiding in plain sight on the trunk of a tree. It relies on its mottled forewings to blend it into the bark. However, should an overly curious predator get too near, the moth shows its hidden underwings, creating a shocking flash of red that scares predators away.

FACT FILE	
Distribution:	Europe
Habitat:	Woodland and gardens
Diet:	Nectar, willow and poplar
Reproduction:	Eggs laid in September
Status (IUCN Red List):	Not evaluated

Twenty-plume Moth

Alucita hexadactyla

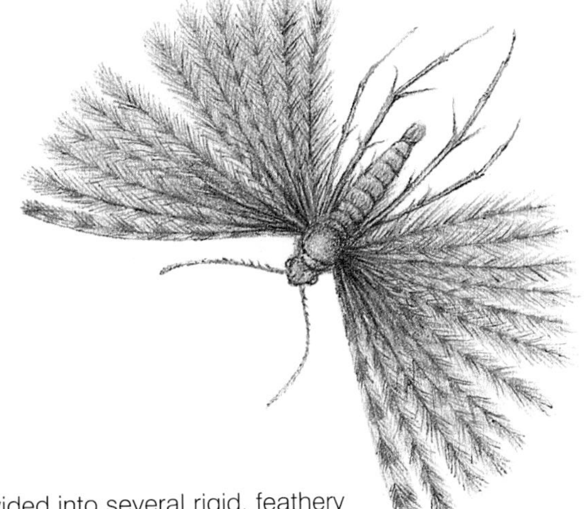

The wings of this bizarre moth have become divided into several rigid, feathery spines. Despite its name, there are nearer to 24 plumes than 20. The moth can still just about fly; it flutters weakly at dusk. The adults do not feed – not unusual for lepidopterans – and devote themselves to finding a mate.

FACT FILE	
Distribution:	Europe
Habitat:	Gardens
Diet:	Larvae eat honeysuckle leaves
Reproduction:	Eggs laid on honeysuckle
Status (IUCN Red List):	Not evaluated

Atlas Moth

Attacus atlas

The mighty Atlas moth is the largest lepidopteran in the world. The larger females can achieve a wingspan of 30cm (12in). The adults do not have working mouth parts and do not feed. The caterpillars weave fluffy cocoons and are used to create an inexpensive alternative to silk.

FACT FILE	
Distribution:	East and southeast Asia
Habitat:	Forests
Diet:	Larvae eat citrus fruits
Reproduction:	Eggs laid under leaves
Status (IUCN Red List):	Not evaluated

Indian Moon Moth

Actias selene

This is one of several moon, or luna, moths found in warm regions of the world. All of them are known for long 'tails' that trail behind the back wing. As their name suggests, moon moths are very much nocturnal creatures, although their bright colours make them stand out as they bask on walls and tree trunks.

FACT FILE	
Distribution:	Southeast Asia
Habitat:	Forests and woodland
Diet:	Leaves
Reproduction:	150 eggs laid
Status (IUCN Red List):	Not evaluated

At first, moon moth caterpillars are red and black. After a couple of moults, they become leaf green. A moon moth caterpillar is covered in feathery spines that break off when the larva is handled, causing irritations on the skin of an attacker. The bright yellow and black tufts also serve as a warning that the insect tastes nasty.

Madagascan Sunset Moth

Chrysiridia riphearia

While the axiom that moths are nocturnal and butterflies are daytime creatures generally holds true, the Madagascan sunset moth is the exception to the rule. The species is found only on the island of Madagascar and, as is typical of a day-active insect, it has very colourful wings. These serve as a warning to predators that the insect is toxic, filled with poisons harvested from the spurge plants it feeds on when a caterpillar.

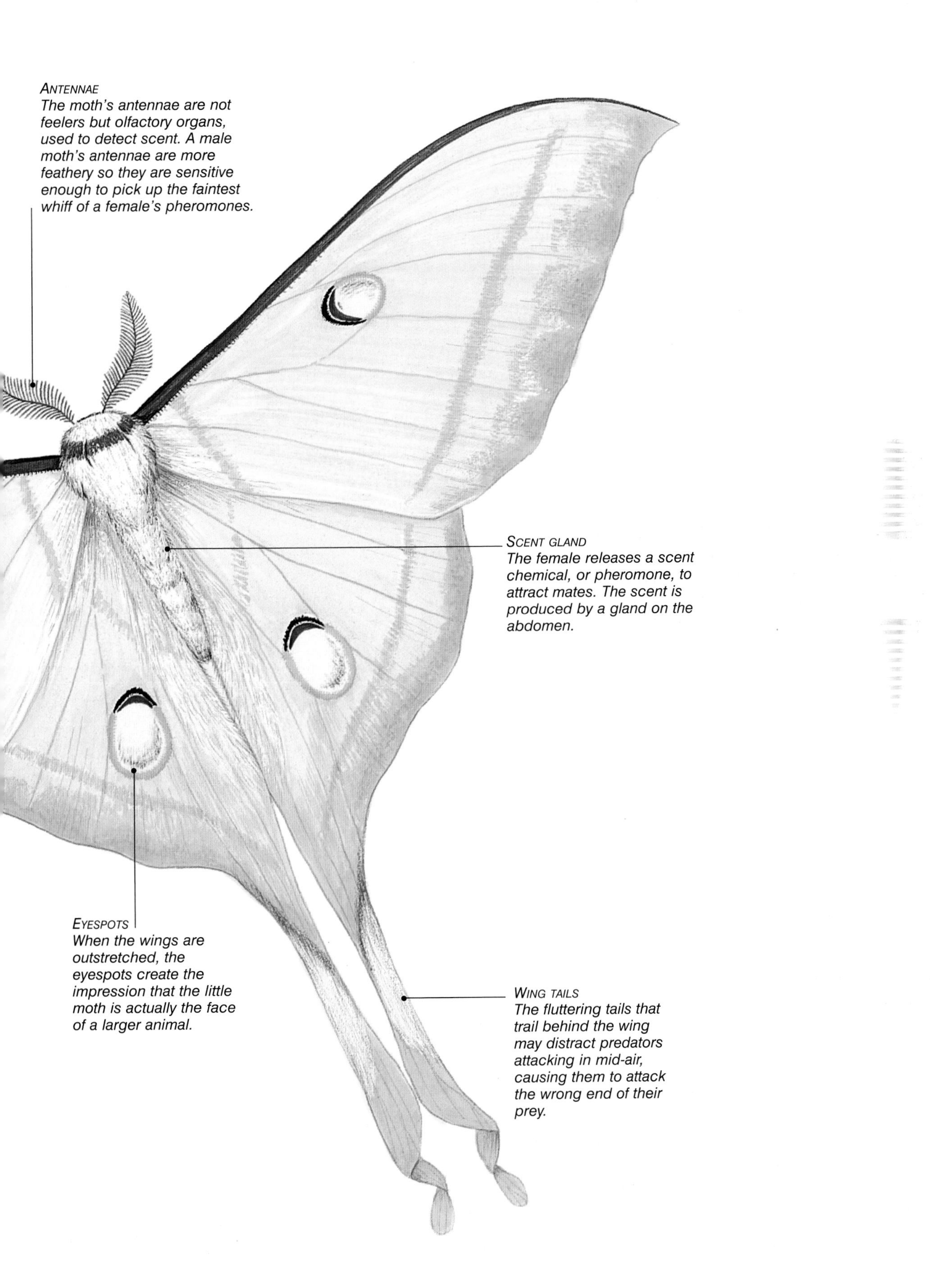
ANTENNAE
The moth's antennae are not feelers but olfactory organs, used to detect scent. A male moth's antennae are more feathery so they are sensitive enough to pick up the faintest whiff of a female's pheromones.
SCENT GLAND
The female releases a scent chemical, or pheromone, to attract mates. The scent is produced by a gland on the abdomen.
EYESPOTS
When the wings are outstretched, the eyespots create the impression that the little moth is actually the face of a larger animal.
WING TAILS
The fluttering tails that trail behind the wing may distract predators attacking in mid-air, causing them to attack the wrong end of their prey.

Wasps, Ants and Bees

The order Hymenoptera is made up of wasps, ants, bees and sawflies. These insects are characterized by a narrow 'waist' between thorax and abdomen, and a pair of small hind wings that are hooked to forewings to make a single flying surface. The order is known for its many social species.

Sawfly

Cimbex femorata

Sawflies look like large metallic wasps and are mistakenly regarded as a danger to people. However, they have no stinger. The stingers of wasps, bees and ants are modified ovipositors. The sawfly uses its serrated ovipositor for its original purpose – to lay eggs.

FACT FILE	
Distribution:	Central Europe to Siberia
Habitat:	Woodland
Diet:	Leaves
Reproduction:	200 eggs implanted in plants
Status (IUCN Red List):	Not evaluated

Hyperparasite Wasp

Torymus bedeguaris

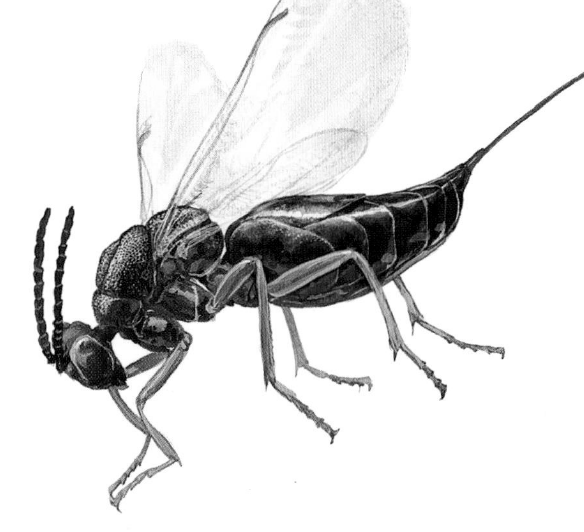

Many tiny wasps are parasitic and lay eggs on or inside the bodies of other insects. The larvae then eat their hosts alive. This wasp is special: it is a parasite of a parasite, laying eggs inside pincushion galls on rose shrubs. These galls are themselves created by the larvae of another wasp, which are in turn eaten by this wasp's young.

FACT FILE	
Distribution:	Europe
Habitat:	Dog rose shrubs
Diet:	Wasp larvae
Reproduction:	Eggs laid in gall wasp eggs
Status (IUCN Red List):	Not evaluated

Leafcutter Ant

Atta sexdens

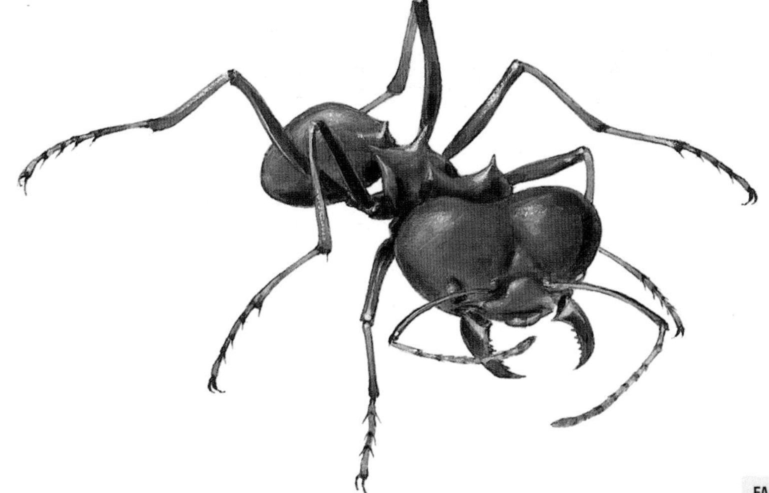

The sight of a column of leafcutter ants trooping in and out of their nest is one of the wonders of the animal kingdom. The worker ants are often dwarfed by the leaf slabs they have cut from the surrounding trees. The leaves are not the ants' food, but are used as fertilizer for underground fungus gardens.

FACT FILE	
Distribution:	Southern U.S. to northern Argentina
Habitat:	Forests
Diet:	Fungus
Reproduction:	Colonies have millions of workers
Status (IUCN Red List):	Not evaluated

Yellowjacket

Paravespula vulgaris

This species is the main social wasp in North America, outside of which these insects and others very like them are simply called 'wasps'. The yellowjacket lives in a nest made from papery wood pulp. The workers help their mother, the queen wasp, to feed and clean their larval sisters.

FACT FILE	
Distribution:	North America
Habitat:	Woodland and fields
Diet:	Meat and fruits
Reproduction:	Colonies reach 8000 workers
Status (IUCN Red List):	Not evaluated

Giant Honeybee

Apis dorsata

Honeybees collect nectar from flowers and store it in the hive's cells. The bees then fan the nectar to drive away the water – the result is the sticky, sugary goo called honey, which is the colony's main food. Giant honeybees are the largest honey-producing species, growing to 2.5cm (1in) long.

FACT FILE	
Distribution:	Himalayas
Habitat:	Trees on cliffs
Diet:	Meat, fruits and pollen
Reproduction:	Colonies reach 5000 workers
Status (IUCN Red List):	Not evaluated

Other Insects

There are dozens of insect orders, containing at least a million species. They are divided roughly in half into the exopterygotes, which hatch out as wingless nymphs that look like tiny adults, and the endopterygotes, which develop as larvae that look completely different from the adults, and survive in a very different way, too.

Emperor Dragonfly

Anax imperator

These dragonflies are also known as darners, due to a folk tale claiming that they sew up children's lips during the night. They have exceptionally large eyes, which are comprised of more than 28,000 lenses. They are also accomplished aerial acrobats, and can fly at speeds of up to 40km/h (24.9mph).

FACT FILE	
Distribution:	Europe, Asia and Africa
Habitat:	Freshwater ponds and streams
Diet:	Larvae: insects and tadpoles; adults: insects
Reproduction:	Lays eggs on water plants
Status (IUCN Red List):	Least concern

Linnaeus Leaf Insect

Phyllium siccifolium

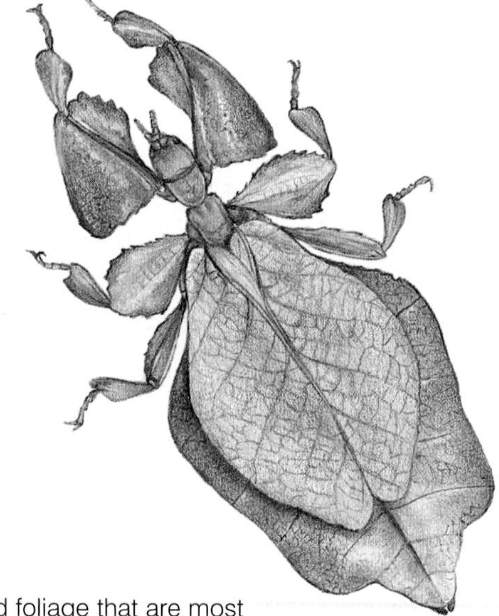

These insects have evolved to look like the leaves and foliage that are most common in their rainforest habitats. Some species also mimic the movements of leaves as they sway in the breeze. This camouflage even extends to the leaf insect's unhatched eggs, which look like small seeds.

FACT FILE	
Distribution:	Southeast Asia
Habitat:	Tropical rainforests
Diet:	Green leaves
Reproduction:	Eggs laid on ground
Status (IUCN Red List):	Not evaluated

Migratory Locust

Locusta migratoria

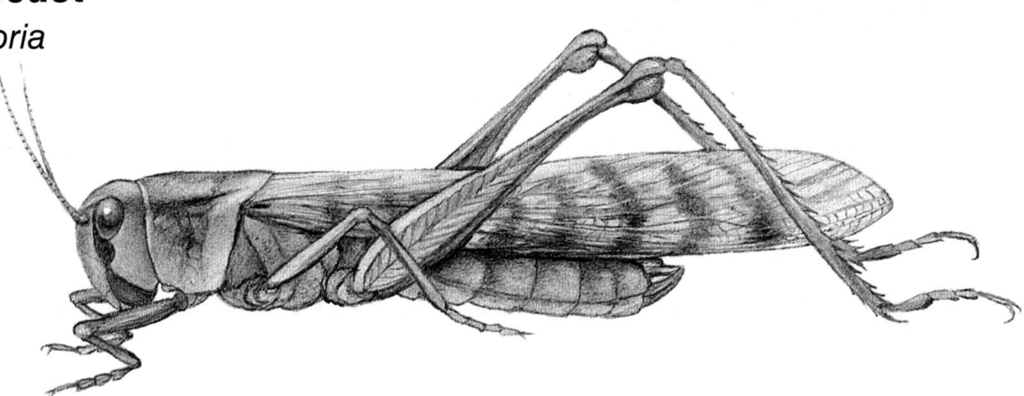

FACT FILE	
Distribution:	North Africa, Arabia and Asia
Habitat:	Grassland
Diet:	Any vegetation
Reproduction:	Eggs laid in soil
Status (IUCN Red List):	Not evaluated

Locusts are a type of migratory grasshopper. In crowded conditions, the insects develop into a swarming form, which can contain 150 billion insects, and can eat 100,000 tonnes (90,720 tons) of food a day. In the Bible, desert locusts were one of the ten plagues sent by God to punish the Egyptians.

Oriental Rat Flea

Xenopsylla cheopis

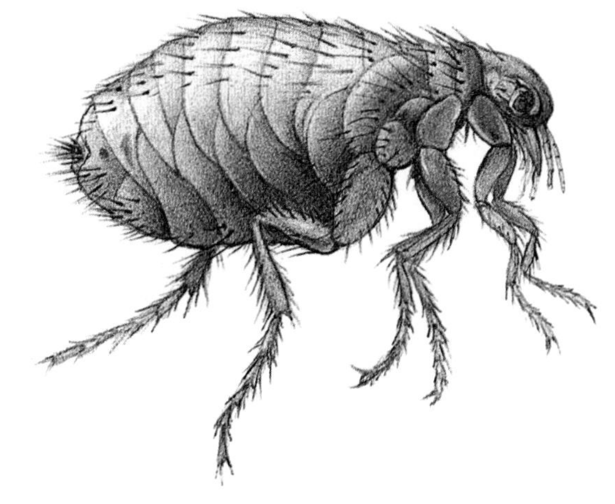

FACT FILE	
Distribution:	Tropical and subtropical regions
Habitat:	On rats
Diet:	Fresh blood
Reproduction:	Eggs laid in host burrows
Status (IUCN Red List):	Not evaluated

This insect is one of the biggest killers in history. It spread the Black Death, or bubonic plague, which killed one-third of Europe's population in the fourteenth century. The fleas picked up the disease from the blood of rats. It drove them wild with hunger, forcing them to bite humans and pass the disease to them.

Antlion

Palpares libelluloides

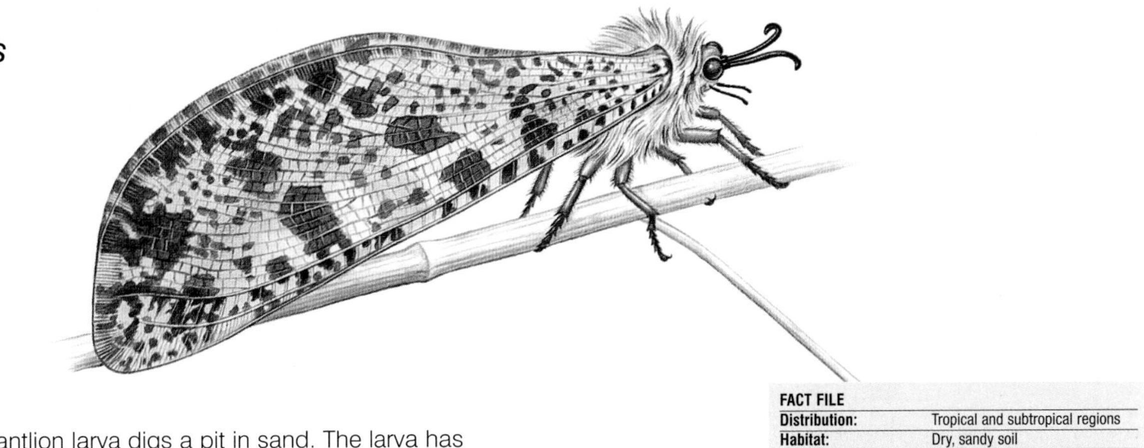

FACT FILE	
Distribution:	Tropical and subtropical regions
Habitat:	Dry, sandy soil
Diet:	Larvae: insects; adults: no food
Reproduction:	Eggs laid in soil
Status (IUCN Red List):	Not evaluated

Soon after hatching, the stout antlion larva digs a pit in sand. The larva has spiked legs, which hold it in place in the slippery trap. Any insects that fall into the pit cannot escape, and are killed by the larva's pincer-like mouth parts. After three years, the larva transforms into a flimsy-looking adult.

Other Arthropods

The Arthropoda is the largest phylum in the animal kingdom. It contains any creature with a hard outer skeleton (exoskeleton) and jointed appendages. The phylum includes insects, arachnids and crustaceans, but there are several smaller subgroups that indicate where the arthropods may have evolved from.

Atlantic Horseshoe Crab

Limulus polyphemus

Despite its name, this is closer to a spider than a true crab, though it does not bear much resemblance to any other living animal. The head and thorax form a single unit encased in a horseshoe shield. Beneath are eight walking legs and four other appendages. Horseshoe crabs are burrowing predators.

FACT FILE	
Distribution:	Western North Atlantic
Habitat:	Shallow sandy offshore seabeds
Diet:	Molluscs and worms
Reproduction:	Spawns on land annually
Status (IUCN Red List):	Near threatened

House Centipede

Scutigera coleoptrata

Despite its name, this centipede does not have 100 legs, just one pair of legs for each section of its body. That makes these predators neither insects nor spiders, but members of the Myriapoda. This species lives in houses worldwide and was originally from the Mediterranean. It is also called the 'moustache bug'.

FACT FILE	
Distribution:	Worldwide
Habitat:	Houses
Diet:	Spiders and insects
Reproduction:	Female guards 100 eggs
Status (IUCN Red List):	Not evaluated

Flat Backed Millipede

Polydesmus complanatus

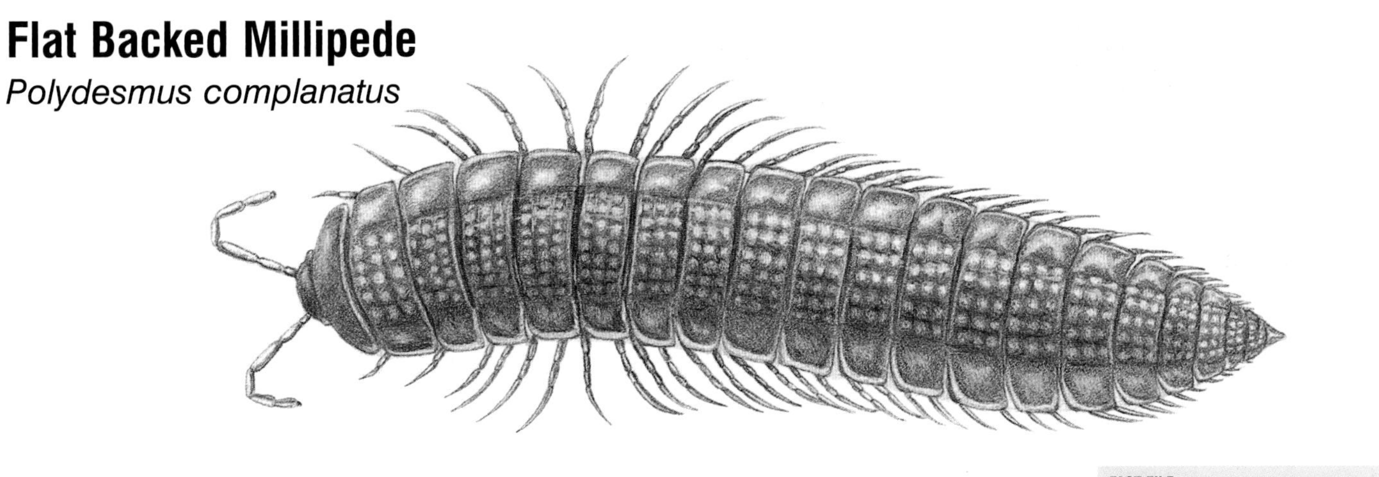

FACT FILE	
Distribution:	Worldwide
Habitat:	Woodland
Diet:	Dead leaves
Reproduction:	Eggs laid in nest
Status (IUCN Red List):	Not evaluated

Millipedes are myriapods, like centipedes. However, they have two pairs of legs attached to each body segment. Most have no more than a few dozen legs, although some have several hundred. Millipedes eat plant food. This species has flattened armour plates to protect it from attack.

Sea Spider

Nymphon gracile

FACT FILE	
Distribution:	Worldwide
Habitat:	Deep ocean seabeds
Diet:	Corals, hydroids, sea anemones
Reproduction:	Male brood fertilized eggs
Status (IUCN Red List):	Not evaluated

Sea spiders live in the sea and are only cousins of land spiders. Most have eight walking legs, though some have more. Most sea spiders live on the ocean floor, feeding on corals, hydroids and anemones by puncturing the outer membrane with a long proboscis and sucking at the internal tissues.

Velvet Worm

Peripatopsis capensis

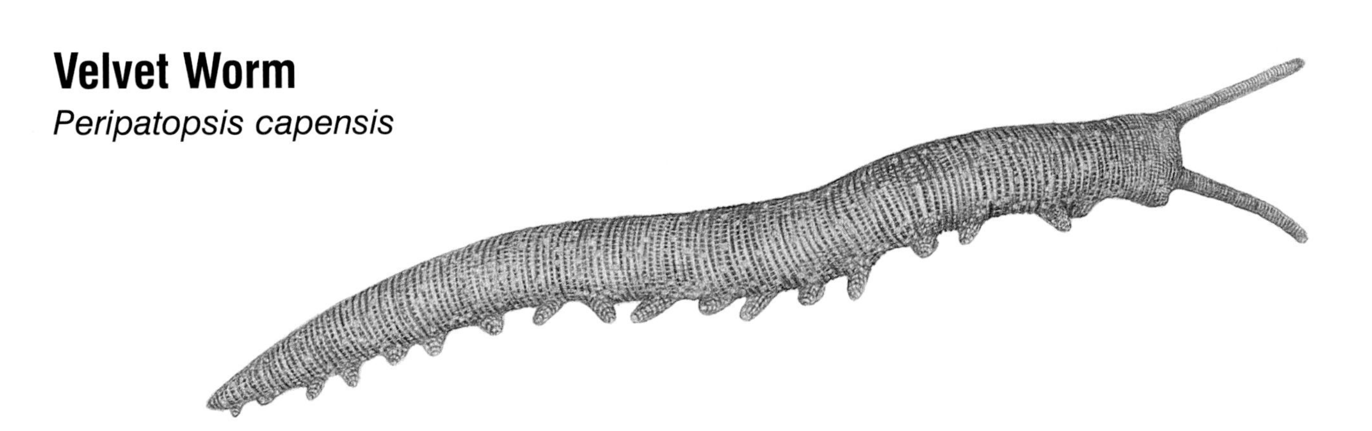

FACT FILE	
Distribution:	South Africa
Habitat:	Humid forest
Diet:	Insects
Reproduction:	40 babies born each year
Status (IUCN Red List):	Not evaluated

Velvet worms are thought to form a link between the worms and the arthropods, since they show features of both. Any common ancestors would probably have been marine creatures. Today, all velvet worms live on land, where they catch prey by squirting them with a glue-like spit that renders them immobile.

Glossary

Abdomen The last section of an animal's body, usually containing the intestines and sex organs.

Algae Microscopic plant-like organisms that live in water or grow in mats on damp surfaces.

Blubber Fatty deposits found under an animal's skin that act as insulation.

Canid A member of the family Canidae, embracing wolves, foxes and dogs.

Canine The long, pointed tooth often located at each corner of the mouth, especially in carnivores.

Carapace The name given to the upper part of the shell of a tortoise, terrapin or turtle.

Carnivore An animal which has a diet largely consisting of meat; a large group of mammals, including cats, bears and otters, are known as the Carnivora.

Carrion Dead animals, whose carcasses may be scavenged rather than being left to decompose.

Cartilage A flexible connective tissue made from proteins that performs a structural role similar to bone.

Caudal fin The tail fin of a fish.

Cetacean A member of the order Cetacea, which covers whales, dolphins and porpoises.

Climate The average weather experienced by a region over the year; the climate remains constant, or changes slowly, while the term weather refers to conditions that can change from day to day, minute to minute.

Colony A community of animals.

Constriction The method used by large snakes to kill prey; they wrap their body around a victim and gradually squeeze. The force does not crush the prey as such, but makes it impossible for it to breathe.

Crepuscular Animal active between the hours of dawn and dusk.

Dorsal fin A fin located on the backs of fish and aquatic mammals, used mainly to control direction.

Echolocation The use of sound-wave emissions to detect objects and shapes, used by certain species of animals including bats and dolphins.

Ecological niche The role in an ecosystem exploited by a particular species.

Evolution A change in the physical characteristics of animals that is believed to happen over time.

Family In the system of animal classification (taxonomy) animals are split into groups based on biological similarities. For every animal there are seven distinct groupings: Kingdom, Phylum, Class, Order, Family, Genus and Species.

Froglet A young frog that has grown legs from its tadpole form but may still retain its tail.

Foetus A baby mammal developing inside its mother.

Folivorous To eat leaves above all other foods.

Genus A biological grouping between species and family, denoting animals with common characteristics. The plural is genera.

Gland A body part that produces active chemicals for use inside or out of the body.

Habitat The natural home environment of an animal or plant.

Harem A group of females controlled by a single male, which mates with then exclusively and drives other males away.

Herbivore A plant-eating animal.

Hermaphrodite An animal that is both male and female during its lifetime. It may have male and female sex organs at the same time, or develop from one sex to the other as it gets older.

Insectivore An animal that feeds on invertebrates.

Invertebrate An animal without a backbone.

Keratin A fibrous protein material occurring in the formation of structures such as hair, nails, horns, hooves, feathers and claws.

Larva A young insect that looks very different to its adult form and lives in a very different way; for example, a caterpillar is the larva of a butterfly. Not all insects have a larva stage, some start out as nymphs instead.

Mammal A warm-blooded animal with a hair-covered body that feeds its young on milk.

Mandible The upper or lower jaw of a vertebrate animal.

Marsupial A subgroup of mammals, where the young are born after a few week development and they complete their growth inside a marsupium – a pouch, generally on the mother's underside. Opossums, kangaroos and wombats are marsupials.

Monogamous When an animal breeds exclusively with one mate only; monogamous pairs often stay together for life and work as a team to raise offspring.

Monotreme A rare type of mammal that lays eggs; echidnas and platypuses are monotremes.

Mucus Slimy liquid produced by animals to protect and waterproof their skin and internal surfaces.

Nocturnal Active at night, under cover of darkness.

Noxious So unpleasant that it forces an animal to flee.

Nymph A young form of an insect that looks and lives like the adult form, although a nymph is always wingless. Cicadas and other bugs develop as nymphs.

Omnivore An animal that eats both meat and plant material.

Order A biological classification of animals between class and family.

Parasite An animal that obtains food or other such benefits by living off the body of another animal.

Passerine A bird with feet adapted to perching on twigs and branches. Most birds are passerines, which includes finches, tits, and sparrows.

Pectoral fin One of the first pair of fins on a fish.

Pelvic fin One of the back pair of fins on a fish.

Pharynx The upper portion of the throat above; in lunged animals it is the location where the windpipe and oesophagus join into a single tube.

Phylum The largest classification group of animals; familiar phylum's include chordates (vertebrates), molluscs, arthropods and annelids (worms).

Plankton Generally small organisms, plants, animals and fungi, that float in water, drifting with the currents.

Plumage The colours of a bird's feathers.

Predator A hunting animal that tracks down and kills its food.

Prehensile Grasping and hand-like; several animals have prehensile tails and tentacles that can wrap around objects.

Primate A general term for any species within the order Primates, which includes lemurs, monkeys, apes and ourselves.

Raptor A hunting bird with grasping claws or talons in their feet; raptors include eagles, harriers and vultures.

Rhinarium A cleft that connects a mammal's lips to its nostrils. The cleft is moist and helps to combine the senses of smell and taste. Animals that lack a rhinaria tend to have poor senses of smell.

Rodent The most abundant and diverse group of mammals, which include rats, squirrels and guinea pigs. Typically rodents have long front teeth used for gnawing a wide range of foods.

Saliva The liquid produced in the mouth, which moistens food making it easier to swallow and beginning the digestion process.

Scute A bony plate covered in skin

Species A group of animals that can breed with other members – but not with those outside the group.

Spinal cord The cable of nerves that runs down a vertebrate's back connecting the brain to the rest of the body.

Squamate A member of a large group of reptiles that includes the lizards and snakes. Non-squamate reptiles include turtles and crocodiles.

Solitary A species which lives alone, only coming together with its own kind for mating.

Territorial In the animal kingdom, groups or individuals will often fight to defend their territory from intruders.

Thorax In insects, the second body region, between the head and thorax. It is the area where the legs and wings are attached.

Troop A name often given to a group of primates.

Tundra The treeless frozen habitat that surrounds the Arctic. There is very little tundra in the Antarctic region because there are no land masses. Tundra-like habitats also exist on high mountains.

Ultrasound Sound that is too high-pitched for humans to hear.

Ungulate An animal that walks on hooves. A hoof is effectively a thickened toenail or claw which allows the animal to stand on its tiptoes and fingertips. That extends the leg to its maximum length and allow the animal to run faster.

Venom A poisonous liquid that is pumped or injected into prey during a bite or sting.

Vertebra The bone units that make up a vertebrate's backbone or spine.

Vertebrate An animal with a backbone.

Warm-blooded Animals that produce their body heat through metabolic processes and maintain a core temperature within a constant, narrow range. All mammals are warm-blooded.

Wattle A fleshy growth hanging from the head or neck

Weaning The stage at which a young mammal no longer depends on its parents to suckle it, or, more generally, when a young animal is able to live independently.

Web A fine structure spun from silk by spiders, and used primarily as a means of catching prey such as flies.

Animals Index

Aardvark 17
Acanthaster planci 404
Acanthurus achilles 381
Acanthurus sohai 381
Acherontia atropos 428
Achilles Tang 381
Acinonyx jubatus 30
Acipenser sturio 330–1
Acrocinus longimanus 421
Actias selene 430–1
Aechmophorus occidentalis 170
Aegypius monachus 201
Aeoliscus strigatus 360
Aetobatus narinari 329
African Buffalo 85
African Bullfrog 312
African Bushpig 65
African Devil Flower Mantis 417
African Dwarf Dormouse 115
African Elephant 18–19
African Fish Eagle 193
African Grey Parrot 222
African Wild Ass 103
African Wild Dog 37
Afropavo congensis 209
Agalychnis callidrias 316
Agapornis fischeri 223
Ailuropoda melanoleuca 44–5
Ailurus fulgens 46
Alaska Rabbit 128
Alcedo atthis 242
Alcelaphus buselaphus 76
Alexandrine Parakeet 222
Alligator sinensis 288
Alouatta caraya 144
Alouatta palliata 144
Alouatta seniculus 145
Alpine Marmot 106
Alpine Swift 239
Alucita hexadactyla 429
Amazona aestive 225
Amblonyx cinereus 48
Amblysomus hottentotus 20
American Badger 51
American Bison 85
American Black Bear 42
American Black Swift 238
American Black Vulture 200
American Bullfrog 312
American Crocodile 289
American Flag Fish 358
American Flamingo 180–1
American Red Squirrel 109
American Robin 259
Amia calva 333
Amitermes meridionalis 417
Ammotragus lervia 94
Amphiprion melanopus 375
Amphiprion ocellaris 374
Anableps anableps 359
Anarhichas lupus 376
Anas platyrhynchos 174–5
Anax imperator 434
Andean Condor 200
Androctonus australis 408–9
Anglerfish 356
Anglo-Nubian Goat 97
Angora Rabbit 129
Anhinga melanogaster 173
Anser tabalis 179
Antarctic Krill 415
Anthochaera paradoxa 264
Antilope cervicapra 80
Antlion 435
Aotus trivirgatus 139
Apis dorsata 433
Apodemus sylvaticus 111
Apteryx owenii 166
Aquila chrysaetos 194
Ara ararauna 225
Ara macao 224
Ara militaris 224
Arabian Tahr 90
Araneus diadematus 406
Archilochus colubris 241
Architeuthis dux 401
Arctic Lemming 111
Ardea cocoi 182
Ardeoia ralloides 183
Argali 95
Argyrodes gibbosus 407
Argyropelecus olfersi 348
Arion hortensis 397
Armadillidium vulgare 414
Asian Elephant 16
Asian Fairy Bluebird 249
Asian House Shrew 23
Asio otus 235
Asterias rubens 404
Ateles geoffroyi 145
Athene noctus 235
Atlantic Halibut 387
Atlantic Horseshoe Crab 436
Atlantic Puffin 218–19
Atlantic Salmon 350
Atlantic Tarpon 334
Atlantic Thorny Oyster 398
Atlas Moth 429
Atta sexdens 433
Attacus atlas 429
Aulacocephalus temminckii 366
Australian Bittern 185
Australian Lace-lid 316
Avahi laniger 135

Baboon Spider 406
Balaena mysticetus 58
Balaenoptera musculus 58
Balaenoptera physalus 59
Bald Eagle 192
Bald Uakari 141
Balistoides conspicillum 382
Baltimore Oriole 266
Banded Water Snake 303
Banded Whiptail 349
Banjo Catfish 344
Barbary Macaque 151
Barbary Sheep 94
Barn Owl 234
Barn Swallow 250
Barred Warbler 258
Basking Shark 325
Bassaricyon gabbii 46
Bassariscus sumichrasti 47
Bat-eared Fox 40
Bataleur 195
Bean Goose 179
Beauty Rat Snake 302
Beaver 104–5
Beluga Whale 61
Berber Skink 296
Betta splendens 365
Bicoloured Shrew 23
Bielzia coerulans 397
Bighorn Sheep 94
Birgus latro 413
Bishari Camel 72
Bison bison 85
Blaberus giganteus 416
Black-backed Jackal 36
Black Caiman 288
Black-crested Bulbul 249
Black-faced Sheathbill 213
Black-handed Spider Monkey 145
Black-headed Uakari 140
Black Howler Monkey 144
Black Kite 191
Black Mamba 304
Black Rat 112–13
Black Rhinoceros 98–9
Black Skimmer 217
Black-tailed Jackrabbit 126
Black Widow 407
Black Woodpecker 247
Blackbuck 80
Blatella germanica 416
Blood Python 301
Bloodhound 39
Blue-and-yellow Macaw 225
Blue-fronted Amazon 225
Blue Monkey 158
Blue Mussel 399
Blue Poison Dart Frog 319
Blue Shark 325
Blue-webbed Gliding Tree Frog 317
Blue Whale 58
Bluethroat 256
Boat-billed Heron 183
Bobolink 267
Bolinus brandarius 395
Bongo 82
Bontebok 76
Bos gaurus 86
Bos mutus 84
Bos sauveli 84
Bos taurus 86, 87
Botaurus pinnatus 185
Botaurus poiciloptilus 185
Bottlenose Dolphin 60
Bowfin 333
Bowhead Whale 58
Brachyteles arachnoides 145
Bradypodion thamnobates 291
Bradypus tridactylus 14
Brahminy Kite 190
Brambling 271
Branta canadensis 179
Brazilian Porcupine 123
Brazilian Tapir 100
Breviceps macrops 319
Brill 386
Brittle Star 405
Broad-bordered Bee Hawkmoth 428
Bronze Cory 345
Brosme brosme 354
Brown Hare 127
Brown Mouse Lemur 134
Brown-throated Wattle-eye 257
Brown Trout 350
Bubalus quarlesi 85
Buceros bicornis 243
Budgerigar 230
Budorcas taxicolor 90
Bufo marinus 314–15
Bulldog 38
Bunocephalus coracoideus 344
Bunolagus monticularis 127
Buphagus erythrorhynchus 274–5
Burbot 355
Burton's Snake Lizard 295
Bushy-tailed Olingo 46
Buteo regalis 199
Butorides striatus 183

Cacajao calvus 141
Cacajao hosomi 140
Cacatua moluccensis 228
Cacatua roseicapilla 228
Cacicus uropygialis 266
Cacomistle 47
Cairina moschata 176
Calandrella brachydactyla 248
Calidris canutus 215
Callagur borneoensis 285
Callicebus personatus 140
Callithrix jacchus 138
Calloplesiops altivelis 364
Calocitta formosa 279
Caloenas nicobarica 221
Camelus dromedarius 72, 73
Canada Goose 179
Cancer pagurus 413
Canis lupus 36
Canis lupus familiaris 38, 39

Canis mesomelas 36
Canis simensis 37
Canthigaster coronata 382
Cape Barren Goose 179
Capra aegagrus 96
Capra falconeri 91
Capra hircus 97
Capreolus capreolus 71
Capricornis crispus 91
Capromys pilorides 121
Capuchin Monkey 142–3
Capybara 120
Caranx hippos 364
Carcharodon carcharias 325
Cardinal 263
Cardinal Tetra 341
Cardinalis cardinalis 263
Carduelis carduelis 270
Carduelis flammea 270
Carpathian Blue Slug 397
Cassowary 166
Castor Bean Tick 411
Castor fiber 104–5
Casuarius casuarius 166
Catocala rupta 429
Cavia aperea 120
Cebuella pygmaea 138
Cebus apella 142–3
Centrolene prosoblepon 319
Cepaea hortensis 397
Cephalopholis miniatus 366
Ceratotherium simum 101
Cercopithecus erythrotis 159
Cercopithecus mitis 158
Cercopithecus neglectus 158
Cercopithecus nictitans 159
Cercopithecus pogonias 159
Cereopsis novaehollandiae 179
Cerocebus galeritus 156
Cerocebus torquatus 157
Cetorhinus maximus 325
Chaetophractus villosus 15
Chamaeleo jacksonii 292–3
Chamois 91
Channel-billed Cuckoo 232
Charadrius mongolus 213
Charinus milloti 411
Chauliodus macouni 348
Chauna torquata 178
Cheetah 30
Cheilinus undulatus 377
Chelmon rostratus 370
Chelodina longicollis 284
Chestnut-winged Cuckoo 232
Chimpanzee 162–3
Chinchilla lanigera 122
Chinese Alligator 288
Chinese Egret 185
Chinese High Fin Banded Shark 339
Chinese Paddlefish 332
Chinook Salmon 351
Chionis minor 213
Chlamydosaurus kingii 291
Chlorocebus pygerythrus 157
Chloroceryle americana 242
Chondropython viridis 300
Chrysiridia riphearia 430
Chrysocyon brachyurus 41
Ciconia ciconia 186
Cimbex femorata 432
Cinereous Vulture 201
Cinnamon Clownfish 375
Circaetus gallicus 195
Circus cyaneus 198
Cissa chinensis 278
Clamator coromandus 232
Cleaner Wrasse 378–9
Click Beetle 420
Clown Coris 376
Clown Tree Frog 317
Clown Triggerfish 382
Clypeaster humilis 405
Coccinella septempunctata 421
Coccothraustes coccothraustes 271
Cochlearius cochlearius 183
Cockatiel 229
Cocoi Heron 182
Coelacanth 332
Coelorhynchus fasciatus 349
Coendou prehensilis 123
Colburn's Tuco-tuco 123
Cold Water Coral 392
Collared Mangabey 157
Collared Peccary 65
Colobus guereza 147
Columba livia 220, 221
Columba palumbus 220
Comb-billed Duck 177
Comet 364
Common Carp 336–7
Common Crossbill 271
Common Earwig 417
Common Egg Cowrie 395
Common Eider 177
Common Kingfisher 242
Common Limpet 394
Common Lobster 413
Common Marmoset 138
Common Octopus 402–3
Common Prawn 412
Common Raven 280–1
Common Redpoll 270
Common Sand Frog 313
Common Sawfish 329
Common Snakeneck Turtle 284
Common Spiny Bandicoot 11
Common Spiny Lobster 412
Common Squirrel Monkey 139
Common Starfish 404
Common Stingray 328
Common Tern 217
Common Vampire Bat 28
Common Waxbill 272
Common Wood Pigeon 220
Common Yellowthroat 248
Condylura cristata 20
Conepatus chinga 49
Conger conger 335
Congo Peafowl 209
Copperband Butterflyfish 370
Coragyps atratus 200
Coral Hind 366
Cordylus polyzonus 296
Coris aygula 376
Corvus albicollis 278
Corvus corax 280–1
Corydoras aeneus 345
Corythaeola cristata 233
Cougar 31
Coypu 121
Crax rubra 208
Crested Gibbon 160
Crested Oropendola 267
Crested Serpent Eagle 195
Crested Shelduck 177
Crested Shriketit 253
Crested Tit 252
Crevalle Jack 364
Cricetus cricetus 116
Crimson Chat 265
Crimson Horned Pheasant 209
Crocidura leucodon 23
Crocodylus acutus 289
Crown of Thorns Starfish 404
Crowned Guenon 159
Crowned Hairstreak 427
Crowned Puffer 382
Ctenomys colburni 123
Cuban Boa 300
Cuban Hutia 121
Cuban Solenodon 22
Cuccyzus americanus 233
Cusk 354
Cutthroat Trout 351
Cuttlefish 400
Cyanocorax yncas 279
Cyclopterus lumpus 360
Cygnus cygnus 178
Cylindrophis rufus 301
Cyprinus carpio 336–7
Cystophora cristata 56

Daboia russelii 305
Dacelo novaeguineae 244–5
Dactylopsila trivirgata 11
Dama Gazelle 81
Damaliscus pygargus 76
Dartford Warbler 258
Dascyllus melanurus 374
Dascyllus trimaculatus 375
Dasyatis pastinaca 328
Dasyurus hallucatus 10
De Brazza's Monkey 158
Death's-head Hawkmoth 428
Deep-sea Hatchetfish 348
Delichon nipalensis 251
Delphinapterus leucas 61
Dendrelaphis pictus 303
Dendroaspis polylepis 304
Dendrobates azureus 319
Dendrocopos major 246
Dendrohyrax dorsalis 16
Dermochelys coriacea 286–7
Desert Kangaroo Rat 114
Desert Rain Frog 319
Desert Warthog 64
Desmodus rotundus 28
Dewdrop Spider 407
Dicerorhinus sumatrensis 101
Diceros bicornis 98–9
Dicrostonyx torquatus 111
Didunculus strigirostris 221
Diodon holacanthus 383
Diomedea epomophora 172
Diopsis tenuipes 424
Dipodomys deserti 114
Discus 373
Distichodus sexfasciatus 340
Dolichonyx oryzivorus 267
Dolichotis patagonum 121
Dolomedes fimbriatus 407
Domestic Pigeon 221
Domino Damsel 375
Dorking Chicken 207
Dreissensa polymorpha 399
Drill 153
Dromaius novaehollandiae 167
Dromedary 72
Dryocopus martius 247
Dugong 17
Dugong dugon 17
Dynastes hercules 421
Dytiscus marginalis 422
Dzungarian Dwarf Hamster 116

Earthworm 390
Eastern Bearded Dragon 291
Eastern Bluebird 259
Eastern Chipmunk 108
Eastern Coral Snake 305
Eastern Meadowlark 267
Eastern Paradise Whydah 273
Eastern Woolly Lemur 135
Echymipera kalubu 11
Ectophylla alba 29
Ecuadorian Hillstar 240
Edible Crab 413
Edible Sea Urchin 405
Edible Snail 396
Egretta eulophotes 185
Egyptian Rousette 27
Electric Catfish 345
Electric Ray 328
Electus Parrot 230–1
Electus roratus 230–1
Elegant Water Shrew 23
Elephantfish 333
Elephas maximus 16
Elf Owl 234
Eliomys quercinus 115
Emberiza citrinella 262
Emerald Glass Frog 319
Emerald Green Snail 396
Emperor Angelfish 371
Emperor Dragonfly 434
Emperor Tetra 341
Emu 167
Emydocephalus annulatus 305
English Cocker Spaniel 39
Ensifera ensifera 241
Epicrates angulifer 300
Epinephelus striatus 367
Eptesicus serotinus 29
Epthianura tricolor 265
Equus africanus 103
Equus caballus 102
Equus hemionus kulan 103
Equus kiang 103
Equus quagga 102
Eremochelis bilobatus 411
Erethizon dorsatum 124–5
Erinaceus europaeus 22
Erythrura gouldiae 273
Esox lucius 352–3

Estrilda astrild 272
Ethiopian Wolf 37
Eubalaena glacialis 59
Eublepharis macularius 294
Euchoreutes naso 114
Eudyptes chrysocome 168–9
Eumeces schneideri 296
Eumetopias jubatus 56
Eumyias thalassina 257
Euoticus elegantulus 130
Euphausia superba 415
Eurasian Hobby 205
Eurasian Woodcock 214
European Badger 50
European Conger 335
European Garden Spider 406
European Goldfinch 270
European Ground Squirrel 106
European Hake 354
European Hamster 116
European Hedgehog 22
European Mole 21
European Otter 48
European Peacock 427
European polecat 53
European Rabbit 128
European Squid 401
European Sturgeon 330–1
Eurostopodus argus 236
Eutoxeres aquila 240
Exotic Shorthair Cat 35

Falco rusticolus 205
Falco subbuteo 205
Falco tinnunculus 205
Falcunculus frontatus 253
False Clownfish 374
False Gharial 289
Fat-tailed Scorpion 408–9
Felis catus 34, 35
Felis silvestris 34
Ferret 53
Ferruginous Hawk 199
Ficedula hypoleuca 254–5
Fin Whale 59
Firebug 419
Fischer's Lovebirds 223
Fisher 49
Flat Backed Millipede 437
Flounder 387
Flying Squid 401
Fogstand Beetle 422–3
Forcipiger longirostris 370
Forficula auricularia 417
Four-eyed Fish 359
Four Stripe Damselfish 374
Fratercula arctica 218–19
Freshwater Angelfish 372
Frill-necked Lizard 291
Fringilla montifringilla 271
Fulgora laternaria 419
Fundulopanchax gardneri 358

Gabar Goshawk 198
Galago senegalensis 130
Galah 228
Galapagos Petrel 173
Galeocerdo cuvier 324
Galictis vittata 53
Gallotia galloti 297
Gallus gallus 206, 207
Gambusia affinis 359
Garden Dormouse 115
Garden Slug 397
Gastromyzon sp. 339
Gaur 86
Gazella dama 81
Gazella thomsonii 81
Gelada 153
Geochelone radiata 285
Geococcys californianus 233
Geothlypis trichas 248
German Cockroach 416
Giant Anteater 15
Giant Clam 399
Giant Cockroach 416
Giant Eland 82
Giant Forest Hog 64
Giant Grebe 170
Giant Honeybee 433
Giant Hummingbird 241
Giant Kingfisher 244
Giant Otter 49
Giant Panda 44–5
Giant Squid 401
Giant Water Bug 418
Gila Monster 298–9
Giraffa camelopardalis 74–5
Giraffe 74–5
Glass Catfish 344
Glaucomys volans 108
Glossina palpalis 425
Gloucester Old Spot Pig 66
Golden Eagle 194
Golden Hamster 117
Goldribbon Soapfish 366
Goose Barnacle 415
Gorilla gorilla 161
Gouldian Finch 273
Granite Night Lizard 297
Graphiurus murinus 115
Graptemys oculifera 284
Grass Snake 303
Great Blue Turaco 233
Great Curassow 208
Great Diving Beetle 422
Great Grebe 171
Great Grey Shrike 260–1
Great Hornbill 243
Great Tit 252
Great White Shark 325
Greater Bird of Paradise 277
Greater Black-backed Gull 216
Greater Bulldog Bat 28
Greater Crested Newt 310–11
Greater Grison 53
Greater Kudu 83
Greater Roadrunner 233
Greater Short-toed Lark 248
Greater Spot-nosed Guenon 159
Greater Spotted Woodpecker 246
Green-back Heron 183
Green Bottle Fly 425
Green Iguana 290
Green Jay 279
Green Kingfisher 242
Green Magpie 278
Green Shield Bug 419
Green Tree Python 300
Green Woodpecker 247
Grey-cheeked Mangabey 156
Grey Four-eyed Opossum 14
Grey Fox 41
Grey-headed Fish Eagle 193
Grey-rumped Treeswift 239
Grey Wolf 36
Ground Pangolin 24–5
Guereza 147
Guinea Pig 120
Guppy 359
Gypaetus barbatus 202–3
Gyrfalcon 205

Haddock 355
Haliaeetus albicilla 192
Haliaeetus leucocephalus 192
Haliaeetus vocifer 193
Haliastur indus 190
Halieutaea stellata 357
Hamadryas Baboon 153
Hammerhead Shark 326–7
Hampshire Pig 67
Hanuman Langur 146
Harbour Porpoise 61
Harlequin Beetle 421
Harlequin Rasbora 338
Harlequin Tuskfish 377
Harpia harpyja 194
Harpy Eagle 194
Harris's Hawk 199
Hartebeest 76
Harvestmen 410
Hawfinch 271
Helarctos malayanus 43
Heleophryne rosei 318
Helix pomatia 396
Helmeted Friarbird 265
Helmeted Guineafowl 207
Heloderma suspectum 298–9
Helostoma temmincki 365
Hemaris fuciformis 428
Hemichromis lifalili 373
Hemiprocne longipennis 239
Hemitragus jayakari 90
Hen Harrier 198
Heniochus acuminatus 371
Hercules Beetle 421
Hereford Cattle 87
Herichthys cyanoguttatus 372
Herpetotheres cachinnans 204
Highland Cattle 87
Hillstream Loach 339
Himalayan Blue Sheep 95
Hippocamelus bisulcus 71
Hippocampus ramulosus 361
Hippoglossus hippoglossus 387
Hippopotamus 68–9
Hippopotamus amphibius 68–9
Hippotragus niger 77
Hirudo medicinalis 391
Hirundo rustica 250
Hoatzin 210–11
Holopedium gibberum 415
Holstein 87
Homarus gammarus 413
Honey Badger 51
Honey Buzzard 191
Honey Gourami 365
Hooded Seal 56
Hoopoe 243
Horned Grebe 171
Hottentot Golden Mole 20
House Centipede 436
House Mouse 110
Housefly 425
Hoverfly 424
Huemel 71
Humpback Whale 59
Humphead Wrasse 377
Hydrochaeris hydrochaeris 120
Hydrometra stagnorum 418
Hydrurga leptonyx 57
Hyla leucophyllata 317
Hylobates concolor 160
Hylobates lar 160
Hylobates syndactylus 161
Hylochoerus meinertzhageni 64
Hyperparasite Wasp 432

Iberian Lynx 31
Ichthyophaga ichthyaetus 193
Icterus galbula 266
Idolum diabolicum 417
Iguana iguana 290
Illuminated Netdevil 357
Inachis io 427
Inca Tern 217
Indian Gerbil 117
Indian Giant Squirrel 107
Indian Moon Moth 430–1
Indian Roofed Turtle 285
Indian Verditer Flycatcher 257
Indigo Bunting 263
Indri 135
Indri indri 135
Irene puella 249
Irish Wolfhound 38
Ixobrychus eurhythmus 184
Ixodes ricinus 411

Jackson's Chameleon 292–3
Jacob Sheep 97
Jaguar 31
Japanese Harlequin Rabbit 129
Japanese Macaque 150
Japanese Shrew 91
Java Sparrow 272
Javan Rhinoceros 101
Jerdon's Courser 212
Jordanella floridae 358

Kachuga tecta 285
Kakapo 226–7
Karoo Girdled Lizard 296
Kea 229
Kestrel 205
Kiang 103
Killer Whale 60
Killifish 358
King Cobra 306–7
King Vulture 201
Kingsnake 302

Kissing Gourami 365
Ko Shamo Chicken 207
Koala 11
Kob 77
Kobus kob 77
Kodiak Bear 42
Kouprey 84
Kribensis 373
Kryptopterus bicirrhis 344
Kuhl's Flying Gecko 295
Kulan 103

Lab Rat 111
Labroides phthirophagus 378–9
Lagidium peruanum 122
Lama glama 73
Lammergeier 202–3
Lampropeltis getula 302
Lanius excubitor 260–1
Lantern Bug 419
Lar Gibbon 160
Large Hairy Armadillo 15
Large White Pig 67
Larosterna inca 217
Larus marinus 216
Larus pacificus 216
Latimeria chalumnae 332, 333
Latrodectus mactans 407
Laughing Falcon 204
Laughing Kookaburra 244–5
Lavia frons 27
Leaf-tailed Gecko 294
Leafcutter Ant 433
Leafy Sea Dragon 361
Least Weasel 52
Leatherback Turtle 286–7
Lemur catta 132–3
Leopard Gecko 294
Leopard Seal 57
Lepas anatifera 415
Lepilemur mustelinus 134
Leptoptilos crumeniferus 187
Lepus californicus 126
Lepus europaeus 127
Lesser Rhea 167
Lesser Sand Plover 213
Lethocerus indicus 418
Lialis burtonis 295
Lienardella fasciata 377
Lifalili Jewel Cichlid 373
Limulus polyphemus 436
Linnaeus Leaf Insect 434
Linophryne arborifera 357
Lion 30
Lion-tailed Macaque 151
Lionfish 362–3
Little Owl 235
Little Spotted Kiwi 166
Llama 73
Lobatus gigas 394
Locusta migratoria 435
Loligo vulgaris 401
Lonchothrix emiliae 123
Long-eared Jerboa 114
Long-eared Owl 235
Long-snouted Seahorse 361
Long-tailed Chinchilla 122
Long-tailed Skua 213
Long-tongued Nectar Bat 26
Longnose Butterflyfish 370
Longspined Porcupinefish 383
Lophelia perstusa 392
Lophiomys imhausi 110
Lophius americanus 357
Lophius piscatorius 356
Lophocebus albigena 156
Lophotus capellei 349
Loris tardigradus 131
Lota lota 355
Loxia curvirostra 271
Loxodonta africana 18–19
Lucilia sericata 425
Lumbricus terrestris 390
Lumpsucker 360
Luscinia svecica 256
Lutra lutra 48
Lycaon pictus 37
Lynx pardinus 31

Macaca arctoides 150
Macaca fuscata 150
Macaca mulata 151
Macaca silenus 151
Macaca sylvanus 151
Macroglossus minimus 26
Madagascan Sunset Moth 430
Magnetic Termite 417
Magnificent Riflebird 276
Malapterurus electricus 345
Malayan Tapir 100
Mallard 174–5
Mandarinfish 380
Mandrill 154–5
Mandrillus leucophaeus 153
Mandrillus sphinx 154–5
Maned Rat 110
Maned Wolf 41
Manis gigantea 24–5
Manta birostris 329
Manta Ray 329
Mantis Shrimp 414
Mantled Howler Monkey 144
Mara 121
Marabou Stork 187
Marine Toad 314–15
Markhor 91
Marmota marmota 106
Marsh Frog 313
Martes pennanti 49
Masked Titi 140
Medicinal Leech 391
Mediterranean Monk Seal 57
Mediterranean Moray 334
Megaceryle maxima 244
Megalops atlanticus 334
Megaptera novaeangliae 59
Melanodera melanodera 263
Melanogrammus aeglefinus 355
Melanosuchus niger 288
Meleagris gallopavo 206
Meles meles 50
Mellivora capensis 51
Melopsittacus undulatus 230
Melursus ursinus 43
Menura novaehollandiae 268–9
Merluccius merluccius 354
Mesocricetus auratus 117
Micrathene whitneyi 234
Microcebus rufus 134
Micronisus gabar 198
Micrurus fulvius 305
Midshipman Fish 356
Migratory Locust 435
Mikado Pheasant 208
Military Macaw 224
Milos Wall Lizard 297
Milvago chimachima 204
Milvus migrans 191
Miopithecus talapoin 157
Mirounga leonina 57
Mola mola 383
Molina's Hog-nosed Skunk 49
Monachus monachus 57
Mongolian Gazelle 81
Monk Saki 141
Monkfish 357
Monocled Cobra 304
Monodon monoceros 61
Monticola saxatilis 259
Mormolyce phyloides 420
Morpho rhetenor 427
Mosquitofish 359
Mouflon 96
Mountain Anoa 85
Mountain Goat 92–3
Mudskipper 384–5
Muraena helena 334
Muriqui 145
Mus musculus 110
Musca domestica 425
Muscovy Duck 176
Muskox 88–9
Muskrat 118–19
Mustela erminea 52
Mustela nivalis 52
Mustela putorius 53
Mycteria americana 186
Mycteroperca venenosa 367
Mydaus javanensis 50
Myobatrachus gouldii 318
Myocastor coypus 121
Myrmecobius fasciatus 10
Myrmecophaga tridactyla 15
Mytilus edulis 399
Myxocyprinus asiaticus 339

Naja kaouthia 304
Narwhal 61
Nasalis larvatus 148–9
Nassau Grouper 367
Natal Midlands Dwarf Chameleon 291
Natrix natrix 303
Nautilus 400
Nautilus pompilius 400
Nectogale elegans 23
Needle-clawed Galago 130
Nematobrycon palmeri 341
Nepal House Martin 251
Nephoecetes niger 238
Nerodia fasciata 303
Nesolagus netscheri 127
Nestor notabilis 229
Nicobar Pigeon 221
Noble Pen Shell 398
Noctilio leporinus 28
North American Porcupine 124–5
North Atlantic Right Whale 59
Northern Bushbaby 130
Northern Owl Monkey 139
Northern Quoll 10
Northern Viscacha 122
Notoryctes typhlops 21
Numbat 10
Numida meleagris 207
Nyala 83
Nyctereutes procyonoides 40
Nycticebus coucang 131
Nyctidromus albicollis 237
Nyctimene robinsoni 26
Nyctimystes dayi 316
Nyctinomops femorosaccus 29
Nymphicus hollandicus 229
Nymphon gracile 437

Oarfish 349
Oceanic Sunfish 383
Ochotona roylei 126
Octopus vulgaris 402–3
Odobenus rosmarus 54–5
Odocoileus virginianus 71
Oilbird 237
Olive Baboon 152
Ommastrephes sagittatus 401
Oncorhynchus clarkii 351
Oncorhynchus mykiss 351
Oncorhynchus tshawytscha 351
Ondatra zibethicus 118–19
Onymacris unguicularis 422–3
Ophiocomina nigra 405
Ophiophagus hannah 306–7
Opisthocomus hoazin 210–11
Opistognathus aurifrons 380
Orcinus orca 60
Oreamnos americanus 92–3
Oreotrochilus chimborazo 240
Oribi 80
Oriental Darter 173
Oriental Rat Flea 435
Oriental Small-clawed Otter 48
Orthriophis taeniurus 302
Orycteropus afer 17
Oryctolagus cuniculus 128, 129
Osprey 188–9
Ostrich 167
Otocyon megalotis 40
Ourebia ourebi 80
Ovibos moschatus 88–9
Ovis ammon 95
Ovis aries 97
Ovis canadensis 94
Ovis dalli 95
Ovis orientalis musimon 96
Ovula ovum 395
Oxyura leucecephala 176

Pacific Gull 216
Pacific Viperfish 348
Padda oryzivora 272
Painted Bronzeback 303
Painted Terrapin 285
Palaemon serratus 412

Pale-throated Sloth 14
Palinurus vulgaris 412
Palomena prasina 419
Palpares libelluloides 435
Pan troglodytes 162–3
Panaque nigrolineatus 381
Pandion haliaetus 188–9
Panthera leo 30
Panthera onca 31
Panthera tigris 32–3
Papilio machaon 426
Papio anubis 152
Papio cynocephalus 152
Papio hamadryas 153
Papustyla pulcherrima 396
Parabuteo unicinctus 199
Paracentrotus lividus 405
Paracheirodon axelrodi 341
Paradisaea apoda 277
Paravespula vulgaris 433
Parotia sefilata 276
Parus cristatus 252
Parus major 252
Parus spilonotus 253
Passerina cyanea 263
Patagonia gigas 241
Patella vulgata 394
Pauraque 237
Pecari tajacu 65
Pedetes capensis 107
Pelvicachromis pulcher 373
Pennant Coralfish 371
Pericrocotus flammeus 260
Periopthtalmus koelreuteri 384–5
Peripatopsis capensis 437
Pernis apivorus 191
Perodicticus potto 131
Pesques's Parrot 229
Phacochoerus aethiopicus 64
Phalacrocorax aristotelis 173
Phalangium opilio 410
Phascolarctos cinereus 11
Philander opossum 14
Philemon buceroides 265
Philippine Warty Pig 65
Philomachus pugnax 215
Phocoena phocoena 61
Phodopus sungorus 116
Phoenicopterus ruber 180–1
Phrynosoma douglassi 290
Phycoduras eques 361
Phyllidia ocellata 395
Phyllium siccifolium 434
Phyllurus cornutus 294
Physalia physalis 392–3
Physeter catodon 62–3
Pickerel Frog 313
Picus viridis 247
Pied Bushchat 256
Pied Flycatcher 254–5
Pike 352–3
Pill Woodlouse 414
Pinna nobilis 398
Pipa pipa 320–1
Piranga olivacea 262
Pithecia monachus 141
Pithecia pithecia 141
Plains Zebra 102
Platalea ajaja 187
Platichthys flesus 387
Platydoras costatus 345
Platysteira cyanea 257
Plum-headed Parakeet 223
Pocketed Free-tailed Bat 29
Podarcis milensis 297
Podargus strigoides 236
Podiceps auritus 171
Podiceps major 171
Podilymbus gigas 170
Poecilia reticulata 359
Pogona barbata 291
Polydesmus complanatus 437
Pomacanthus imperator 371
Pomacentrus sulfureus 375
Porichthys notatus 356
Portuguese Man o' War 392–3
Potamochoerus porcus 65
Potto 131
Prionace glauca 325
Pristis pristis 329
Proboscis Monkey 148–9
Procapra gutturosa 81
Procolobus badius 147
Procyon lotor 47
Prosthemadera novaeseelandiae 264
Przewalskium albirostris 70
Psarocolius decumanus 267
Psephurus gladius 332
Pseudoceros ferrugineus 390
Pseudochelidon sirintarae 250
Pseudois nayaur 95
Pseudoryx nghetinhensis 83
Psittacula cyanocephala 223
Psittacula eupatria 222
Psittacula krameri 223
Psittacus erithacus 222
Psittrichas fulgidus 229
Pterinochilus murinus 406
Pterocnemia pennata 167
Pterodroma phaeopygia 173
Pterois radiata 362–3
Pteronura brasiliensis 49
Pterophyllum scalare 372
Pterosynchiropus splendidus 380
Ptiloris magnificus 276
Ptychozoon kuhli 295
Puma concolor 31
Purple Dye Murex 395
Pycnonotus melanicterus 249
Pygathrix nemaeus 147
Pygmy Marmoset 138
Pygocentrus nattereri 342–3
Pygoplites diacanthus 371
Pyrrhocoris apterus 419
Python curtus 301
Python regius 301
Pyxicephalus adspersus 312

Queen Conch 394
Queen Parrotfish 368–9
Queensland Tube-nosed Bat 26

Raccoon 47
Raccoon Dog 40
Radiated Tortoise 285
Raft Spider 407
Rainbow Trout 351
Rajah Brook's Birdwing 426
Ramphastos toco 246
Rana catesbeiana 312
Rana palustris 313
Rana ridibunda 313
Raniceps raninus 355
Raphael Catfish 345
Rasbora heteromorpha 338
Rashaida Camel 73
Rattus novegicus 111
Rattus rattus 112–13
Ratufa indica 107
Razorfish 360
Red-bellied Piranha 342–3
Red-billed Blue Magpie 279
Red-billed Oxpecker 274–5
Red-eared Guenon 159
Red-eyed Tree Frog 316
Red Fox 41
Red-handed Tamarin 139
Red Howler Monkey 145
Red Junglefowl 206
Red Knot 215
Red Panda 46
Red Ruffed Lemur 135
Red-shanked Douc Monkey 147
Red Squirrel 107
Red-tailed Pipe Snake 301
Red Underwing Moth 429
Redeye Piranha 340
Redunca redunca 77
Reedbuck 77
Reef Stonefish 361
Reeve's Pheasant 209
Regalecus glesne 349
Rhacophorus reinwardtii 317
Rhaphidura sabini 238
Rhesus Macaque 151
Rhetenor Blue Morpho 427
Rhincodon typus 324
Rhinelander 129
Rhinoceros sondaicus 101
Rhinopithecus avunculus 146
Rhinoptilus bitoquatus 212
Rhynchopsitta pachyrhyncha 225
Ring-tailed Lemur 132–3
Ringed Sawback 284
Riverine Rabbit 127
Robber Crab 413
Rock Pigeon 220
Roe Deer 71
Rose-ringed Parakeet 223
Roseate Spoonbill 187
Rostrhamus sociabilis 190
Rousettus aegyptiacus 27
Royal Albatross 172
Royal Angelfish 371
Royal Pleco 381
Royal Python 301
Royle's Pika 126
Ruby-throated Hummingbird 241
Ruff 215
Rufous-tailed Rock-thrush 259
Rupicapra rupicapra 91
Rusa alfredi 70
Russell's Viper 305
Russian Blue Cat 34
Rynchops niger 217

Sabine's Spinetail 238
Sable Antelope 77
Saccopharynx ampulaceus 335
Sacred Ibis 187
Sagittarius serpentarius 196–7
Saguinus midas 139
Saiga 78–9
Saiga tatarica 78–9
Saimiri sciureus 139
Salmo salar 350
Salmo trutta fario 350
Salmon-crested Cockatoo 228
Sand Dollar 405
Saola 83
Sarcoramphus papa 201
Sarkidiornis melanotos 177
Sawfly 432
Saxicola caprata 256
Scarlet Macaw 224
Scarlet Minivet 260
Scarlet-rumped Cacique 266
Scarlet Tanager 262
Scarus vetula 368–9
Sciurus vulgaris 107
Scolopax rusticola 214
Scophthalmus maximus 386
Scophthalmus rhombus 386
Scutigera coleoptrata 436
Scythrops novaehollandiae 232
Sea Slug 395
Sea Spider 437
Secretary Bird 196–7
Seleucidis melanoleuca 277
Semioptera wallacii 277
Semiotus distinctus 420
Semnopithecus hector 146
Sepia officinalis 400
Serassalmus rhombeus 340
Serotine Bat 29
Serrivomer beani 335
Seven-spot Ladybird 421
Shag 173
Short-beaked Echidna 12–13
Short-horned Lizard 290
Short-toed Eagle 195
Sialia sialis 259
Siamang 161
Siamese Cat 35
Siamese Fighting Fish 365
Silurus glanis 346–7
Sixbar Distichodus 340
Slender Loris 131
Sloth Bear 43
Slow Loris 131
Sludge Worm 391
Snail Kite 190
Snipe Eel 335
Sohal Surgeonfish 381
Solenodon cubanus 22
Somateria mollissima 177
South American Bittern 185
Southern Elephant Seal 57
Southern Flying Squirrel 108
Southern Lapwing 212

Southern Marsupial Mole 21
Southern Rockhopper Penguin 168–9
Southern Screamer 178
Southern Three-banded Armadillo 15
Spectacled Bear 43
Sperm Whale 62–3
Spermophilus citellus 106
Spermophilus tridecemlineatus 109
Sphynx 35
Sphyrna mokarran 326–7
Spilornis cheela 195
Spiny anteater 12–13
Spondylus americanus 398
Spotted Eagle Ray 329
Spotted-eared Nightjar 236
Spotted Redshank 214
Springhare 107
Squaacco Heron 183
Squilla empusa 414
Stalk-eyed Fly 424
Star-nosed Mole 20
Starry Handfish 357
Steatornis caripensis 237
Steller Sea Lion 56
Stercorarius longicaudus 213
Sterna hirundo 217
Stoat 52
Strigops habroptilus 226–7
Striped Possum 11
Struthio camelus 167
Stump-tailed Macaque 150
Sturnella magna 267
Sulphur Damsel 375
Sumatran Rhinoceros 101
Sumatran Short-eared Rabbit 127
Sun Bear 43
Suncus murinus 23
Superb Lyrebird 268–9
Suriname Toad 320–1
Sus philippensis 65
Sus scrofa 66
Sus scrofa domesticus 66, 67
Swallower 335
Swallowtail 426
Sword-billed Hummingbird 241
Sylvia nisoria 258
Sylvia undata 258
Symphysodon aequifasciatus 373
Synanceia verrucosa 361
Syncerus caffer 85
Syrigma sibilatrix 182
Syrmaticus mikado 208
Syrmaticus reevesii 209
Syrphus ribesii 424

Table Mountain Ghost Frog 318
Tachycineta albiventer 251
Tachyglossus aculeatus 12–13
Tachymarptis melba 239
Tadorna cristata 177
Tadpole Cod 355
Taeniopygia guttata 273
Takin 90
Talapoin 157
Talpa europaea 21
Tamias striatus 108
Tamiasciurus hudsonicus 109
Tana River Mangabey 156
Tapirus indicus 100
Tapirus terrestris 100
Tarsier 136–7
Tarsius bancanus 136–7
Tatera indica 117
Tawny Frogmouth 236
Taxidea taxus 51
Teledu 50
Tench 338
Tenerife Lizard 297
Terathopius ecaudatus 195
Texas Cichlid 372
Texas Longhorn 86
Texel Sheep 97
Thecla coronata 427
Theropithecus gelada 153
Thick-billed Parrot 225
Thinhorn Sheep 95
Thirteen-lined Ground Squirrel 109
Thomson's Gazelle 81
Thorold's Deer 70
Thoroughbred Horse 102
Threskiornis aethiopicus 187
Tiger 32–3
Tiger Shark 324
Tigriornis leucolophus 184
Tinca tinca 338
Toco Toucan 246
Tolypeutes matacus 15
Tomistoma schlegelii 289
Tomopterna cryptotis 313
Tonkin Snub-nosed Langur 146
Tooth-billed Pigeon 221
Torpedo torpedo 328
Torymus bedeguaris 432
Tragelaphus angasii 83
Tragelaphus derbianus 82
Tragelaphus eurycerus 82
Tragelaphus strepsiceros 83
Tragopan satyra 209
Tremarctos ornatus 43
Trichechus manatus 17
Trichogaster chuna 365
Tridacna gigas 399
Tringa erythropus 214
Triturus cristatus 310–11
Trogon viridis 243
Trogonoptera brookiana 426
Trombidium holosericeum 410
Tsetse 425
Tubifex tubifex 391
Tuft-tailed Spiny Tree Rat 123
Tui 264
Turbellarian 390
Turbot 386
Turdus migratorius 259
Turkey 206
Tursiops truncatus 60
Turtle Frog 318
Turtle-headed Seasnake 305
Twelve-wired Bird of Paradise 277
Twenty-plume Moth 429
Tyto alba 234

Unicornfish 349
Upupa epops 243
Urocissa erythrorhyncha 279
Urocyon cinereoargenteus 41
Ursus americanus 42
Ursus arctos middendorffi 42

Vanellus chilensis 212
Varecia rubra 135
Variola louti 367
Velvet Mite 410
Velvet Worm 437
Vervet 157
Vidua paradisaea 273
Violin Beetle 420
Visayan Spotted Deer 70
Von Schrenck's Bittern 184
Vulpes vulpes 41
Vultur gryphus 200

Wallace's Standardwing 277
Walrus 54–5
Water Flea 415
Water Measurer 418
Weasel Sportive Lemur 134
Wels Catfish 346–7
West Indian Manatee 17
Western Grebe 170
Western Lowland Gorilla 161
Western Parotia 276
Western Red Colobus 147
Western Tree Hyrax 16
Whale Shark 324
Whip Scorpion 411
Whistling Heron 182
White Bat 29
White-bridled Finch 263
White-crested Tiger Heron 184
White-eyed River Martin 250
White-faced Saki 141
White-headed Duck 176
White-necked Raven 278
White Rhinoceros 101
White Stork 186
White-tailed Deer 71
White-tailed Eagle 192
White-tailed Trogon 243
White-throated Magpie-jay 279
White-tipped Sicklebill 240
White-tipped Snail 397
White-winged Swallow 251
Whooper Swan 178
Wild Boar 66
Wild Goat 96
Wild Yak 84
Wildcat 34
Wind Spider 411
Wolf Fish 376
Wood Mouse 111
Wood Stork 186

Xantusia henshawi 297
Xenopsylla cheopis 435

Yellow Baboon 152
Yellow-billed Cuckoo 233
Yellow-cheeked Tit 253
Yellow-Edged Lyretail 367
Yellow-headed Caracara 204
Yellow Wattlebird 264
Yellow-winged Bat 27
Yellowfin Grouper 367
Yellowhammer 262
Yellowhead Jawfish 380
Yellowjacket 433
Yorkshire Terrier 39

Zebra Finch 273
Zebra Mussel 399

General Index

Africa
- antelopes 76–7, 80, 81, 82–3
- birds 184, 222, 223
- cats 30
- monkeys 147, 152–9, 161
- reptiles 292–3
- wild hogs 64–5
- wild horses 103
- *see also* Middle East; North Africa; South Africa; sub-Saharan Africa

alligators 288

America
- birds 176, 186, 188, 233, 266–7
- fish 358
- mammals 46–7, 71
- reptiles 289, 290
- see also North America; South America

amphibians 308–21

Andes mountains 73

angelfish 370

anglerfish 356–7

Antarctic circle 57, 212

anteaters 12–13, 15

antelopes 76–7, 80–1, 82–3

ants 433

apes 160–3

aquarium fish 338, 341, 345, 359, 380–1

arachnids 406–11, 437

Arctic circle
- birds 205, 215
- mammals 54–5, 58, 61, 88–9

armadilloes 15

Asia
- birds 202–3
- Central Asia 70, 96
- mammals 16, 32–3, 78–9, 103, 116, 117, 150–1
- *see also* China; Eurasia; India; Japan; South Asia; Southeast Asia

Atlantic Ocean
- birds 218–19
- fish 330–1, 334, 350, 354, 355, 364, 367, 387
- penguins 168–9
- whales 59

Australia
- amphibians 314, 316
- birds 166–7, 179, 185, 228–9, 230, 244–5, 264, 265, 273
- geckos 294
- mammals 10–11, 12–13

baboons 152–3

badgers 50–1

baleen whales 58–9

barnacles 415

bats 26–9

bears 42–3

beavers 104–5

bees 433

beetles 420–3

birds 164–281

birds of prey 190–205

bitterns 184–5

bivalves 398–9

blackbirds 266–7

boas 300

Borneo 146–7

bugs 418–19

buntings 262–3

butterflies 426–7

butterflyfish 370

camels 72–3

Canary Islands 297

capuchins 142–3

carnivores
- small 48–9, 52–3
- *see also individual carnivores*

carp 336–9

catfish 344–7, 381

cats 30–5

cattle 84–7

centipedes 436

Central America see America; South America

Central Asia 70, 96

cephalopods 400–3

chameleons 291, 292–3

chickens 207

chimpanzees 162–3

China 44–5, 288, 339

cichlids 372–3

clams 399

clownfish 374, 375

cockroaches 416

conches 394

coral reefs 392
- fishes in 360, 367, 370, 371, 375, 377, 378–9, 382
- invertebrates in 395

coralfish 371

crabs 413, 436

crocodiles 288, 289

crows 278–81

crustaceans 412–15

Cuba 121, 300

cuckoos 232–3

damselfish 374–5

deep-sea fish 348–9

deer 70–1

dogs 36–41

dormice 115

dragonflies 434

ducks 174–7

eagles 7, 192–5

earwigs 417

East Asia 184, 185

eels 334–5

elephants 16, 18–19

endangered species
- antelopes 83
- birds 177, 250
- cats 31, 32–3
- cattle 84
- dogs 37
- fish 329, 330–1, 332
- goats 90
- pandas 44–5
- rabbits 127
- reptiles 284, 288
- rhinoceros 98–9
- rodents 122
- saigas 78–9
- seals 57
- whales 59

Eurasia
- birds 171, 176, 177, 178, 179, 183, 214
- birds of prey 192, 205
- fish 336–8, 346–7
- mammals 116, 127
- *see also* Arctic circle; Asia; Europe

Europe
- amphibians 313
- birds 246–7
- mammals 22, 48, 50, 53, 71, 96, 106–7, 128

see also Eurasia; Mediterranean region
extinct species 170

falcons 204–5
finches 270–1, 273
fish 322–87
fish eagles 192–3
fish-eating birds 172–3
flamingos 180–1
flatfish 386–7
flatworms 390
fleas 435
flies 424–5
flightless birds 166–7
flycatchers 254–7
fowl 206–9
foxes 40–1
frogs 312–13, 316–19
fungi 6

Galapagos islands 173
gazelles 81
geckos 294–5
geese 179
gerbils 117
gibbons 160
goats 90–3, 96–7
gorillas 161
grebes 170–1
groupers 366–7
guenons 158–9
guinea pigs 120–1
gulls 216

hake 354
hamsters 116–17
hares 126–7
harriers 198
hawkmoths 428
hawks 198–9
hedgehogs 22
herons 182–3
heterotrophs 6
Himalayan mountains 90, 95, 126
hogs, wild 64–5
honeyeaters 264–5
horses 102–3
howler monkeys 144–5
hummingbirds 240–1

iguanas 290–1
India 86, 107, 212, 257, 305
Indian Ocean
fishes in 366, 378–9, 384–5
invertebrates in 395
insectivores 22–3
invertebrates 388–437

Japan 91
jawfish 380
jays 279

killifish 358
kingfishers 242–5
kites 190–1
krill 415

ladybirds 421
land snails 396–7
landfowl, wild 208–9
leaf insects 434
leaf monkeys 146–7
leeches 391
lemmings 111
lemurs 132–5
limpets 394
live bearers 358–9
lizards 290–9
loaches 339
lobsters 412–13
locusts 435

macaques 150–1
Madagascar 132–5, 285, 430
magpies 278, 279
mallards 174–5
mammals 9–163
mandrills 154–5
mangabeys 156–7
mantises 417
marmosets 138
marsupials 10–11, 21
martins 250, 251
Mediterranean region 57, 297, 334, 398
mice 110, 111, 114–15
Middle East 72, 186
millipedes 437
mites 410
moles 20–1
monkeys 142–63
monotremes 12–13
moths 428–31
mussels 399

Namib desert 422
New Guinea 12–13, 166, 229, 276, 277, 396
New Zealand 166, 172, 226–7, 229, 264
newts 310–11
nightbirds 236–7
North Africa 72, 94
North America
amphibians 312, 313
beavers 104–5
birds 170, 171, 183, 238, 241, 259
birds of prey 192, 198
fish 351, 372
goats and sheep 92–3, 94, 95
hamsters and gerbils 116–17
mammals 42, 49, 51, 85, 124–5, 126
reptiles 298–9, 305
squirrels 108–9
see also America
Northern hemisphere
birds 174–5, 177, 188–9, 194, 198, 270–1
fish 352–3, 355
reptiles 303
see also Arctic circle; Asia; Eurasia; Europe; North America

octopus 388, 402–3
ostriches 167
otters 48–9
owls 234–5
oxpeckers 274–5

Pacific Ocean
fishes in 351, 366, 378–9, 384–5
invertebrates in 395
pandas 44–5
pangolins 24–5
parrotfish 368–9
parrots 222–31
penguins 168–9
perch 364–5
pheasants 208–9
Philippines 65, 70
pigeons 220–1
pigs 64–7
pike 352–3
piranhas 340, 342–3
plants 6
polecats 53
porcupinefish 383
porcupines 123, 124–5
prawns 412
primates 130–63
primitive bony fish 332–3
prosimians 130–5
puffers 382
pythons 300–1

rabbits 126–9
raccoons 46–7

raptors see birds of prey
ratites 166–7
rats 110, 111, 112–13
ravens 278, 280–1
rays 328–9
reptiles 282–307
rhinoceros 98–9, 101
rivulids 358–9
rodents 120, 121, 122–3
see also guinea pigs; hamsters; mice; porcupines; rats; squirrels

sakis 141
salamanders 308, 310
salmon 350, 351
Samoa 221
sandpipers 214–15
scavenging raptors 200–1
scorpions 406–7, 411
sea dragons 361
sea lions 56
sea snails 394–5
sea snakes 305
seahorses 361
seals 56–7
sharks 322, 324–7
sheep 94–7
shorebirds 212–15
shrews 23
shrikes 260–1
shrimps 412, 414
skinks 296
slugs 397
snails 394–7
snake eagles 195
snakes 300–7
songbirds 248–9, 252–3, 258–61, 264, 270–3
South Africa 127, 291, 318
South America
amphibians 320–1
Andes mountains 73
birds 167, 171, 182, 183, 185, 210–11, 212, 224–5, 240–1
birds of prey 194, 198, 200, 201, 204
fish 340–1, 342–3
mammals 14–15, 31, 49, 53, 100
monkeys 138–45
reptiles 288
rodents 120, 121, 122–3
waterfowl 178, 180–1
see also America
South Asia
birds 222, 223
birds of prey 193, 195
mammals 43, 90
monkeys 146–7
see also India
Southeast Asia
amphibians 317
fish 365
invertebrates 430–1
mammals 48, 50, 84, 100, 101, 160, 161
reptiles 288, 301, 302, 303, 305, 306–7
Southern hemisphere 172
see also Antarctic circle; Australia; New Guinea; New Zealand; South America
spider monkeys 145
spiders 406–7, 411, 437
squid 401
squirrels 106–9
starfish 404–5
storks 186–8
sturgeons 330–1
sub-Saharan Africa
amphibians 312, 313
birds 167, 186, 274–5
birds of prey 193, 195, 198
fish 340, 373
mammals 18–19, 37, 74–5, 85, 98–9
reptiles 296, 304
see also Africa; South Africa
Sulawesi 85
Sumatra 127
swallows 250, 251
swans 178
swifts 238–9

tangs 381
tapirs 100
tarsiers 136–7
termites 417
terns 217
terrapins 285
tetras 340, 341
thrushes 258–9
ticks 411
titis 140
tits 252–3
toadfish 356
toads 314–15, 320–1
tortoises 285
toucans 246
tree frogs 316–17
triggerfish 382–3
tropical oceans 324, 325, 326–7, 349, 367
trout 350–1
turtles 284, 285, 286–7

uakaris 140–1
urchins 405

venomous snakes 304–7
vultures 200–1

waders 182–8, 212–13
walrus 54–5
warblers 258
wasps 432, 433
waterfowl 174–81
waxbills 272
weasels 52
whales 58–63
whitefish 354–5
wolves 36, 37, 38, 41
woodlice 414
woodpeckers 246–7
worms 390–1, 437
wrasses 376–9

Picture Credits

All images © The Magic Group except the following:

Corbis Royalty Free: 5, 7, 8/9, 164/165
Dreamstime: 282/283, 308/309, 388/389 (John Abramo)
IMP AB: 12–13, 18–19, 24–25,32–33, 44–45, 54–55, 62–63,68–69, 74–75, 78–79, 88–89,92–93, 98–99, 104–105, 112–113, 118–119, 124–125, 132–133, 136–137, 142–143, 148–149, 154–155, 162–163, 168–169, 174–175, 180–181, 188–189, 196–197, 202–203, 210–211, 218–219, 226–227, 230–231, 244–245, 254–255, 260–261, 268–269, 274–275, 280–281, 286–287, 292–293, 298–299, 306–307, 310–311, 314–315, 320–321, 326–327, 330–331,336–337, 342–343, 346–347, 352–353, 362–363, 368–369, 378–379, 384–385, 392–393, 402–403, 408–409, 422–423, 430–431
iStockphoto: 322/323 (Klaas Lingbeek-van Kranen)